Prime Minister Corby

… and other things that never

PRIME MINISTER CORBYN ...

... AND OTHER THINGS THAT NEVER HAPPENED

edited by

DUNCAN BRACK

and

IAIN DALE

First published in Great Britain in 2016 by
Biteback Publishing Ltd
Westminster Tower
3 Albert Embankment
London SE1 7SP

ISBN 978-1-78590-045-7

10 9 8 7 6 5 4 3 2 1

A CIP catalogue record for this book is available from the British Library.

Set in Bembo by Adrian McLaughlin

Printed and bound in Great Britain by
CPI Group (UK) Ltd, Croydon CR0 4YY

Contents

Introduction

Duncan Brack and Iain Dale

Here in this book you will find twenty-three examinations of things that never happened, from William Gladstone being drowned at sea in 1885, to Lyndon Johnson being shot down over the Pacific in 1942, to Britain losing the Falklands War in 1983, to Tony Blair sacking Gordon Brown as Chancellor in 2004, to the Scottish people voting 'yes' in the independence referendum of 2014. You will also find three chapters on things that haven't happened *yet*...

This is the fourth in a series of books of political counterfactuals one or both of us has produced, the others being *Prime Minister Portillo and Other Things That Never Happened* (2003), *President Gore and Other Things That Never Happened* (2007) and *Prime Minister Boris and Other Things That Never Happened* (2011). As we have observed before, although 'serious' historians have tended to look down their noses at the study of counterfactuals, they have a distinguished record. Winston Churchill contributed a chapter (on what if Robert E. Lee had won the battle of Gettysburg) to a 1931 collection called *If It Had Happened Otherwise*, and other counterfactual analyses have been published by historians and sociologists such as Robert Fogel, Geoffrey Hawthorn and Niall Ferguson. Indeed, counterfactual history is increasingly popular, with an ever-expanding range of books, novels, documentaries and films produced in recent years.

We believe that counterfactual history has value in the analysis of history in several different sets of circumstances – all illustrated by chapters included in this book. To achieve this analytical aim, the counterfactuals must of course be plausible. Start to change one decision or happening or event in history, and it can be difficult to justify not changing others. There have to be boundaries, and the more rigorously these are policed the more convincing – and the more analytically useful – the results become. So the chapters in this book are limited to occasions where very little needed to have happened differently for the ultimate outcome to have been transformed – and, mostly, to changed individual choices or actions set against unchanged economic and social backgrounds.

One group of chapters, accordingly, focuses on instances where historical outcomes depended on finely balanced decisions or actions taken by key individuals or small groups of people; the counterfactual enables us to analyse the range of factors that influenced their decisions, to weigh up their relative importance and to consider whether the decision that was actually reached was the 'right' one given what the individuals themselves hoped to achieve. Thus we have the French Cabinet voting to accept Winston Churchill's offer of unification with Britain in June 1940 (Churchill himself thought that they might have done had French Prime Minister Reynaud held on to his post for one day longer); the British Cabinet deciding to float sterling in 1952 (the proposal was seriously discussed, and could have avoided the debilitating cycle of boom and bust that crippled the British economy in the 1950s and 1960s); the German politician Lothar Späth deciding to stand against Helmut Kohl for Chancellor in 1989 (he almost did – and, far less keen than Kohl on German reunification, he could have turned down the expensive and risky project that in reality Kohl embarked on in 1990); the UK joining the euro in 2000 (which our author argues could have been good for the euro system as well as the UK); Yevgeny Primakov standing for Russian President in 2000 (a popular and effective Prime Minister, he almost did – which could have meant no President Putin); Tony Benn deciding to back Respect when it was launched in 2004 (thus helping to split the Labour Party); Tony Blair opting to sack Gordon Brown as Chancellor in 2004 (he was given plenty of opportunity...); George Osborne resigning as shadow Chancellor in 2008 in the wake of the 'Yachtgate' donations scandal; and, extremely entertainingly, though perhaps less plausibly (though read through to the end), Lynton Crosby switching sides during the 2015 general election.

Other chapters do not depend on decisions being taken differently, but examine the impact of the decision-makers themselves being absent, or of different key figures being present. So we have Gladstone falling overboard on his yachting trip to Norway in 1885 (a trip he actually took); Lyndon Johnson being shot down over the Pacific in 1942 (an observer on a long-distance bomber, he switched planes at the last moment – and the plane he should have been on was shot down with the loss of all its crew); and RAF pilot Michael Wedgwood Benn *not* being killed in 1944 (his younger brother Tony thus not inheriting the Stansgate viscountcy in 1960). Each of these is entirely plausible, and it is difficult not to conclude that the absence of Gladstone or Johnson would have made a considerable difference to British and American politics, respectively; and how would Tony Benn's career have developed had he not been radicalised so early by the fight to turn down his peerage?

These 'what ifs' remind us of the critical role of contingency in history. The outcome of battles often being a particularly chancy thing, many other books of counterfactuals concentrate on military history. One chapter here takes a different military outcome – British defeat in the Falklands War – and applies it to politics; it is difficult not to conclude that British political history after 1983 would have been very different had the Falklands been lost.

This being a book of political counterfactuals, several chapters deal with different outcomes of elections, both general and party leadership. Thus we have Chris Huhne instead of Nick Clegg winning the Liberal Democrat leadership in 2007 (indeed, as our contributor here argues, perhaps he did) or the Conservatives winning outright in the 2010 general election (they only needed 10,000 voters – just one in every 3,000 of those who cast their ballots in May 2010 – to vote differently to win). No less than three chapters deal with different outcomes of Labour leadership elections: David Miliband or Ed Balls winning in 2010, rather than Ed Miliband (David Miliband almost did, of course, and the outcome could plausibly have been different if the election had been held quickly, rather than being the long-drawn-out affair it was), and Andy Burnham winning in 2015. Two chapters look ahead to the chances of a Labour general election victory in 2020, installing Jeremy Corbyn as Prime Minister; in one, things work out badly, in the other, rather better – at least to start with...

Two chapters look at the impact of possible alternative outcomes of referendums: the UK voting to leave the EEC in 1975 (as seemed likely at the beginning of the campaign) and Scotland voting to leave the UK in 2014 (with perhaps unexpected consequences). The remaining chapter deals with the aftermath of the UK's vote to leave the EU in 2016 (a chapter which divides in two, where in one future things go well, and in the other, not so much; both feature a starring role for Boris Johnson, and other characters you might recognise...).

As in the previous three books, the authors have adopted a variety of approaches, including scholarly analyses of the possibilities and causalities of different outcomes, and fictional accounts of alternate political histories – and sometimes both. And, quite apart from their analytical value, helping us to think about political history and what determines how politicians act, these chapters have high entertainment value; at some of them, you will laugh out loud.

If any reader has ideas for topics, or authors, for a potential further volume, we would be very pleased to hear them; send us your ideas via email at dbrack@dbrack.org.uk and/or iain@iaindale.com. In the meantime, we hope you are stimulated, provoked and entertained by *Prime Minister Corbyn and Other Things That Never Happened* – but could have.

~

Acknowledgements
Our warmest thanks go to Ian Cawood, Mark Egan, David Howarth, Neal Lawson, Caron Lindsay, James Nixey, Tim Oliver, Greg Rosen, Christian Schweiger, Neil Stockley, Alun Wyburn-Powell and – in particular – Sam Macrory for reviewing draft chapters; to Olivia Beattie and Victoria Godden, of Biteback, for their constant encouragement and support; and, above all, to all the chapter authors, for producing high-quality work to a demanding timetable.

Duncan Brack and Iain Dale
August 2016

Authors

Francis Beckett is an author, journalist and contemporary historian. He edited *Prime Ministers Who Never Were* (Biteback, 2011) and the series of short lives, *The 20 British Prime Ministers of the Twentieth Century* (Haus, 2006.) His latest books are *1956: The Year That Changed Britain* (Biteback, 2015) and *Fascist in the Family* (Routledge, 2016).

Asa Bennett is assistant comment editor at the *Daily Telegraph*, and writes its morning briefing politics email.

David Boyle is a former Liberal Democrat parliamentary candidate and policy-maker. He is co-director of the New Weather Institute and the author of *Scandal*, *Before Enigma* and other books. He is the author of the forthcoming *V: The radio campaign that shaped wartime resistance* (The Real Press).

Duncan Brack has co-edited and contributed to all three previous volumes of political counterfactuals published by Politico's or Biteback. He is also editor of the *Journal of Liberal History* and has edited or co-written several reference books on Liberal history. Professionally he works on international environmental policy.

Tina Burrett is associate professor of Political Science at Sophia University, Japan. She holds a PhD in Political Science from Cambridge University. Her recent publications include *Television and Presidential Power in Putin's Russia* (Routledge, 2013) and 'Russia's Competing Nationalisms and Relations with Asia' in Jeff Kingston (ed.), *Asian Nationalisms Reconsidered* (Routledge, 2015). Her op-eds appear regularly in the *Japan Times*.

Peter Cuthbertson is a public affairs consultant. In his own time, he runs a non-profit organisation aimed at reducing offending and reoffending, the Centre for Crime Prevention. He was the Conservative parliamentary candidate for Darlington in 2015 and candidate for Darlington and Durham Police Commissioner in 2016.

Stephen Daisley is a political journalist and commentator based in Glasgow. His areas of interest include the rise of nationalism in Scotland and the decline of the Labour Party across the UK. He tweets as @JournoStephen.

Iain Dale is managing director of Biteback Publishing. He presents the *Drivetime* show on LBC Radio and is winner of the Arqiva Radio Presenter of the Year award 2013 and 2016.

Tom Harris is a columnist for the *Daily Telegraph* and director of his own public affairs company, Third Avenue Communications Ltd. He was a Labour MP between 2001 and 2015, and served as a government minister at the Department for Transport under Tony Blair and Gordon Brown.

Chris Huhne founded the City of London's largest team of economists at Fitch Ratings, was economic columnist on *The Guardian* and *Independent on Sunday*, and has served on the council of the Royal Economic Society and as visiting fellow of Nuffield College, Oxford. He was an MEP, MP and minister between 1999 and 2013.

Julian Huppert was the Liberal Democrat MP for Cambridge from 2010 to 2015, and is now a lecturer in Public Policy at the University of Cambridge, trying to teach students how to do public policy properly. He also works on technology and science policy, and is a director of the Joseph Rowntree Reform Trust.

Tom King worked as a caseworker and parliamentary researcher before moving to a consultancy specialising in political due diligence. He is now business development manager for an international network of journalists investigating organised crime and corruption. He lives in Sarajevo and enjoys pretending to be a musician.

Graham Kirby writes on culture and politics as well as short fiction. He has translated numerous plays for theatre and, working with educational charity the Iris Project, has adapted ancient political satire for schoolchildren and modern audiences. He contributes regularly to *Tribune* magazine and is the editor of *Disclaimer*.

Alexander Larman is an author and journalist whose previous books include *Blazing Star* (Head of Zeus, 2014), a biography of the poet and libertine the Earl of Rochester, and *Restoration* (Head of Zeus, 2016), a social and narrative history of the year 1666. He writes about literature and politics for titles including *The Observer* and *Huffington Post*.

Tony Little is the chairman of the Liberal Democrat History Group, and joint editor of and a contributor to the History Group's books *British Liberal Leaders* (Biteback, 2015) and *Great Liberal Speeches* (Politico's, 2001). He has also contributed a chapter to *Peace, Reform and Liberation* (Biteback, 2011) and entries to the *Dictionary of Liberal Thought* (Politico's, 2007).

Tony McNulty was Labour MP for Harrow East from 1997 to 2010. He was a minister variously for housing, planning and regeneration (ODPM), transport, immigration, police and security, employment and London (attending Cabinet). He continues to be very active in Labour politics – and in writing, occasional broadcasting, teaching and reflecting.

Andy Mayer was formerly general secretary of the Pro-Euro Conservative Party and chair of the Young European Movement. Today he works in public affairs and supported Remain in the 2016 EU referendum.

Ted Morris works in financial services, and is a keen student of modern political history.

Adrian Moss is an award-winning screenwriter who worked in publishing for sixteen years before setting up a specialist video production company. Having invested heavily in a Tory majority at 10–1, he spent the latter half of 2015 hiding from his bookie. He might live in Gloucestershire.

Dr Tim Oliver is a Dahrendorf Fellow at the London School of Economics. He has worked in the House of Lords and the European Parliament, at research institutions in Berlin and Washington DC and has taught at LSE, UCL and the Royal Military Academy Sandhurst.

Dr Mark Pack worked at Liberal Democrat HQ between 2000 and 2009, running the party's digital campaigns through two general elections. He is co-author of *101 Ways To Win An Election* (Biteback, revised edition, 2016) and edits *Liberal Democrat Newswire* (www.LibDemNewswire.com).

Paul Richards joined the Labour Party in 1986. He has been a parliamentary candidate, local activist and special adviser to two Cabinet ministers. He is a former chair of the Fabian Society. Among his many books and pamphlets is *Tony Blair In His Own Words* (Politico's, 2004) and *How to Be a Spin Doctor* (Biteback, 2016).

Andrew Stone teaches history and politics and is the NUT rep at Saint Francis Xavier Sixth Form College in south London. He is an assistant editor of *rs21* magazine and *Education for Liberation*. He also contributes to Politics Review Online. He is currently failing to prevent the gentrification of Hackney.

Stuart Thomson is a public affairs and communications consultant with Bircham Dyson Bell, and honorary research fellow in the Department of Politics and International Relations at the University of Aberdeen. He is also a regular media commentator, frequent blogger and author; his latest book is *Public Affairs: A Global Perspective* (Urbane Publications). He tweets as @redpolitics.

Dr Robert Waller is a former Fellow and lecturer at Magdalen, Trinity and Wadham Colleges, Oxford. He is currently Head of History and Politics at Greenacre School for Girls, Banstead.

Michael Wuliger lives in Berlin. He is a former features editor of the German Jewish weekly *Jüdische Allgemeine* and author of a satirical book on contemporary Jewish life in Germany, *Der koschere Knigge* (S. Fischer, 2009).

Chapter 1

What if Gladstone had died in 1885?

The birth of the welfare state

Tony Little

At the end of 1884, Gladstone's Liberal government had just secured its greatest triumph, the passage of the Third Reform Act, with an accompanying redistribution of seats. Such a widening of the electorate to incorporate large numbers of agricultural labourers in both Britain and Ireland would necessitate an election as soon as the new registers became available. This election required an innovative set of policies to seduce the new voters, and Joseph Chamberlain knew just the man to proclaim them. John Stuart Mill had already commissioned a series of articles on what he saw as the principal controversial issues and brought them together in a book – *The Radical Programme*.

Historically, the Liberal Party's role had been, in Mill's words, 'activity which does not impede, but aids and stimulates, individual exertion and development' – removing the barriers to freedom. Chamberlain was offering the party a new purpose: constructive government. He summarised that initial programme as 'an extension of popular government to the counties, free education, land for the labourers, artisans' dwellings, a revision of taxation'.[1] In our eyes, these proposals might seem modest, but the principle of using government endeavour on behalf of the working citizen – a welfare state – was almost revolutionary.

Ignoring the conventions of Cabinet responsibility and the sensibilities of the Queen, Chamberlain popularised the programme during a speech to his Birmingham constituents in January 1885 with the ill-chosen sound bite: 'What ransom will property pay for the security it enjoys?' This was the first of a series of blows endured by the Liberal Party in the first half of the year. Chamberlain's intemperate speech exacerbated tensions with moderates in the Cabinet, who put up G. J. Goschen to make a public response, and caused Gladstone unnecessary worry in soothing Victoria's ruffled feathers. In February, the government learned that the mission to relieve the siege of Charles Gordon's forces in Khartoum had arrived too late. Gladstone was blamed for the subsequent murder of General Gordon and the government barely survived a vote of censure. In April, the government abandoned attempts to recover Sudan to confront Russia in Afghanistan, nearly leading to the resignation of Lord Hartington, the Whig (or moderate) leader and Secretary of State for War.

Divisions within the Liberal Cabinet worsened at the end of the month, when Radicals objected to proposals to raise alcohol taxes and Lord Spencer proposed to renew the emergency 'coercion' powers constraining the violence of Irish home rule protests. Chamberlain countered Spencer's proposal with a scheme for devolving some – principally local – powers to an elective central board in Dublin, a scheme that Chamberlain had been misled into believing was acceptable to Charles Parnell, the home rule leader. Despite support from Gladstone, the scheme was rejected. The Cabinet was still arguing over coercion when it was defeated on an amendment to the Budget and gratefully acquiesced in the chance to resign.

Liberal thinking appears to have been that a period of minority Conservative government under Lord Salisbury would allow the party to reunite and campaign more effectively in the autumn general election. They were surprised when the Tories made a play for Irish support. Salisbury abandoned coercion and introduced a Bill allowing Irish tenant farmers to buy their land on affordable terms.

The Conservative administration also allowed Gladstone time to contemplate his position. At seventy-five, did he have the stamina and the ambition to continue? Was it his duty to lead if he alone, as he thought, could paper over the divisions among his Cabinet colleagues?

A death at sea

On 8 August, Gladstone and his family boarded Thomas Brassey's yacht *Sunbeam* for a trip to the Norwegian fiords. Among the guests was Lewis ('Loulou') Harcourt, the son of Gladstone's combative Home Secretary Sir William Harcourt. On 9 August, Loulou recorded in his diary:

> [T]he breeze has freshened a little during the night and … we are making about eight knots under sail … We had two services today and Mr Gladstone sat in his room to hear them as he did not feel safe enough of his stomach to come into the saloon.

Two days later, he recorded their arrival at Stavanger: 'We got in here at 5 o'clock this morning after a fearful night with a heavy sea running…'[2] As they disembarked, they realised that Gladstone had not joined them.

A fruitless search of the vessel revealed only Gladstone's draft notes for his election manifesto and a routine letter to Lord Granville, the Liberal leader in the Lords. His companions could only speculate that he had stumbled overboard during the storm and drowned. From Stavanger, Brassey sent telegrams to the Queen, to Lords Granville and Hartington and, after a suitable delay, to the Associated Press Agency; Loulou Harcourt telegraphed his father, who immediately sent news to Chamberlain. Gladstone's body was never recovered, and it was an empty coffin that lay in state at Westminster Hall before the funeral, a coffin whose pallbearers included the Prince of Wales and Arthur Balfour, the nephew of Lord Salisbury.

Any contest for the leadership of the Liberal Party would be between Hartington and Chamberlain. Hartington had led the Liberals in the Commons between 1875 and 1880, during Gladstone's temporary 'retirement'. The heir to the Duke of Devonshire, he personified the Whig tradition: honourable, capable, experienced, slightly raffish and willing to advocate reform but never too soon. Chamberlain had been known to refer to him as a drag on the wheel of progress and it was rumoured that his mistress, the Duchess of Manchester, constantly influenced him in a conservative direction.

Chamberlain was a self-made businessman who had built his political reputation as an energetic executive Mayor of Birmingham, the leader of the campaign for secular state education and the founder of the National Liberal Federation (NLF). The NLF was not then the representative body of the grassroots Liberals that it later became but a caucus, whose purpose was to push the party in a more radical direction at the expense of Whigs and moderates. Quick and inventive but prickly, Chamberlain's impatience with the Westminster club made him difficult to manage in a subordinate role, but he was, in Winston Churchill's short pen portrait, 'one who made the weather'.[3]

Gladstone's funeral brought most of the prominent political figures back to London from their country estates. Granville and Hartington took the opportunity for widespread consultations. Anxious to avoid a destructive leadership contest immediately before an election, the Chief Whip advised Hartington to negotiate with Chamberlain. On the other side, Chamberlain recognised that he did not command the loyalty of sufficient MPs in the old House to win, though he expected better from the MPs elected on the new franchise. At roundtable talks held in Harcourt's house, Hartington was surprised to discover that Chamberlain was more interested in the delivery of his Radical Programme than in the role in which he delivered it. He was also pleased to discover that Chamberlain was now much more critical of Parnell than previously, and more imperialist than Hartington had understood. Though Hartington conceded that he considered Chamberlain's programme 'inexpedient' rather than 'revolutionary',[4] he was reluctant to commit himself to some of its proposals. After some reflection, the two men established sufficient common ground on which to fight the election. Following these successful talks, a meeting of the Liberal MPs at the Reform Club endorsed Hartington's leadership by acclamation.

A new premier

The outcome of the election in November 1885 was the final Liberal disappointment that year. The expectations had been for an overwhelming Liberal majority, in line with the experience of the Reform Acts of 1832 and 1867. In the event, while Liberals and their allies gained an 84-seat margin over the Conservatives, this was offset by the eighty-six seats held by the Irish nationalists.[5] This could have led to a bidding war for Irish support but neither of the British parties was tempted. When Parliament met in January 1886, Salisbury almost immediately introduced a coercion Bill, which divided the Liberals and was carried with sufficient unofficial Liberal support to offset vehement Irish opposition. Having lost its Irish support, Salisbury's government was turned out on a vaguely worded motion for land reform and the Queen sent for Lord Hartington.

Hartington seized the opportunity to drop some of the older and less effective Gladstonian ministers: Granville, Derby, Selborne and Carlingford. Contrary to earlier plans, Harcourt took the Exchequer, Rosebery was brought in as Foreign Secretary, Goschen replaced Harcourt at the Home Office and Chamberlain was made president of the Local Government Board. Spencer remained in Ireland, supported by a newcomer, John Morley, and another newcomer, Campbell-Bannerman, was given the War Office. Among the Radicals, Dilke was unavailable because of the Crawford divorce scandal and Forster through illness.[6]

Hartington's manifesto for the 1885 election had been vaguely worded but had contained pointers towards the issues that the government could tackle without enlarging the split between Whigs and Radicals, which had so frequently threatened Gladstone's last government. Parliamentary procedure, education, local government, land law and Ireland were all issues that at least partly overlapped with the Radical Programme.[7]

The disruptive opposition of the Irish home rulers delayed the reforms to the procedures of the Commons; the Irish had been effective exploiters of the old loose procedures to blackmail previous governments. However, in the long run, this obstruction proved beneficial to the government by enabling Hartington and Chamberlain to construct a working relationship without the mediation of Gladstone. The establishment of county councils, including a county council for London, in addition to the City Corporation, was the government's greatest achievement of 1887. The legislation's patient management through the House by Chamberlain enhanced his reputation and brought him closer to the premier without stunting his inventiveness.

Arrangements for Ireland were more controversial. Ireland did secure county government, but a Bill to provide a Grand Committee to sit in Dublin was announced the day before *The Times* published revelations implicating Parnell in agrarian violence. The resulting anti-Irish sentiment allowed the Conservative majority in the Lords to veto the Bill. Neither Hartington nor Chamberlain fought hard to save it, leaving Morley and Spencer to handle Irish affairs through the traditional mix of coercion, half-hearted amelioration and a gradual extension of the Acts providing government funding for tenants to purchase their farms. In killing home rule with kindness, cheap land offered benefits that were more tangible to farmers than devolution. After a protracted public inquiry revealed that *The Times* had been deceived by forged letters, Parnell was vindicated, but shortly afterwards he was revealed as a guilty party in the O'Shea divorce case. The scandal brought condemnation from the Catholic Church and split the home rule party. Parnell's distractions undermined the effectiveness of the Irish opposition and allowed the government to function even without a significant majority.

The county councils were empowered to provide substantial allotments for farm workers but the powers were constrained by Whig hostility to interference with property rights and, more importantly, by a lack of demand to take up subsistence farming on any great scale. 'Three Acres and a Cow', as the allotments policy was commonly known, provided only an illusory popularity. The quid pro quo for the Whigs was the reform of land law, allowing for the easier sale of land and greater flexibility to divide estates on inheritance, which slipped quietly through Parliament in 1888.

The other great achievement of the government's first term was free primary education, in line with Hartington's promise that 'the burdens imposed on the working classes for the education of their children may be diminished',[8] although this was only achieved after the usual controversy over the funding of church – particularly Anglican – schools by Nonconformist taxpayers. Chamberlain's plan to fund free schools through the disestablishment and disendowment of the Church of England were rejected in Cabinet.

The completion of the local government reforms left Chamberlain with the time to prepare for the election expected around 1891. In 1885, he had anticipated a 'solid Liberal victory' of 360 seats and for the party to perform well in its traditional urban areas.[9] The Radical Programme, with its appeal to agricultural labourers, had helped the Liberals in rural areas but the switch from multi-member to single constituencies had hurt it in the suburbs. There had been no equivalent to 'Three Acres and a Cow' for industrial workers. Something better was needed for the next election.

Preparing the ground

The frustrations of the working classes and their search for solutions outside the Liberal Party were amply demonstrated during Hartington's first government. In 1887, there were riots in Trafalgar Square during a demonstration on behalf of the unemployed. In 1888, the Match Girls' strike pitted Radical MP Charles Bradlaugh and the socialist feminist activist Annie Besant against a leading Liberal, the owner of Bryant & May. In 1889, surprisingly well-organised dockworkers struck to secure a pay rise to six pence an hour.

Despite the distractions of government, Chamberlain maintained his policy-making drive after 1886. He used his local party activists to assess working-class opinion. He brought together informed participants to debate and test his proposals. His biographer, Peter Marsh, gives the example of a dinner to discuss temperance, which pitted a brewer against clergymen and a teetotaller while he watched out for the practical implications.[10] He brought to his investigations his skills as a businessman, crafting proposals that would work and would answer immediate needs cost-effectively.

His techniques were shown most clearly during 1890, when he took up the cause of pensions. The better-remunerated and organised workers paid into friendly societies to cover themselves for ill health and their families against their deaths. The less well-off became a burden on their families when they could no longer work. As the process of pauperisation continued, the poorest, forced into workhouses, became stigmatised as a burden on the community. When Chamberlain had been criticised for his 'ransom' speech in 1885, he recognised the rashness of his words but was not diverted from his purpose. As he continued to campaign, he rephrased the question, asking what *insurance* the better-off would pay for civil harmony. The pensions proposals were the fruit of this thinking.

He envisaged a contributory pension scheme payable to men aged over sixty-five with some provision for widows and children up to the age of twelve. Payment would be made through the Post Office. He allowed for direct contributions to the government scheme or for the state to supplement the pensions of those contributing to friendly societies. He invited Charles Booth, the famous investigator of London poverty, to his Birmingham home, Highbury, and arranged for an actuary to consider the cost. He met the spokesmen for the provident societies, who proved uncooperative, and he also failed to win over organised labour; for the unions, retirement at sixty-five was too late, as many manual working men did not live that long, but to Chamberlain the cost to the Exchequer of a lower retirement age was prohibitive and he concluded that the scheme would be popular with the wider public.[11]

By the time of the election in 1891, his programme for retaining labour voters within the Liberal fold was ready. In addition to his pension proposals, he backed legislation restricting miners' hours and promised reforms of employer liability. At that time, compensation for industrial injuries applied only where employers could be shown to be culpably negligent. Chamberlain proposed compensation in all cases where the employee was not himself the cause of the accident. Employers would be compelled to pay for insurance and thus pass the costs onto consumers.[12] Chamberlain retained his faith in the old shibboleths of Radicalism, such as disestablishment, but had little expectation that any such proposal would escape the veto of the Lords or that his party would undertake fundamental reform of that institution while it was led by so many aristocrats.

Although Chamberlain had learned lessons in policy formulation from the criticisms of the Radical Programme, in other ways he had not become a better politician. He remained keener to communicate his ideas to the nation than to consult either his leader or the rest of the Cabinet; keener to differentiate himself from the Whigs than to present a united front to the electorate. While Hartington had no inhibitions about expressing his exasperation with this breach of etiquette in private, in public he was restrained.

Hartington's letter to the electors of Rossendale – by default the official Liberal manifesto – defended the government's record of colonial expansion in Africa and warned of the growing rivalry with other European empires, which presaged a rise in military expenditure. He spoke strongly against Irish nationalist ambitions, seeing them as a means of breaking up the empire. While endorsing the proposals for employer liability and restrictions on miners' hours, he cautioned about the costs of pensions and spoke only of careful investigation of the possibilities.

A reconstruction

The outcome of the election was a modest gain for the Liberals but at the end of 1891 Hartington was elevated to the Lords when he succeeded his father as Duke of Devonshire. This required a reconstruction of the government and, in particular, a new Leader of the House. Should it be Chamberlain or Harcourt? Both were talented and effective ministers but neither was a great team player. Chamberlain always sought to preserve his independence of action and was frequently suspected of leaking Cabinet discussions when it suited his ambitions. Harcourt was given to irascible outbursts against colleagues during Cabinet discussion followed by lengthy memorandums reinforcing his arguments. Though he quickly recovered his good humour, he failed to recognise the lasting offence that his victims sometimes took.

In the end, the Duke concluded that thwarting Chamberlain would be the more dangerous option. Chamberlain requested that his new role of Leader of the House be combined with the presidency of the Board of Trade so that he had the best opportunity to implement his proposals for the welfare of the working man. The employers' liability legislation passed without much argument, but restrictions on the hours of labour for miners were more contentious. Ideologues argued over whether it was reasonable to legislate for able-bodied men capable of bargaining for themselves. Others were more concerned with setting precedents that would extend the regulation of hours to more and more trades. Despite these doubts, the legislation passed and the precedents were indeed set for ever more intrusive state regulation of working conditions.

Harcourt was left, aggrieved and quarrelsome, at the Treasury. Nevertheless, it was he who made Chamberlain's state pension scheme practical through his 1894 Budget. The government already faced a deficit and the prospect of increased military expenditure combined with the funding required to subsidise the pensions proposals necessitated innovative thinking; the savings anticipated in the poor rate from the reduced need for workhouse provision covered only a fraction of the anticipated costs. In addition to the usual increases in excise duties on alcohol, Harcourt proposed a substantial reform of death duties and a graduated income tax, imposing higher rates on higher earners. A fierce controversy was sparked by the income tax proposals both within the Cabinet and between the parties, a controversy that threatened the survival of the government. On top of that, both Devonshire and Rosebery opposed the rates proposed for the death duties – hardly surprisingly given the scale of their estates. Despite having to drop the graduated tax and moderating the rate of death duty, Harcourt's reforms significantly increased revenue over the long term.

On the back of the Budget, pensions were introduced and the beginnings of a welfare state secured. The illustrated papers were afforded the opportunity to photograph Chamberlain handing over the first pension from behind the counter of the main post office in Birmingham, wearing his trademark orchid in his buttonhole. With the principle of a state or national insurance scheme established, the way was open for later governments to extend the scope of state pensions, to provide insurance for temporary periods of unemployment and to extend the role of government in providing labour exchanges. The welfare state was born.

For Devonshire's government, however, its greatest achievement was also the beginning of its end. Harcourt's death duties took time to generate revenues. The state pension, free education and the competition to build ever-larger navies all proved more expensive than first thought and ever-larger Budget deficits undermined an already disputatious Cabinet. As Foreign Secretary, Rosebery was reluctant to share his thinking with colleagues and was quick to take offence at Harcourt's blustering.

The imperialist tendency shared by Devonshire, Rosebery and Chamberlain was resented by Morley and Harcourt.

Chamberlain's fertile mind finally tipped the scale. Anxious to promote the cohesion of the empire and to generate the tax revenues needed to expand his 'socialist' schemes for the benefit of working men, Chamberlain promoted the idea of 'imperial preference'. Impressed by the German customs union used by Bismarck to fund his social security schemes, Chamberlain proposed that Britain, in conjunction with the self-governing colonies, introduce tariffs, with mutual concessionary rates for fellow members of the empire. The new import duties would act as retaliation for the tariff walls erected by the Germans, Americans and other protectionist states. The concessionary rates would, he argued, benefit the economic development of both Britain and its colonies, while the revenue provided by the new taxes on imports would fund the expansion of social security. As usual, he made his proposals public, in a speech at Birmingham's Town Hall, in 1895, before enlightening his Cabinet colleagues.

This assault on free trade was too much for the orthodox Chancellor, Harcourt, who gave Devonshire an ultimatum: either he or Chamberlain must go. Devonshire was as much a free trader as Harcourt and, despite mediation by Morley, Chamberlain was forced to resign. Never one to back away from a challenge, he set out to convert the nation to his new imperial vision. Although unsuccessful outside his Birmingham 'Duchy', his fair trade crusade split sufficient local parties to cause the loss of the election in 1897. He never again held office, suffering a stroke in 1906, shortly after his seventieth birthday, which limited his political activities, though he lived on until 1914.

In life, Chamberlain's divisiveness condemned him, but to posterity he is more fondly remembered as a father of the welfare state, of free primary education and the modern political party.

Assessment

In reality, Gladstone did not suffer the fate of Robert Maxwell. He returned from Brassey's yacht ready to capitalise on his indispensability by leading the Liberals into the 1885 election. His election manifesto, drafted on the voyage, is his longest, but is famous in posterity only for the ambiguity of the final section, on Ireland:

> In my opinion, not now for the first time delivered, the limit is clear within which any desires of Ireland, constitutionally ascertained, may, and beyond which they cannot, receive the assent of Parliament. To maintain the supremacy of the Crown, the unity of the Empire, and all the authority of Parliament necessary for the conservation of that unity, is the first duty of every representative of the people. Subject to this governing principle, every grant to portions of the country of enlarged powers for the management of their own affairs is, in my view, not a source of danger, but a means of averting it, and is in the nature of a new guarantee of increased cohesion, happiness, and strength.[13]

It was only after the election had delivered a hung parliament, with the Irish nationalists holding the balance, that Gladstone's son flew the 'Hawarden Kite', leaking his father's intention to introduce home rule. This unanticipated initiative split the Liberal Party. Hartington declined to join Gladstone's government; Chamberlain joined, taking responsibility for local government, but subsequently resigned when Gladstone finalised his Irish proposals. On 8 June 1886, the Government of Ireland Bill was defeated in the Commons by 341 to 311; Hartington and Chamberlain led ninety-three Liberals in voting against it.

The two rebels separately formed Unionist parties and fashioned an electoral alliance with the Conservatives, which swept the Liberals out of power in the election that followed in July. Hartington refused to accept the premiership but the Liberal Unionists supported Salisbury in office. Roundtable talks held at Harcourt's house in 1887 failed to appease the dissident Liberals. When Hartington moved to the Lords, Chamberlain took over the leadership of the Liberal Unionists in the Commons. After 1895, the Liberal Unionists formed a coalition with the Conservatives, with both Devonshire and Chamberlain joining the Cabinet. In 1903, Chamberlain split the Unionists over his proposals for imperial preference.

In examining the counterfactual, I have tried to stay as close as possible to events and personalities. Admirers of Chamberlain believe that he could have succeeded Gladstone. I think this improbable. It is very unlikely that Queen Victoria, for whom Gladstone was a 'half-mad firebrand', would have sent for a man with such offensive views on the establishment as Chamberlain when Hartington was available. It is also unlikely that the Liberal Party as it was constituted in the 1880s would have preferred him; there were not enough radical Liberals and he was not altogether popular even with older Radicals who resented the bullying of Chamberlain's NLF. Having led the Liberals in the Commons during Gladstone's retirement, in 1885 Hartington was still, indisputably, the heir apparent.

In the Liberal Unionists, Hartington and Chamberlain proved that they could work together, though the relationship was never entirely harmonious. The two men reflected their different backgrounds and lived different lifestyles. They represented different traditions, with Hartington seeking to protect liberty and property from interference from either the mob below or the monarchy (government) above. Hartington tended to be slow to reach conclusions and was a man of applied common sense. Nevertheless, he was a Liberal and had adapted to the party's reforms up to 1885; he undoubtedly favoured the county councils (introduced, in fact, by the Conservatives in 1889) and was not an opponent of old-age pensions.

Chamberlain was building on the activist local government he had helped to create in Birmingham, a proponent of the constructive positive role for government that foreshadowed the New Liberalism of the next century. Chamberlain's 'caucus' was the new cutting edge of party organisation, but he envisaged the NLF as a means of depriving Whigs like Hartington of the power they had held over Liberal governments. Chamberlain had all the prickly consciousness of the outsider and the guile of a self-made businessman.

Consequently, the counterfactual presents a rosier view of Cabinet life after 1885 than seems probable. Tussles between the two men would have hindered progress and were more likely to have occurred if they had remained within Liberalism than in the adversity they faced jointly as Unionists.

The other feature of political life that has been too lightly skated over in this sketch is Ireland. In reality, Parnell's troubles were as outlined, but his MPs were well versed in the arts of obstruction. Even without him, they remained well placed to make demands for land reform and 'the management of their own affairs' that Hartington was most unlikely to concede. This would inevitably have limited Liberal achievements.

Chamberlain first wrote about old-age pensions early in 1892, and it would not have been unreasonable for him to have included such proposals in 1891 if an election had taken place that year, though he did not at that time propound a means of financing pensions beyond employees' contributions. I have similarly anticipated the other reforms for working men that he proposed in 1892. What might be thought surprising is the modesty of his programmes in 1885 and 1892. In the speech at Smethwick he explained:

> When a man tells you he is going to pass, not five or six, but twenty or thirty, omnibuses through Temple-bar, I do not believe him; and when a man puts before you a programme of the kind of the Newcastle programme, with so many items, with promises to oblige everybody all over the place, you may be quite certain that these are promises not intended to be fulfilled but only promises to catch votes.[14]

Chamberlain was the innovative executive, not the idealist visionary.

Gladstone's magnificent but futile Irish home rule crusade deprived the Liberal Party of Hartington's leadership and Chamberlain of the opportunity to deliver his Radical Programme. For a decade, British problems were neglected and the ambitions of the new working-class electorate frustrated. The seeds of Liberal decline and the rise of the Labour Party were both sown.

While Hartington was merely an effective administrator, Chamberlain was a visionary of the modern political party and the practical welfare state: a force Liberalism should not have lost and a force from which Conservativism gained, in his lifetime and through his sons, Austen and Neville. In thinking the unthinkable too often and in his ruthless political professionalism, Chamberlain was always likely to overreach. And, yet, an earlier birth of the welfare state, in the 1890s, was a practical possibility, and a Chamberlain-influenced Liberal Party might have prevented the birth of an independent Labour Party – but that is a story for another day.

Notes

1. C. H. D. Howard (ed.), *A Political Memoir, 1880–92 by Joseph Chamberlain* (The Batchworth Press, 1953), p. 110.
2. Patrick Jackson (ed.), *Loulou: Selected Extracts from the Journals of Lewis Harcourt (1880–1895)* (Associated University Presses, 2006), p. 108.
3. Winston Churchill, *Great Contemporaries* (Fontana 1965 reprint), p. 63.
4. T. J. Spinner, 'George Joachim Goschen', *Oxford Dictionary of National Biography*.
5. C. Cook and B. Keith, *British Historical Facts 1830–1900* (St Martin's Press, 1975).
6. Jackson, op. cit., p. 76.
7. *The Times*, 30 October 1885, p. 7.
8. Ibid.
9. Peter T. Marsh, *Joseph Chamberlain: Entrepreneur in Politics* (Yale University Press, 1994), pp. 212–13.
10. Ibid., p. 334.
11. Ibid., pp. 334–5; *The Times*, 10 June 1892, p. 10.
12. Chamberlain's speech at Smethwick, *The Times*, 10 June 1892, p. 10.
13. *The Times*, 19 September 1885.
14. *The Times*, 10 June 1892, p. 10.

Chapter 2

What if Britain and France had unified in 1940?

David Boyle

> 'Although vain, the process of trying to imagine what would have happened if some important event or decision had been different is often tempting and sometimes instructive. The manner of the fall of France was decided on June 16 by a dozen chances, each measured by a hair's-breadth.'
>
> – *Winston Churchill, The Second World War, Vol. II*

It is 20 June 1940. Nazi troops occupy Paris and France teeters on the edge of collapse. The British Prime Minister Winston Churchill, only ten days in office, sits at the microphone in a studio in Broadcasting House. The red light flashes and he is broadcasting to a Europe that is now under Nazi control from Brest to Warsaw.[1]

'I am speaking to you now as the voice of free Europe,' he intones in the rotund phraseology that was to become so familiar, but sounded at the time a little as if Edward VII has risen from the dead, to embody the values of Victorian speech and Victorian England. Churchill continues:

> Yesterday, a final note was broadcast to Hitler warning that, if he did not state by noon this morning that he would withdraw his troops from France, then a new nation would arise to push him back to Berlin, and his forces into well-deserved oblivion. I have to tell you now that no such undertaking has been received, and consequently this nation is now subsumed into an indissoluble union with France.

> This is an historic moment in the destinies of our two nations. The genius of them both, forged together into one mighty alliance, now form the champion who is called upon to defend the world against tyranny. We will not fail humanity in this monumental task. We Britons will defend our island home, but we will also fight alongside our French compatriots. There is now no French and no British, no French Empire and no British Empire, but one impregnable nation that will not rest until the curse of Hitlerism is lifted from the brows of mankind.

~

In fact, Churchill made no such speech. Nor did he, as far as anyone knows, even write notes for it. It isn't even very well understood that he was working towards making it – but he was. For a few days in June 1940, the proposed unification of Britain and France was at the forefront of his mind and the subject of the most frenetic activity among his Cabinet members and closest aides. It was Britain's chosen response to the imminent fall of France and the threat that the powerful French fleet would fall into Nazi hands, an eventuality that would give Hitler a fighting chance of making a successful invasion of the UK. It didn't happen because of the fall of his French opposite number, Paul Reynaud, who had backed the plan.

But what if it had? What if the two nations, after centuries of rivalry, had suddenly found themselves one? The rest of this chapter didn't happen – but it might have.

~

Churchill's broadcast was stirring stuff and it was intended to be. But the speech was received with astonishment in the homes of the United Kingdom, where little idea of his emergency plan for national union had filtered through to the wider populace. Indeed, the idea of a union between Britain and France was really only understood by Churchill, his Cabinet and his immediate circle of advisers.

A thousand questions came into everyone's minds, and the minds of the newspaper editors – questions and a new note of fear. The peril must be great indeed for the nation to cast aside a thousand years of independence to unite with their traditional enemies across the English Channel – and not just as a temporary arrangement, but as an 'indissoluble union'.

Could such a union survive, when the cultures and administrative systems of the two nations were so different? Churchill's worrying use of the word 'indissoluble' seemed to emphasise the problem – it begged the question. If it could not be dissolved, what was it, and how could it stand in the first place? Were the British still a monarchy? Was France still a republic? Which Parliament and Cabinet would prevail? Who would decide in disputes between them? How would the Napoleonic legal code mesh with Anglo-Saxon legal complexities and nuance? Who would have command of the armed forces – the navy and air force? Would there be a new Marshal Foch as commander-in-chief, as there had been in the Great War? And, perhaps most urgently: how could the new nation conduct itself equally when half of it was under Nazi rule or the rule of Nazi sympathisers?

The truth was that Churchill himself had not really addressed these questions, even to himself – except that there would be an Anglo-French super-state, in practice a working committee that met in London and managed the war effort on behalf of both nations. The French government would continue in North Africa, and would control the French Navy from Dakar. The French fleet would sail from its base in southern France, beyond the reach of the Nazis. Both Parliaments would continue as before to oversee the administration of their own empires.

This arrangement was also controversial in defeated France. Some, like Marshal Pétain and General Weygand, feared that it was some kind of plot by the British to take control of their empire. If it had not been for Prime Minister Reynaud unilaterally closing the Cabinet meeting on 16 June, when the reaction to Churchill's proposal for a Declaration of Union ran into such vociferous opposition from Pétain, the union would never have taken place.

Reynaud understood that his ministers had met expecting to hear a British response to their request to renege on their agreement not to make a separate peace, made only two and a half months before. Some of the ministers had heard about the proposal for union only because all sides in the unravelling and complex melee were then tapping each other's phones.

When Pétain made his famous charge that it would be like 'fusion with a corpse', Reynaud closed the meeting and agreed to convene again the next day. There was uproar, and he realised that he must stay in office for at least twenty-four hours more, if he could. Armed guards were placed around his office. De Gaulle, Defence Minister in his government, agreed to take responsibility for security around the centre of Bordeaux, where the French government had fled.

At noon on 17 June, Churchill himself docked at Bordeaux and made for the French Cabinet room, accompanied by Clement Attlee and Archibald Sinclair, the Labour and Liberal leaders, and the three service chiefs. They had left the Cabinet room in Whitehall at 6 p.m. the previous evening by special train from Waterloo and steamed by cruiser though the night to arrive just before lunchtime. A small detachment of British troops formed a defensive shield around the British dignitaries.

Churchill summarised his proposal in the following terms: 'No release from the obligation of 28 March unless the French fleet is sailed to British ports. On the other hand, we offer an indissoluble Anglo-French Union. Go to Africa and let us fight it out together.'[2]

He and his delegation were greeted with suspicion by the despairing French Cabinet, and the confrontation was not slow in coming. When Jean Ybarnégaray, Reynaud's Minister of State, said, 'Better be a Nazi province; at least we know what that means,' Reynaud turned on him and replied, 'I prefer to collaborate with my allies rather than with my enemies.'[3]

The power of Churchill's oratory, backed up by skilful interpretation by General Sir Edward Spears – a close friend of de Gaulle's – began to convince the waverers. It gave them hope. Churchill had written two addresses during the night, one for when his back was against the wall – as he predicted it would be. It foresaw that the union between France and Britain would form the basis of a United States of Europe that was powerful enough, intellectually, technically and economically, not just to expel tyranny, but to found a new era of peace that would provide a bedrock for the stability of the world.

Once again, Churchill read his amended declaration: 'At this most fateful moment in the history of the modern world, the governments of the

United Kingdom and the French Republic make this declaration of indissoluble union and unyielding resolution in their common defence of justice and freedom against subjection to a system which reduces mankind to a life of robots and slaves. The two governments declare that France and Great Britain shall no longer be two nations...'[4]

Reynaud achieved a slim majority in support of the proposal, and Pétain and Weygand stormed out of the room, where they were placed under arrest by British troops, taken quickly to a waiting plane and flown to London.[5] They were imprisoned in the Tower of London.

Reynaud and his closest colleagues accompanied Churchill on the cruiser back to London. The Colonies Minister, Georges Mandel, went by the destroyer HMS *Berkeley* to Dakar to establish the new seat of French government and administration. Spears accompanied de Gaulle and the Blockade Minister Georges Monnet by plane to London. It was therefore Reynaud who stood next to Churchill as he made his BBC broadcast, and took his turn at the microphone to assert that France would fight on. This is what he said:

> France is not alone. We are now part of a great empire, a Franco-British Empire that holds the seas and has access to the vast industrial resources of the United States. The French government is now in North Africa, our capital is occupied and the days seem dark with the suffering and difficulties to come. I do not want to belittle the challenge that faces my country. But France remains France and, in a greater whole, the new union will be triumphant.[6]

With Reynaud and de Gaulle in London, assisted by the diplomat Jean Monnet, and Mandel in North Africa, the French government was at a huge disadvantage in the new Union – divided by geography. The fact that it stayed united was entirely due to the trust that existed between Reynaud and his predecessor Édouard Daladier, who continued as Foreign Minister from Morocco; he understood that – despite his suspicions – it was critical to their survival that the relationship should last.[7] If London and North Africa remained on the same side, then the union could stand.

The new nation was known as the Union of European Democracies. Four decisions became critical to its success.

First, it was important that there was to be no head of state. The two Parliaments delegated their powers to the new joint union War Cabinet. King George and the French President, Albert Lebrun, also met regularly and retained their original powers in relation to their own people. The decision about the final status of the union after the war was put off until then, though a joint socialist platform began to emerge urging that the union should be a republic. There was also a conservative move to restore some kind of joint monarchy, but it was always sketchy as to how this was to be achieved – though there was much celebration of the 1421 Treaty of Troyes, the last time the two nations were on the verge of becoming one. The Cross of Lorraine became a symbol of resistance to the union just as Joan of Arc had resisted the Treaty of Troyes.

Second, the union needed some kind of formal identity. Although designers tried to merge the Union Jack and the Tricouleur, it was eventually decided that an entirely new symbol should be constructed. Jean Monnet borrowed the symbol of the crown of stars around the head of the Virgin Mary, though he was never explicit about its source. The final design, as produced by Paul Lévy, the Belgian journalist who escaped from occupied Europe to join the staff of the European broadcasting service, was a flag of twelve yellow stars on a blue background.[8]

Third, the decision was made that the French Navy would concentrate first on the Mediterranean, supported by elements of the British fleet and using the British bases at Gibraltar and Malta. The Italian Navy was destroyed at anchor in Taranto Harbour.[9] Rome was hit by French bombers from North African airfields, meaning that, instead of spreading out from Greece and into Africa, the war concentrated on the Greek–Italian border. Rommel was diverted there: the Afrika Korps became the Adriatic Corps. The Italian armies in Africa surrendered within months in 1940. Hitler briefly drew up plans for the invasion of North Africa through Spain, but realised that this would jeopardise his more critical plans for invading Soviet Russia, and he eventually opted for the latter.

The final decision that cemented the union was the dismemberment of the BBC, which was anyway under consideration by the Foreign Office.[10] The union would take over the BBC European Service, with the *Manchester Guardian*'s former Paris correspondent Darsie Gillie as joint Director with the BBC's European news editor Noel Newsome. The two men fought throughout the war, but, under their joint control, the European Broadcasting Service became the biggest broadcasting operation in history.[11] For anyone who wanted accurate war news, free – at least to some extent – of spin, the European Broadcasting Service was the only one to listen to, aware of the propaganda value of getting its side's own bad news out before the other side's. It gathered to itself all the resource of European history and culture and flung them over the airwaves at the Nazis.

~

The date of the invasion of Europe was a source of huge friction among the Allies, with the British side linking with the Americans to urge delay and certainty, and the French side allied with the Russians to urge haste. A compromise was agreed for D-Day in 1943, a joint operation with French, British and Canadian troops landing in Normandy and French and American troops landing in Provence. It was de Gaulle – still Defence Minister – who was appointed supreme commander of the northern invasion. Fighting was difficult as de Gaulle faced a fearsome opponent in Rommel, but the winter of 1943/44 marked the turn of the tide, with the Nazis facing their most bitter defeat in Stalingrad just as de Gaulle led French tank columns to liberate Paris in the snow. The European Broadcasting Service took over Radio Luxembourg when that city was liberated, and the polyglot broadcasters moved there to become the voice of the victorious allies.[12]

The combination of a successful invasion in the west and defeat in the east hastened the end of the war; hostilities ended in early 1945 after Hitler committed suicide in the ruins of his bunker in Berlin. The politicians in both previous nations then turned their attention to the central post-war issue: should the indissoluble union continue? The consensus between both former nations was that it should not.

Leading French and British politicians had felt constrained by the need for consensus during the war effort. They had been scarred by battles within the War Cabinet about priorities and by the British insistence that naval power should reside with a British admiral. When the battleship *Bismarck* had been sunk off the French coast by a French squadron, it had irritated the French side that this fact had not been sufficiently celebrated. De Gaulle's trenchant and intolerant style as military commander-in-chief had not won him many friends either, and there were constant difficulties about the overall command of the union air force.

But, especially in London, there had been a cadre of senior French politicians – led by Georges Monnet and encouraged by Reynaud himself – who had looked to the post-war future with the union still in place. When they began to think more clearly about the future shape of Europe, the union between France and Britain seemed to them to be a largely successful pattern, forged by two sets of armed forces fighting side by side in France, and underpinned by the success of the European Broadcasting Service over the airwaves – and by the request of the Belgian government that they should become partners in the union as well.

A joint War Cabinet committee of both former nation's Cabinets met in London in the final year of the war to broker proposals about the post-war shape of the union. Clearly, if it were to continue in this present form, then some of the issues that had been postponed – whether the union was a monarchy or republic, for example – would have to be faced. There was also a limit to how long the debate between the advocates of an established church and those of a secular state could be prevented from arguing bitterly in public.

The request of the Belgian government was followed by expressions of interest by other nations that had been under occupation – the Netherlands, Poland, Denmark and even Norway. One of the effects of ending the war early in 1945 was that Soviet forces had not yet pushed the Nazis back beyond the Polish border. The Iron Curtain descended further east; paradoxically, this meant less establishment fear of the Red Menace – and the French and British Communist parties linked together to form a formidable electoral unit. NATO, when it was formed, was correspondingly both more controversial and less powerful. The issue of nuclear weapons was to become more fraught, as they were among the deepest secrets that had not been fully shared between the new partners in the joint nation.

But the key question was the future of this new Europe, stretching from Brest to Brest-Litovsk. The chair of the joint War Cabinet committee, Jean Monnet, realised that the union could form the basis for the dream sketched out by Reynaud for a United States of Europe. This was therefore the blueprint that was put forward.

Aware that the new union would find it hard to be fully democratic on its own if the nations within it – with their democratic institutions – were to disappear, the new union was proposed not as a super-state but as a *supra*-state. It was not intended that it would aim at statehood itself, but to continue the values of democracy that had been forged during the war and articulated by the polyglot broadcasting service. Monnet was also careful not to let economics come within the remit of the new Union. It was to be based on the cultural union forged by the broadcasters during the war. The model was not to be the United States of America; it was the example of the cacophony of the European Broadcasting Service in its headquarters at Bush House, which would remain in existence in Luxembourg as the beating heart of the new union.

The new European Union was given a constitution based on the original Anglo-French Union of 1940. This was the date that marked its anniversaries, as the moment a peaceful new kind of Europe emerged. It was supported by the extreme right who, like Oswald Mosley, regarded the new entity as an antidote to free trade, a new customs union supplied by the twin empires of Britain and France. It was supported by the imperialists who had tasted an empire that included Francophone Africa and India and much of the English-speaking and French-speaking worlds. It was supported by the left, as a bastion against a resurgent United States. It was supported by Liberals in both nations on the grounds that this was internationalism in action, and it led to a resurgence of Liberalism in France. It was supported by both Cabinets, now in the grip of social reformers in both nations, as the foundation for a new social settlement. The Communists opposed it, on the grounds that Stalin was unsure how to respond.

There were of course diehard opponents, including wide swathes of the public who complained that the other side had not suffered as much as they had – the British had been bombed and the French had been starved, and these were not considered equivalents. They complained that the union had led to compromised decision-making. There were also complaints about the number of French people living in England, setting up bakeries that pushed out native British businesses. But it was a foundation for the Europe of the future, forged in war and with all the advantages and disadvantages of that. It continues to this day.

So Britain and France went back to being Britain and France, but with their main focus elsewhere – as twin pillars of a new institution that covered the whole of Europe and was based, as Monnet hoped, not on trade but on culture.

~

As we know, this is not quite how it happened. Churchill's proposals for the union were thrown out by Reynaud's Cabinet on 16 June after a furious meeting that led to his resignation. De Gaulle, who had backed the union, was spirited out of the country by Spears on a light plane the following day. Reynaud's car crashed as he drove south from Bordeaux and he was arrested by the new administration. So was Mandel, who had succeeded in getting to North Africa, after refusing a seat in the plane that took de Gaulle to London. Reynaud's place was taken by Pétain, as head of state for the new Vichy regime. Not satisfied with the Vichy government's assurances about the French fleet, the ships were attacked and put beyond use by British naval forces at Oran and Toulon in July 1940. French forces were bogged down in the Middle East and North Africa in what amounted in effect to a civil war, the wounds of which have never entirely healed. The rest is history.

The idea that the new European Union might have been based on Radio Luxembourg is not as far-fetched as it might seem. The nations of Western Europe were all joint controllers of the radio station in 1945, and the Americans and French backed the plan to turn it into a permanent institution dedicated to objective news and international understanding. One of the last acts of Churchill's wartime coalition was to veto this idea by withdrawing British involvement, to the horror of the Americans and those who had been shaping it until then.

It is next to impossible to predict what the military implications of the union would have been, except to guess that D-Day would have come earlier, the fighting would have been fiercer, the war might have ended sooner and the great divisions of the Cold War would have been further east. But any number of other factors might then have come into play. And since it didn't happen, we don't have a laboratory to find out.

But it was so nearly different. Certainly Churchill believed so. 'If Paul Reynaud had survived the 16th, I should have been with him at noon on the 17th, accompanied by the most powerful delegation that has ever left our shores, armed with plenary [*sic*] powers in the name of the British nation,'[13] he wrote in the second volume of his Second World War history, for which he was awarded the Nobel Prize for Literature. 'It seems to me probable that we should have uplifted and converted the defeatists round the table, or left them in a minority or even under arrest.'

Churchill's speculations about how the war effort would have been changed if this had happened form the basis for this chapter.

Notes

1. Although Churchill never made this broadcast, a similar one, with a different message, was made by Charles de Gaulle from the same studio.
2. Winston Churchill, *The Second World War, Vol II: Their Finest Hour* (reprint, London: Cassell, 1951), p. 188.
3. Ibid., p. 182.
4. Ibid., p. 179.
5. There was actually a waiting plane, but it was in reality used to take de Gaulle to London instead.
6. He made no such speech, of course.
7. In fact, Daladier did escape to Morocco where he was arrested and tried by the Vichy regime. His rivalry with Reynaud would have made their relationship critical if the London–Morocco link at the heart of Franco-British unity was to work.
8. Remarkably like the one he actually designed, actually.
9. As they were, in fact.
10. The BBC European Service actually came under joint Foreign Office and Ministry of Information control early in 1941.

11. As the BBC European Service did in fact become, broadcasting from Bush House on three channels and in twenty-five different languages (including English) for a total of thirty-six hours a day. Newsome was actually the inspirational Director of European Broadcasts; Gillie was head of the French service.
12. In reality, Radio Luxembourg became the voice of SHAEF as it advanced westwards.
13. Churchill, *The Second World War, Vol. II*, p. 188f.

Chapter 3

What if Lyndon Johnson had been shot down in 1942?

Robert Waller

On 9 June 1942, Representative Lyndon Baines Johnson of the tenth district of Texas flew on his one and only combat mission of the Second World War. A lieutenant commander in the US Naval Reserve since 1940, he had been sent by President Roosevelt to report on conditions in the South West Pacific in April 1942. Always a man with an eye for a chance of gaining publicity to bolster his overwhelming drive to further his political career, Johnson volunteered to act as an observer on a 900-mile bombing raid from Garbutt Field near Townsville, Australia, on the Japanese air base in Lae, in north-eastern New Guinea.

The B-26 Marauder bomber in which he was flying, named the *Heckling Hare*, was attacked on the outward journey by Japanese Zero fighters. Its right engine generator was put out of action, and bullets tore through the fuselage. Jettisoning its bomb load, it turned and crawled back to Australia. Johnson was later to magnify his single experience of combat and use it in future campaigns. He was awarded the Silver Star medal for gallantry in action. There are those who deny that Johnson's aircraft ever came under fire from the enemy, but his indefatigable biographer Robert Caro's interviews with the *Heckling Hare*'s bombardier and tail gunner support the politician's account.[1]

In any case, this counterfactual exercise does not depend on this issue. Johnson had switched Marauders just before take-off, having stepped off the plane to urinate, being replaced as observer on the *Wabash Cannonball* by Lieutenant-Colonel Francis Stevens of the USAF. The change was so sudden and unplanned that Johnson left his observer's movie camera on the *Cannonball*. The *Wabash Cannonball* never returned to Australia. It too had been attacked by Zeroes and was shot down with the loss of all its crew – and Stevens.

What if Lyndon Johnson had not swapped aircraft at the very last minute? Or what if the *Heckling Hare* had met the same fate if it was indeed damaged by hostile fire? Not only would there never have been an LBJ presidency, but the course of the history of the United States would undoubtedly have been changed significantly in a number of key fields. JFK would never have become President in 1960. Nor would the history of civil rights, of the anti-poverty measures taken in Johnson's Great Society programme, or of the Vietnam War, have transpired in the same way.

Having survived his brush with the Pacific War, Lyndon Johnson went on to be elected as US Senator for Texas in the 'stolen' election of 1948, in which he defeated the former governor Coke Stevenson, the 'greatest vote winner in the history of the state', by manipulating the corrupt counties along the Mexican border. Once a member of Congress's upper chamber, through his extraordinarily energetic and powerful character he rapidly became what Caro's third volume of biography calls the 'Master of the Senate'.[2] Not only does this imply an unprecedented personal dominance, but he revived and promoted the very role of the Senate, which had for a long period fallen into being a negative body controlled by reactionary southern senators, whose seniority – amassed due to Dixie's single-party politics – gave them control of most of the key committee chairs. This counterweight to reform was most evidently seen in the successful obstruction, until the 1950s, of all questions of African-American civil rights, such as anti-lynching measures, despite the efforts of more sympathetic presidents, such as Truman, and of the House of Representatives.

Caro convincingly demonstrates that it was only because of LBJ's status as undisputed master of the upper house, and because of his unique position as a southerner and as a close friend of power brokers such as Senator Richard Russell of Georgia (the de facto leader of the conservative bloc) that he was able to push through the 1957 Civil Rights Act. Although this measure was largely stripped of teeth due to the compromise that removed the Act's proposed Part III, which would have enforced prohibition on segregation in all public locations, it was nevertheless the first civil rights legislation that had broken through the dam of the Senate since the Reconstruction years of 1865–77. As such, it represented a symbolic boost for the non-violent civil rights movement already associated with Martin Luther King. If Lyndon Johnson had been killed in 1942, it can be assumed not only that the 1957 Act would not have passed at all, but that the Senate would have remained a block to progressive legislation of all kinds for much longer, because it was only LBJ's irrepressible energy in pursuit of his own power that enhanced the position of the majority leader at the expense of the Deep South's stranglehold on the committee chairmanships. The consequences for civil rights and the African-American protest movement in the 1960s will be further considered below.

It was Johnson's uniquely self-crafted role as master of the Senate, as well as his attraction as a southern and relatively conservative counterbalance, that persuaded John F. Kennedy, over the strong objections of his brother Bobby, to offer LBJ the position of vice-presidential candidate in the 1960 election. It is also quite clear that without Johnson on the ticket, JFK would not have won that 'damned close-run thing' against Richard Nixon.

The subsequent attention given to the manner in which the state of Illinois may have been carried by the Democrats tells us how narrow Kennedy's victory was. He gained Illinois's twenty-seven electoral college votes, by fair means or foul, by under 11,000 votes out of 5 million cast. But he also won LBJ's Texas's twenty-four votes by only 46,000 out of 2.25 million, which is a margin of 2 per cent. The balance in the electoral college would have been tipped to Nixon if Kennedy had not taken two other southern states, South Carolina and North Carolina, also by less than a 5 per cent margin; and that discounts any bonus Johnson may have brought to his cause in several other extremely close states. Kennedy actually won in terms of the popular vote by just 49.72 per cent to Nixon's 49.55 per cent, and the electoral college vote would have been reversed by the transfer of any four well-populated states.

If LBJ had not been available, Kennedy could not have chosen a well-known running mate in 1960 who would have supplemented his own appeal; the main contenders would probably have been the liberal Hubert Humphrey of Minnesota in the far north or, most likely, Stuart Symington of Midwestern Missouri, who had refused to speak to segregated audiences in his own presidential bid. Kennedy won both Minnesota and Missouri in any case.

~

To embark on our counterfactual trajectory, without Johnson on the ticket we may therefore concede the 1960 race to the Republican Richard Nixon. Nixon beat Kennedy in the key southern states of Texas, its neighbour Arkansas, and the Carolinas, to win the electoral college by 273 to 249, with fifteen unpledged voters who backed the segregationist Robert Byrd. With Nixon as President from his inauguration in January 1961, there would have been no New Frontier programme, no court of 'Camelot' in the White House, and no assassination in Dallas to create the aura of martyrdom and lost hope that surrounded the Kennedy legend (or myth).

Nixon's first term would still undoubtedly have had to deal with the wider forces that impinged upon American politics in the early 1960s. The problems associated with civil rights, for example, would have been even more urgent and divisive if there had been no progress (however nominal) in the form of the passing of an Act in 1957. Nixon, along with many other Republicans, had in the 1950s been in favour of reforms to satisfy some black citizens' demands, if only to discomfit the Democrats by spotlighting the difference between their northern liberal and southern racist wings. However, even if he had wished to enact civil rights legislation, he would have had to overcome a southern bloc in the Senate totally dedicated to resistance, as it would not have been weakened by a desire to support Johnson's ambitions to become the first man elected to the White House from a southern state since the Civil War, as well as by LBJ's own extraordinary capacity to 'get things done'. What is more, Nixon could well have been faced by a different kind of African-American campaign.

As the non-violent campaign typified by the Southern Christian Leadership Conference (SCLC), led by King and other predominantly religious leaders like Fred Shuttlesworth of Birmingham, Joseph Lowery of Mobile and Ralph Abernathy of Montgomery, had apparently made no progress whatsoever in the halls of government, with no Civil Rights Act and the Democrats having been defeated in the 1960 election, the ideas and methods of what came to be known as Black Power advanced more quickly than they otherwise would have done. As Herbert Parmet wrote in *Richard Nixon and His America*, 'the transition from civil disobedience to black power, the transition from movement to revolution ... was plainly shredding established alliances'.[3] For example, the campaign against segregation in public facilities, such as the city's parks in Birmingham, Alabama, included violent elements. For this reason, and because armed intervention in the South would have offended local white sensibilities even more if ordered by a Republican President, with its connotations of the Civil War and Reconstruction, Nixon did not send 3,000 federal troops to Birmingham (as Kennedy did in May 1963). The resulting suppression of the 'Children's Crusade' involving predominantly very young protestors, by fire hoses and police dogs, ordered by the city's 'Commissioner of Public Safety' Theophilus ('Bull') Connor, inflamed the situation across the nation even further. Support for Malcolm X and the Nation of Islam was fuelled among black communities. As discontent spread from the Deep South to northern ghettoes, and the issues spread from voting and segregation to housing, crime and policing, the Nation's own pastoral leaders became as well known as those of the SCLC, men such as the Minister of Temple No. 25 in Newark, New Jersey, James 3X Shabazz. Malcolm himself had already become nationally known as early as 1959 following the publicity gained by the Wallace–Lomax TV series *The Hate That Hate Produced* and his debates on New York City's WMCA radio with the Reverend William James in 1960.[4] Both before and after his break with Elijah Muhammad in 1964, Malcolm X became the most well-known exponent – and then martyr – of the whole African-American struggle of the 1960s.

Whatever his views on civil rights had been, Nixon could not tolerate such extremism and disorder. The Black Panther Party was included on his secret 'List of Enemies',[5] and when Tom Huston of Young Americans for Freedom set out a plan to combat the Panthers along with the Weathermen and other domestic 'terrorist groups' by increasing the budget for the intelligence agencies to carry out covert operations, including 'black bagging', wiretapping and bugging, Nixon approved it when even J. Edgar Hoover had been opposed.[6] He extended the COINTELPRO surveillance programme, including the use of ghetto informants, instituted the 'go-slow' on school desegregation and nominated the southern segregationists Clement Haynsworth and G. Harrold Carswell to the Supreme Court. It was not surprising that the summers of 1963 and 1964 saw serious riots in black ghettoes in the north and west such as Bedford-Stuyvesant and Brownsville in New York, South Chicago, much of Detroit below the 'eight-mile line', and Watts in Los Angeles.

As Vice-President for eight years before entering the White House, Nixon was experienced in the politics of the Cold War. He had already made many trips abroad, including to Vietnam in French Indo-China in 1953 and, notably, to the Soviet Union, meeting Khrushchev in 1959, the occasion of the 'kitchen debate' at the American National Exhibition in Moscow. He knew that he needed to present a response that was superficially strong when Khrushchev ordered the construction of the Berlin Wall in August 1961, while accepting that it was ultimately a stabilising force rather than a *casus belli*. Nixon did back the abortive Bay of Pigs invasion by Cuban exiles in 1961, having 'pushed for action against Cuba as far as he dared' while Eisenhower was still President (according to his biographer Stephen Ambrose) but even the provision of more air cover (there was no question of 'boots on the ground') made no impact on Castro's solid support on the island.[7] His combination of apparent strength with the avoidance of provocation avoided the possibility of a nuclear World War Three in the Cuban Missile Crisis of 1962, as after quarantining Castro's island with an impressive blockade Nixon was ultimately willing to use back channels to secure a compromise which led to the withdrawal of Soviet missiles without bombing or a full-scale American invasion.

Similarly, Nixon's early response to an escalation of tension in Vietnam was relatively cautious. For example, as a long-standing supporter of President Ngo Dinh Diem he refused to sanction CIA involvement in a proposed coup against him in 1963, with the result that Diem narrowly clung on to office.[8] Nevertheless, Nixon had a long history of being determined to stop Communist infiltration of Indo-China, and by the time of the US presidential election in November 1964, there were an increasing number of American 'advisers' there, and the region remained inherently unstable due to Buddhist protests and the widespread insurgency.

It was not surprising that Nixon won a landslide re-election in 1964. No incumbent President in the twentieth century had been denied a second term, apart from the wholly exceptional cases of Herbert Hoover in 1932, in the aftermath of the Wall Street Crash, and William Taft in 1912, thanks to the 'Bull Moose' Republican Party split. The violent turn to the black civil rights demands had frightened the white majority of voters, many of whom, especially in the South, supported Nixon's firm response to the 'extremists' rather than endorsing concessions to black Americans. In foreign policy, Nixon had steered a firm but apparently moderate path. In such circumstances, it was not surprising that potentially strong Democratic candidates eschewed the fight. John F. Kennedy's defeat in 1960 had cast doubt on the likely success of any Catholic candidacy, and in addition, the revelations in an age of ever-developing media of his increasingly severe health problems (principally Addison's Disease), along with growing rumours about his less than religiously correct private life, militated against him running again – and indeed tainted any suggestions favouring his younger brother Robert, who had also made many enemies due to his aggressive personality. Robert Kennedy instead ran for a Senate seat in New York, but was defeated in the November Republican sweep by the incumbent Kenneth Keating. The most prominent liberal, Humphrey, toyed with a challenge but decided that a contest against a popular incumbent promised little chance of success. So, almost by default, the Democratic nomination fell to the ambitious centrist Symington, the runner-up at the 1960 Convention. He won just one state (Massachusetts) plus the District of Columbia, failing even to pick up his own Missouri.

Why, then, many have wondered, did Nixon feel that he needed to adopt or sanction the behaviour that was to end his second term prematurely in disgrace? As has gradually been revealed, the activities of CREEP (the Campaign to Re-elect the President) in 1964 included a variety of dirty tricks, of which the bungled burglary of the Democratic National

Headquarters at 1730 K Street in Washington, not far from the White House, in June has become just the most infamous. Indeed, the notoriety of K Street is why subsequently so many political scandals have had '-street' appended to their names, such as 'Contrastreet' in the Reagan presidency, and even, after an alleged misdemeanour by a Conservative Chief Whip in Britain in 2012, 'Gatestreet'.[9] The story of the connections between the burglary and Nixon's White House, and the subsequent attempts to cover these up, are too well known to need recounting here, as is the role of the Senate Judiciary Subcommittee on Constitutional Rights under its chairman from 1961 to 1974, Sam Ervin of North Carolina. Perhaps the best explanation may simply be that of the ancient fable of the scorpion and the frog: Nixon cheated because it was in his (paranoid) nature to cheat. In any case, the outcome was, of course, his tearful resignation in August 1966. What can be of no doubt was the weakening of the presidency, both personally for Nixon in 1964–66, and of the office itself.

For example, not only did Congress (still with a firm Democrat majority in both houses)[10] take aim at the perceived corruption of American political campaigns in the Federal Election Campaigns Act of 1966, but it also passed the War Powers Act of 1965, a federal law intended to check the President's power to commit the country to an armed conflict without the consent of Congress, in the form of a US Congress joint resolution – something Nixon seemed to be fully intent of doing in 1965.[11] It provided that the President could send US armed forces into action abroad only through a declaration of war by Congress, 'statutory authorisation', or in the case of 'a national emergency created by attack upon the United States, its territories or possessions, or its armed forces'. If it had not been for the War Powers Act, it is quite possible that the US could have become even more embroiled in a widespread and potentially unwinnable conflict in Vietnam, for example, as the Communists in the shape both of the home-grown Viet Cong and Ho Chi Minh's North Vietnamese Army overran the country in the late 1960s. That could have caused serious cultural and generational conflict within the US, especially given the growing protests among students and other young people in support of the civil rights movement and the spread of ideas of 'free love' and 'flower power'.

On the other hand, the paralysis in executive government in the mid-1960s undoubtedly increased divisions *within* the US. Further advances by the separatist Black Power movement, and riots in the summers of 1965 and 1966, emphasised the need for something to be done to assuage the nation's ever-growing racial conflict, but the absence of a strong (and some said the absence of a sympathetic) presidency meant that a Civil Rights Act or a Voting Rights Act could not be passed, even after Martin Luther King's attempted march from Selma to Montgomery in March 1965 was brutally put down by the law enforcement forces of Sheriff Jim Clark and Alabama Governor George Wallace. No presidential support was publicly offered for the Selma campaign, not least as that was the month that – it is now known – was key to the establishment of the K Street cover-up. As the months and years without significant governmental action on civil rights continued, King became more and more of a marginalised figure and ceased to attract much publicity; though perhaps it can be said that this at least saved his life, in the light of the assassination of Malcolm X, the best known of the thousands of victims of the race-related violence of the 1960s.

Discontent within the US was not, of course, confined to African-American communities. Many white Americans also suffered from the privations associated with poverty and gross inequalities in the world's most powerful economy. Were it not for Nixon's own embattled position, a comprehensive programme might have been devised to tackle problems such as unemployment (particularly severe in the Appalachians, a predominantly white region), education and housing, including rent subsidies, rehabilitation grants and urban renewal programmes. There could have been, say, a Job Corps to mirror the Peace Corps. In the fields of health and welfare, an opportunity was missed to introduce what later became Medicare and Medicaid, and the Food Stamp programme remained temporary. Overall, it could be said that in the middle of the 1960s the state of America's society was not so great.

President Henry Cabot Lodge Junior was always something of a lame duck. It is a little unfair that he is best known today as 'the man who pardoned Nixon'. His room for manoeuvre was swiftly limited by the massive Democratic landslide of the 1966 mid-term elections, when the Republicans lost forty-nine seats in the House of Representatives, leaving them with only a bare third of the seats, and the Democrats increased their numbers in the Senate beyond the sixty mark.[12] Lodge, a courtly Massachusetts Brahmin largely overshadowed by the far-from-smooth Californian, had quietly served as Nixon's Vice-President from 1960 to 1966, but as a foreign policy expert (US ambassador to the United Nations 1953–60) he had been a discreetly moderating influence on Cold War and Vietnam policy; as he wrote in his autobiography, 'I reached the conclusion that we should withdraw our troops from Vietnam as fast as this could be done in an orderly way and try to negotiate settlement.'[13] That was in 1963. However, he had no chance of success in his attempt to be elected in his own right in 1968.

The United States was deeply divided and troubled – not over Vietnam, but over the violent civil rights struggle and the issue of whether more should be done to address poverty in a wide range of communities. The Republican brand had been severely damaged by the Nixon scandal, as the mid-term elections had demonstrated. The issue was which Democrat would emerge from the selection process – now more than ever influenced by the fourteen states that ran primaries – rather than the summer convention. Senator Eugene McCarthy of Minnesota was the favourite of the enthusiastic college students who were motivated primarily by sympathy with black civil rights, and in a campaign invigorated by youthful support he achieved over a third of the vote in the first primary, in the snows of New Hampshire, on 8 March 1968. However, the non-peaceful nature of the African-American protest movement limited McCarthy's appeal among mainstream Democrats, and his strength melted away in the warmer weather of the spring and early summer. A potentially serious run had been mooted by Robert Kennedy, but none of his family had ever served in a senior executive position and he was no proven vote-winner, having failed in his 1964 Senate bid. In the end, Kennedy decided to settle for the company of his lucrative law practice and his ten children (with an eleventh on the way). He said it was a pleasure to be able fully to watch them grow up.

The decisive winner of the 1968 Democratic nomination was a man whose time had come – someone with a long and strong enough liberal record to promise real change while well enough connected to the mainstream of the party not to frighten those who felt the dangers of over-correction in the febrile social maelstrom. Hubert Humphrey had been a Minnesota Senator since 1949; he was a passionate advocate of black causes in the 1950s while at the same time gaining something of a reputation for anti-Communism at the height of the Cold War, a serious contender for the Democratic vice-presidential spot in 1960, and one of the finest orators in American politics, recognised ever since his speech on civil rights at the 1948 Democratic Convention. Though less sympathetic than McCarthy to the direction the civil rights movement had taken in the 1960s, Humphrey was liberal (and northern) enough not to stand a chance in the once-solid South – but neither was the all-white electorate of any state in the Old Confederacy willing to vote for so archetypal a Yankee as Lodge.

The consequence was an exceptional level of success for a third-party candidate, George Wallace, running as an American Independent but in effect a segregationist 'Dixiecrat'. Not only did he sweep Mississippi and his own state of Alabama with 70 per cent shares of the vote, but he also took Louisiana, Georgia, Arkansas, South Carolina, Tennessee and North Carolina – nine states in all, which exceeded the number won by the incumbent President. Lodge was confined to Arizona, Idaho, Kansas, Nebraska, North Dakota, Oklahoma and Utah – together worth just thirty-seven electoral college votes to seventy-eight for Wallace. Perhaps the 'American independents' were not such a third party after all, though they did of course run far behind Lodge in terms of the national popular vote. The 1968 presidential election does nevertheless stand out as the high-water mark of American racial division in the twentieth century. It was also the nadir of humiliation for the Grand Old Party.

There was, however, no doubt about the identity of the winner. The eight years of Humphrey's presidency are notable for being the greatest period of reform in the domestic history of the United States, alongside FDR's New Deal of the 1930s.

Consider just some of its achievements. It was abundantly clear that civil rights reform was long overdue. The Civil Rights Act of 1969 and the

Voting Rights Act of 1970, pushed through in the aftermath of the 1968 landslide, are testimony to Humphrey's vision that the teeth of both the organised and disorganised violent African-American reactions to legal, social and political deprivation could be drawn by strong executive and legislative direction from Washington. The provisions of the Voting Rights Act slowly but surely changed the parameters of politics even in the Deep South, as local politicians (including even George Wallace) found that they had to appeal to the gradually enfranchised black voters, who themselves came in time to be represented not only by the first African-American mayors of urban areas but eventually by the creation of 'majority-minority' congressional districts – though of course great inequalities remain in employment, housing and crime and incarceration rates to this day.

Nor was Humphrey's energy confined to improving the lot of ethnic groups. The Economic Opportunity Act of 1969 created an Office of Economic Opportunity to oversee a variety of community-based anti-poverty programmes. Medicare and Medicaid were initiated after the Social Security Act of the same year. In 1970, the Education Act ended a long-standing political taboo by providing significant federal aid to public education, initially allotting more than $1 billion to help schools purchase materials and start special education programmes for those with a high concentration of low-income children. The Housing and Urban Development Act of 1970 greatly expanded federal housing expenditure and created a new executive department of state; together with the New Cities Program started in 1971 it represented an approach to urban renewal that, if patchy in its overall success, served as a breakthrough in governmental intervention in an issue strongly connected with the problems that had so visibly bedevilled the US in the disastrous 1960s.[14] Overall, for intentions alone, the attempts to address the issues of poverty between 1969 and 1971 deserve the overall title trumpeted by the eloquent President at the time – that of the 'Fair Society'.

In foreign affairs, too, although the Cold War was far from over, as long as the USSR maintained its unwanted dominance over the satellite states in its sphere of influence in Eastern Europe (as illustrated by the suppression of Czechoslovakia), relations between the superpowers entered a somewhat warmer phase with the successful strategic arms limitation talks of 1969–72 and Humphrey's visits to Moscow and Beijing – though in truth credit should be given to the work started by Nixon earlier in the '60s, often forgotten because of his domestic catastrophe. It had also become clear by the 1970s that the decision not to more actively resist the Communist takeover of Vietnam had not resulted in a domino effect extending outside Indo-China.

Although no one could claim that the Fair Society solved all of America's problems, and that the effectiveness and popularity of Humphrey's initiatives declined in his second term, after his comfortable re-election in 1972, there can be no doubt that the overall judgement must be that Hubert Horatio Humphrey was one of the greatest ever US presidents. The country inherited by his successor in 1976, the former peanut farmer from Georgia, Jimmy Carter, had moved a long way to redress the grievances over civil rights, and through the interventions against poverty – perhaps most notably in assistance for healthcare – to re-establish the prestige and faith in the presidency that Nixon had damaged. The civil rights legislation and the Fair Society together, along with keeping the US out of major active foreign engagements, add up to among the greatest achievements of any US President.

Therefore, to return to a consideration of the significance of the premature and violent demise of Lyndon Johnson, perhaps if he had survived, his driving ambition and strength of personality, and his talent for the political game – and his ruthless willingness to do whatever was necessary – could have taken him to the very top of the American political system. He had already provided plenty of evidence of these characteristics in his time at San Marcos College, in his early years in Washington as a congressional aide, in his role as the youngest director of a state-wide federal programme in the New Deal, and in his election to Congress at the age of twenty-eight. His experience as a teacher in dirt-poor and majority-Latino rural Texas schools combined with his southern heritage may have put him in a unique position to be able to address the massive and intractable problems of civil rights at an earlier date. His personal upbringing in poverty may have inspired him to attempt a major assault on socioeconomic inequalities. He may have come to be regarded as a great President himself – as long as he could restrain the testosterone-fuelled aggression that had also been evident, which could perhaps have caused major problems in foreign affairs. The complexity of his personality, though, with its unwillingness to back down from a challenge whether for good or ill, may most likely have resulted in a curate's egg of a presidency, with great achievements clouded by ultimate disappointment.

One final line of our fantasy might be pursued. Because without Johnson, the lunar visionary John F. Kennedy did not become President, the space race was not extended to an attempt to land men on the moon. The Soviets continued with their Vostok programme that had put the first man and woman into space, but because the US did not proceed from Mercury to Gemini, the Soviets did not need to respond with Voshkod. Following the Outer Space Treaty signed by Presidents Brezhnev and Lodge, attention was concentrated on orbital space stations, and as the Cold War wound down in the 1970s and 1980s, the beginnings of international cooperation primarily led space programmes to seek advances in scientific understanding rather than competition for prestige. Following the end of the era of superpower conflict, this meant that when it was finally decided that the advent of the twenty-first century could afford – indeed, it demanded – a manned lunar space venture, it ended in the way we all now know and celebrate. After the ballot among the international team of astronauts involved in the programme, in 2016, Britain's Major Tim Peake became the first human to set foot on the moon.

Notes

1. For the details of the raid, see Robert A. Caro, *Means of Ascent* (London, 1990), pp. 39–44.
2. Robert A. Caro, *Master of the Senate* (New York, 2002).
3. Herbert S. Parmet, *Richard Nixon and His America* (Boston, 1990), p. 493.
4. Manning Marrable, *Malcolm X: A Life of Reinvention* (London, 2011), pp. 159, 161, 171.
5. Joshua Bloom and Waldo E. Martin Jnr, *Black Against Empire* (Berkeley, 2013), p. 443 n43.
6. Stephen E. Ambrose, *Nixon: The Triumph of a Politician 1962–72* (London, 1989), pp. 367–8.
7. Stephen E. Ambrose, *Nixon: The Education of a Politician 1913–62* (New York, 1987),

pp. 550, 622 (Nixon said afterwards that as President he would have 'provided more air cover'; he made no suggestion of anything further).

8. Ibid., p. 431.
9. For the address of the headquarters of the DNC in 1964, see Paul A. Smith and Richard E. May (eds), *Official Report of the Proceedings of the Democratic National Convention and Committee, John F Kennedy Memorial Edition* (Washington, 1964), frontispiece.
10. It may be noted that the Democrats still dominated both Houses of Congress in the 1960s due to the South still being 'solid' for them; also, in the real Nixon landslide year of 1972, the Democrats actually gained two seats in the Senate and retained a fifty-seat lead in the House – so Democrat control after a hypothetical Nixon re-election in 1964 is plausible.
11. In reality, Nixon was hawkish on Vietnam during the 1964 presidential election campaign; he supported Johnson on the Gulf of Tonkin resolution; called for more action rather than less in 1965; and vehemently condemned Eugene Genovese of Rutgers University the same year when the professor said that he would welcome a Viet Cong victory. Ambrose writes that Nixon was still 'against negotiations' at the end of 1965 (Ambrose, *The Triumph of a Politician*, pp. 43, 45, 55, 68–9, 73, 77).
12. These results are a translation of what actually happened in 1974 in the mid-term elections during the parallel period of the Watergate scandal.
13. Henry Cabot Lodge, *The Storm Has Many Eyes* (New York, 1973), p. 206.
14. These measures are based on those actually included in Johnson's 'Great Society' programme.

Chapter 4

What if Michael Wedgwood Benn had survived World War Two?

Graham Kirby

On 27 March 2014, Tony Benn died at the age of eighty-six. One of the longest-serving Labour MPs, he had served successively as Postmaster General, Minister for Technology, Secretary of State for Industry and Secretary of State for Energy under Harold Wilson or Jim Callaghan. He opposed the Conservative government's decision to take the UK into the European Economic Community, and argued for a referendum on the issue, which then became a Labour manifesto pledge. When Labour returned to office in 1974, Benn was on the losing 'no' side in the national referendum – Britain's first – on EEC membership in 1975.

When he died, many remembered Benn for his earlier long battle to renounce his peerage, a title he only succeeded to because of the death of his elder brother Michael, who was killed while serving in the RAF during the Second World War.

~

Even before he had sat down, people were describing it as one of the greatest parliamentary performances of all time. Sometimes passionate, sometimes quiet, he was persuasive, even mesmerising. The opposite of demagogical, he spoke with respect and gentleness. In a rare break with custom, when he had finished speaking the House broke into applause; Conservative members joined Labour ones, order papers were waved, cries of 'outstanding' and 'brilliant' could just be heard above the sound of clapping in the packed chamber.

The Right Honourable Member for Leeds Central resumed his seat on the front bench as his colleagues shuffled aside to make space for him; emotionally exhausted, he leant across towards the Dispatch Box to pick up a glass of water, which he drank gratefully.

After hours of tense debate, which had not always seen democratic politics at its best, the sense of release was palpable. The language he had used was both practical and moral; he had achieved something in that packed room which none of the preceding speakers had: he had spoken for a large section of his party, he had also spoken for a large block of left-wing voters. He had made his party feel happy.

In the second decade of the twenty-first century, no political event was complete without a Twitter reaction, and as he took praise from colleagues, his name began to trend on the ubiquitous social media platform. In the lobby, journalists spoke in excited tones about his eloquence, MPs rushed to television cameras to give their verdicts, both in praise and against. Cometh the hour, cometh the man. Yet, one name – apart from his own – cropped up again and again in tweets, before cameras and even in the more politically aware houses where people were watching the debate. For some politicians this might have been a curse, but for Hilary Benn, like the scion of any great dynasty, it was a running and inevitable fact of life.

Benn was used to comparisons with his father; he had the same bearing, a similar speaking voice, the same use of commanding rhetoric and even hand gestures – there was no denying the resemblance, at times almost uncanny, between father and son. He also knew that the sense of ownership that some members of the public felt for his father was a constant. Any deviation from what they saw as his legacy would lead to vitriolic criticism, to angry cries that he had dishonoured his father's memory. There were the predictable accusations that he would have been ashamed of his son, that he would be spinning in his grave at his son's actions. Every time he would politely reply that, with respect, his critics had no idea what either of his parents had thought of him or would have thought of him. As for similar attacks by political opponents – well, they were pretty cheap.

But it was not only the commentators who thought of Tony Benn; it was his son as well. Others might have minded the constant comparisons but, curiously and tellingly, he did not. As he looked around the chamber, he thought of Dad.

~

The first time Hilary could remember seeing his father cry was when father and son had sat together in the public gallery of the House of Lords to watch his uncle, Michael Wedgwood Benn, take his place as the second Viscount Stansgate in the County of Essex. That night his father, elected to the Commons for Bristol South East almost exactly a decade before, talked to Hilary, then aged seven, about his pride in his brother, tinged with sadness at the recent loss of his own father, Air Commodore William Wedgwood Benn DSO, DFC, PC. Even then, Hilary sensed relief that it was the brother, not he, whom primogeniture had destined for the non-democratic chamber of British politics. 'It could have been me,' he said to Hilary. 'Had you ever thought that?'

It was a conversation they were to have many times over the years. Michael, a decorated RAF pilot who had served in Rhodesia and South Africa, could have been shot down and killed during the war. The risks RAF pilots took were immense; many died as a result of accidents or faulty equipment as well as enemy action. His father, who had also served in the RAF, knew the dangers as much as anyone did. The thought that Antony Wedgwood Benn might have become Viscount Stansgate – however briefly – was one that had occupied Hilary's thoughts as well as those of his father. When Hilary eventually asked him what he would have done, Dad replied,

> I would have fought it. I would have changed the law so I could remain a commoner. You either believe in democracy or you don't, and surely it is to be a servant of the public through membership of the elected Commons which is the greatest honour open to any Englishman?

How different would Tony's career have been if he had had to fight to regain a place in the House of Commons? Revered in later life as a rebel and democrat, a battle to change the law against so many obstacles might have made him an earlier radical; any confrontation would have drawn the establishment, both government and party, against him. However, one thing Hilary was sure of was that his dad, whatever the personal cost or loneliness of the battle, would have won.

As it was, the Benn brothers became a feature of British politics. Dad was the senior of the two in political terms. After the war, Uncle Michael had gone on to study for the priesthood. To the Benns, religion and politics were just different forms of moral service, and the horrors of war had given Michael a longing to prevent future generations from suffering as his friends and colleagues had done; more than anything he wanted them to know the happiness and freedom that his family had given him.

Meanwhile, Hilary's father became the face of Labour leader Hugh Gaitskell's approach to politics. Using the skills he had honed as a producer at the BBC, he had quickly become a star of Radio 4's *Any Questions?*. The format suited his quick wit and ability to cross ideological divides when discussing serious policy, and he gained a reputation for withering put-downs. In 1959, together with a languid Woodrow Wyatt, he fronted the Labour Party's television campaign. He was that extraordinarily rare beast: the 'toff' who could speak to ordinary people. But, for all his modernising centre-right tendencies, his heart lay on the left, taking over his father's mantel of opposition to apartheid, and in 1954 joining the H-bomb national committee. Like Michael, it was in his opposition to war that he was at his most ardent: 'all war represents a failure of diplomacy'.

Gaitskell's campaign to replace Clause Four, the totemic commitment to public ownership, led Benn to switch his allegiance to Harold Wilson, a commitment that paid off in 1963, when the former died and was succeeded by the latter. After twelve years of Tory aristocratic rule, Britain in the early 1960s seemed ready for change; Prime Minister Harold Macmillan had lost his sure touch, as demonstrated by his reaction to the Profumo affair and his botched Cabinet reshuffle. Cruelly satirised on television and suffering prostate problems, the ageing Prime Minister, despite fits of doubt, threw in the towel at the beginning of the 1963 party conference.

Hilary remembered watching as Labour turmoil was replaced by Tory chaos. Speculation was rife. After a dull speech from Reggie Maudling, the Chancellor of the Exchequer, the even duller Rab Butler – overlooked for preferment in 1957 – became the choice of both party and public; the 6–4 favourite was preferred by some 39 per cent of voters over 11 per cent for Maudling. Yet Macmillan, rallying in his hospital bed, decided that Butler should not succeed. Hilary thought later that had his father fought and won a battle to renounce his peerage, the Earl of Home, who had acted as front man for Macmillan's plot, could have been a contender himself. As it was, he remained the fourteenth Earl. When the stitch-up was complete, Maudling emerged as the party's new leader; Butler agreed to serve, his friend Iain MacLeod replaced Maudling at the Treasury. Few noticed when the eccentric minister Enoch Powell returned to the back benches.

Labour's victory in 1964 was one that almost never happened. Maudling, a product of Merchant Taylor's School and the Conservative Research Department, was of a different hue to his predecessors: the earlier grouse-moor image of the party was one which even the wily Wilson could no longer use effectively. By leaving it until the last possible moment to call the election, Maudling tried to eke out every vote from his 'dash for growth' policy, but Labour just beat them into office. When Wilson won a convincing majority in 1966, the new Tory leadership rules saw Edward Heath replace an unhappy Maudling.

~

The tumultuous 1960s and 1970s were perhaps the most productive of Hilary's father's career. They were also rewarding for Uncle Michael, who made his first moves into the political world, eventually becoming a minister at the Home Office. The curiosity of two brothers serving together in a left-wing administration caught the public's imagination. However, it was their passionate language that stirred socialist hearts; a language that talked not merely of humanising capitalism but of changing society's values for the better.

Tony served as Postmaster General, then Minister for Technology; he was the modern face of the government. First he tried to remove the Queen's head from postage stamps; then he backed Concorde, a project that combined his fascination with new technology with his internationalism.

In 1969, the brothers formed an alliance with Home Secretary Jim Callaghan to defeat *In Place of Strife*, the proposals to reform trade union law. The alliance helped both and damned its author, Barbara Castle.

Labour's unexpected defeat in 1970 deprived Hilary's dad of his ministerial car, but his energy was undimmed. He critiqued to Michael and Hilary the 1964–70 government, telling them of his sense of its failures. Perhaps he would have been the man to have suggested an alternative, but loyalty – and maybe the influence of Michael – gave him pause. Perhaps it was also a sense that a quick return to power was probable; Heath's majority was slim and his party was split on Europe, oil prices rocketed and industrial action steadily climbed.

His father and uncle, both by nature optimists, did not spend much time lamenting missed opportunities, but if they had one regret, it was that they did not use the period of opposition to propose a popular vote on Heath's signature achievement: British accession to the European Common Market. On the whole, the anti-Marketeers, such as Michael Foot and Enoch Powell, were parliamentarians rather than democrats. Uncle Michael said later that a referendum pledge could have won Labour the 1974 election; Powell's disgust at the absurdity of Heath's 1974 snap 'who governs?' election could have led to a unlikely endorsement for Labour from a man who hoped that Britain would remain a sovereign nation and one who had growing support for his increasingly strident views on immigration. As it was, the impact of Powell's criticism of Heath was minimal. The dozen or so Midlands seats his admirers thought he could shift all stayed Conservative. Heath survived in office, albeit tenuously and in a minority. The *Te Deum* would have to wait.

It was Jim Callaghan who succeeded Harold Wilson as Labour leader, and the following year he was elected Prime Minister when Heath finally lost his battle to cling on to power. Callaghan was able, with a mixture of sunshine and toughness, to harness effectively his junior colleague's undoubted talents; as his deputy, Benn took over the Home Office, where he continued as a pioneering and inventive minister, putting freedom of information, human rights and race relations Bills before Parliament. When Roy Jenkins was shuffled off to Brussels as the European Commission's new president, Benn's disappointment at not being made Chancellor in his place was more than compensated by Uncle Michael's promotion to Lord Privy Seal, leading the two to become the first siblings to sit in the Cabinet simultaneously since Edward, Lord Stanley, and Oliver Stanley in 1938.

The 1975–79 Labour government saw the death of Keynesian economics, the guide to every government's macroeconomic policy since the war. Hilary had watched on TV as the Prime Minister's 1976 conference speech read the rites:

> The cosy world we were told would go on for ever, where full employment would be guaranteed by a stroke of the Chancellor's pen, cutting taxes, deficit spending – that cosy world is gone... We used to think that you could spend your way out of a recession and increase employment by cutting taxes and boosting government spending. I tell you in all candour that that option no longer exists.

David Owen, of whose futile pen Callaghan was speaking, was the first to applaud.

Hilary knew that his father was torn. He felt a residual loyalty to the government of which he and Michael were senior members, and had given no serious consideration to an alternative. However, Owen's deflationary policies, taking £2.5 billion out of the economy, were the greatest recruiting tool for the Campaign for Labour Party Democracy, which aimed to ensure that Labour governments pursued genuine socialist policies. Both Benns, like others on the soft left, were stuck in the middle, believing that the party needed a corrective but worried by the hard left's threat to the Labour movement. Both also admired Callaghan, who charmed and flattered his critics while ignoring the left's more provocative confrontations.

As relations between the government and the unions deteriorated in 1978–79, Callaghan, who for the preceding two years had been reliant on the Liberal and nationalist parties for his survival, was staring at his political mortality. Uncle Michael told Hilary that if the government could survive another twelve months it was just possible that memories of the winter's industrial action would fade and the economy would recover sufficiently strongly for the party to be confident of re-election.

But it was not to be: on 28 March 1979, the government fell.

Hilary watched from the gallery with his uncle as, sitting bolt upright on the opposition benches, the Conservative leader Margaret Thatcher stared at Callaghan, flanked by Owen and Benn, as he gently patronised her position. Tony Benn gave one of his greatest performances from the front bench as he wound up the debate, wooing MPs and giving a forthright defence of the government, lampooning the opposition who had only tabled their own motion of no confidence after the nationalists had got there first:

> Hail, Caesar! Those about to die salute thee... Which brings me to the honourable member, the leader of the Liberal Party. He knows I wouldn't like to miss him out! And here I am sure I will elicit the support of the Right Honourable Lady because she and I have always shared a common interest in this young man, haven't we? What did happen exactly last Thursday night? Did he send for her or did she send for him?

The House loved it. 'He's passed from rising hope to elder statesman without any intervening period whatsoever!' The line would follow the Liberal leader David Steel around for the rest of his career. It was the kind of parliamentary performance only Tony Benn could deliver.

But it was all in vain. Without the Scottish nationalists' support, the government had no majority. And with Callaghan unwilling to deal with Enoch Powell's Unionists – 'He's bottled it,' said Cabinet minister John Smith of the Prime Minister – when the tellers read out the result the government had lost by one vote.

After the drama, neither Hilary nor his father or uncle felt able to join in the gallows humour of party colleagues who spent the night getting drunk in Westminster's various bars. They returned instead first to his father's office and then home to Holland Park, where his mother Caroline was waiting for them. Neither of the elder two were to know it, but it was to be their last time in government.

~

Hilary thought that for all their many ministerial achievements, the greatest irony of the brothers' careers was that the two men who were to effectively lead Labour together to one of its greatest defeats, in 1983, had also saved the party. Once again in opposition, Callaghan had stayed on as leader for eighteen months to time his resignation to suit either of his preferred successors. As the party became bogged down in internal arguments, he then resigned before the new electoral college came into effect. Benn led the first round of voting, with Denis Healey second. The work that Michael and Hilary put in on the campaign paid off: in the final round, his father took 148 votes to the former Foreign Secretary's 120.

It was not a propitious time to take over the party: the 1976 devaluation and the winter of discontent had ruined the party's economic credibility, splits on Europe simmered just below the surface and the far left was in resurgence. In his 1979 Dimbleby Lecture, Roy Jenkins, Wilson's former Chancellor who had been shuffled off to Brussels as Commission President by Callaghan, spoke of a realignment of politics, maybe even a new radical centre party. But realignment did not happen. Labour did not split. Though it was a close-run thing.

Eric Heffer's 1981 deputy leadership challenge to Denis Healey was bitterly fought but the challenger was roundly defeated in the new electoral college. Hilary's uncle, who had at first pleaded with Heffer not to challenge Healey, then supported his brother as he campaigned for Healey, and made sure that the party recognised his brother's support for his beleaguered but robust deputy. The contest marked the high point of the far left's insurrection. It might have been different had they found a substantial tribune behind whom they could rally. Instead, they were effectively leaderless. As Hilary's dad said to him at the time:

> One the one hand, you've got all these people who are simply concerned with power; on the other, you've got sectarians who are simply concerned with ideological purity; and somewhere in the middle somebody has to try to bring it all together for the good of the people we represent.

His father and uncle were the men to bring it all together.

But Hilary knew there were tensions. His father had become increasingly Eurosceptic. Heightened by his experiences as an elected minister, who could be removed at any time, he had come to see 'Europe' as internationalism stifled by unaccountable bureaucracy, with no countervailing advantage to Britain. There was, as well, his support for unilateral nuclear disarmament. Both had the potential to tear the party apart, but his proposed referendum on British membership of the EEC – part of a radical change to Britain's democratic tradition – with the suggestion that shadow ministers could campaign in accordance with their conscience, prevented an absolute meltdown. Extraordinarily, on the key issues he kept the unity of his party without bending his principles. The (left of) centre held.

Labour's 1983 manifesto was described by one wit as 'the most boring suicide note in history'. The two brothers strained to keep the party united; without a substantial figure supporting them, the hard left were unable to force some of their wilder policies into the manifesto. Tim Bell ripped up his 'like your manifesto, comrade' poster and went back to his drawing board at Saatchi & Saatchi. Dismissed by Hilary's uncle as a 'gang of one', Jenkins had joined the Liberal Party, thus ensuring that the mould of British politics remained intact for a while longer. Post-Falklands, when the inevitable defeat came in June 1983, most thought that it could have been worse. A Tory majority of just over 100 was crushing but surely not insurmountable. Only the family saw how devastated Hilary's father was by the defeat. He resigned as leader a week later.

Hilary did wonder, though, what a government led by his father would have looked like. Tony Benn had wanted to be a significant reformer, and saw his socialism in the mould of 1945. If Labour had won in 1983, Thatcherism would have been a historical blip; industry would have remained nationalised and Keynesian economics would have returned. There would have been massive investment, from the revenues of North Sea oil, in jobs, health and education, though Hilary never thought that his father had a definitive plan for public services. The country would have been more democratic, undoubtedly, with Cabinet ministers allowed to dissent on key issues such as the nuclear deterrent, greater devolution and a proposed People's Assembly, yet probably the referendum on the European

Community would have dominated his first years in office. By relaxing Cabinet discipline, he would have given ministers license to attack one another. The Labour Party, which had clung improbably to unity, might well then have found it easier to split.

~

Re-elected to his new Bristol East constituency, but rejected by the voters across the country, Hilary's father became more prodigious, more hard-working and more radical. That summer he read for the first time Marx's *The Communist Manifesto*, a present from Hilary's mother. 'I feel so ignorant that at the age of fifty-eight as a socialist politician,' he confessed, 'I should never have read that basic text before and I am shy to admit it.' He took lessons on English radicalism from a fellow Labour MP, thus beginning his oft-ridiculed fascination with the Levellers and Tolpuddle Martyrs. Approaching his seventh decade, he completed his curiously postponed political education.

Free at last, Hilary's father – strangely, for a man whose history was learned in a Nonconformist oral tradition – wrote: not just diaries and press articles, but books. First came *The Socialist Challenge* (1985), then *Arguments for Democracy*, with Chris Mullin (1987). Theatres and left-wing fringe meetings became used to the whiff of pipe smoke as the former leader, a mug of tea in hand, preached to the converted and the politically engaged. Hilary thought that Dad had been joking, that awful morning after the election defeat, when he said he was returning to the back benches to spend more time on politics, but he most definitely was not. Throughout his doomed election campaign, having barnstormed the country in public meetings with an almost biblical fervour, he found a determination in the face of ruthless mockery from the Tory-inclined press. To Hilary it was as if the experience had opened the floodgates of a steely and self-confident radicalism. Perhaps the seeds had always been there, and it was just a question of when and how they would develop.

The first split with David Owen, Labour's leader since 1983, came over the miners' strike, when the new leader refused to back the NUM and called for a ballot on strike action. He faced opposition from many in the party, not just the Benn brothers, who were inclined to support the strikes, but the end of the strike saw Owen seemingly vindicated. With Tony Benn's frontline career in politics effectively over, his convictions intensified; Hilary watched him increasingly diverge from the party's leadership as he moved leftwards and they moved to the centre ground. It was a journey on which his father took Michael along.

Despite its move back towards the centre ground under Owen, Labour lost the 1987 general election. Owen's forthright – or abrasive – personality meant that he had by then little support left in the party, and he resigned shortly afterwards. The election of John Smith as his replacement was always a foregone conclusion. Hilary wondered why Neil Kinnock, overlooked for promotion when his father had led the party, had even bothered to stand against him. Relations with Smith had always been good, whereas his dad had seen Kinnock as 'not a substantial person' and 'a media figure, really'.

Cannily, Smith left his options open and, unlike the more macho Owen, saw no reason to attack the straw man that was the left. Patience was his watchword. Labour now looked readier for power. The split many had predicted at the beginning of the 1980s had never happened and Smith looked reassuringly prime ministerial. The Tories began to rip themselves apart, first over Mrs Thatcher's poll tax, then over the ever-present, ever-smouldering question of European integration. It was the latter, which, after the Iron Lady's fall in November 1990, dominated Tory strife after the party lost power in 1992.

In later years, strange alliances were formed. Once Hilary's father turned his mind against the 'European question', he was implacable. Unconstrained, he joined his former adversary, Countess Grantham, on a platform to oppose the Maastricht Treaty and its proposed common currency for the European Union, as it had been renamed. Out of office, both were devoted true believers whose lives revolved around politics.

Up and down the country, Hilary, with Uncle Michael, watched his father speak passionately in favour of a nation-wide referendum: 'The European Union is government by people we don't elect and can't remove,' he cried to ripples of applause. 'I will never accept that people can make laws I have to obey if I cannot remove them on polling day ... Europe is run by a group of bureaucrats and however good they are, it lacks the democratic impulse which we are supposed to believe in.'

Europe was a festering grievance. Even though he had come to think of himself as a pro-European, at the time Hilary had thought it strange that to date there had never been a single referendum on the European issue, or indeed any other constitutional issue. Had his father set a precedent with a referendum on EEC membership, or if Jim Callaghan had held one in 1975, it might have been different. However, voting reform, devolution and even the adoption of the euro in 1999 were all passed without public consultation.

When John Smith unexpectedly died, Hilary's father and uncle supported Environment Secretary Michael Meacher's challenge for the leadership. But nothing, not even Gordon Brown, could stop the surging and popular candidacy of Tony Blair, the energetic Education Secretary whom Hilary, more privately, wanted to win. The new Prime Minister, having defeated the left, rebranded the party as 'New' Labour and boldly claimed the future. With an election probable within two years, he startled his internal opponents by proposing, like Gaitskell before him, to abolish Clause Four of the Labour Party's constitution. 'We will govern as New Labour,' he declared as he launched his blitzkrieg. It was a restless, if characteristic, act of party reform not in opposition but in government. Despite their determination to maintain cordial, if dissenting, relations with the leadership, Hilary saw the elder two become rapidly disappointed just as he began to think seriously about a political career for himself. The left, more phantom than actual, had never come close to controlling Labour, but Blair's election, then his ruthless party coup, marked its final obituary. Meacher was returned unceremoniously to the back benches and Clause Four became another sentimental relic of Labour's history. A landslide election victory followed.

~

'Like our father, we grow more left as we grow older,' Viscount Stansgate once said to his nephew. Michael and Tony never missed the Durham Miners' Gala. Together they travelled to Baghdad to secure the release of hostages held by Saddam Hussein after his invasion of Kuwait in 1990. Following the attacks on the World Trade Center in 2001, both forgot the bitter battles of 1981 and spoke, with Islington North MP Jeremy Corbyn, against the proposed invasion of Iraq. Despite the opposition, Tony Blair went ahead and joined US President George W. Bush in the military action. It was the greatest mistake of his political career. By the following year, after ten years as Prime Minister, he had resigned.

Hilary reckoned it was then, in that blaze of autumn sunshine, that both the elder Benns truly became national treasures. They had both been ministers, and his father party leader, but they found their calling as preachers. There were some who still remembered the service they had given to Labour in its darkest days, but increasingly younger voters were carried away with their commanding oratory and socialist faith. The further they travelled from office the more certain they became in their beliefs. Yet the central spine of their arguments, for all their later education, remained unchanged: that power should rest with all the voters, not the wealthy.

Tony found popularity late in life but was never truly understood. Even Hilary had sometimes struggled to grasp his father's complex personality. Perhaps, he surmised, the truth lay in his sense that, in 1983, the establishment had closed itself to him and his brother, marking them as outsiders. But for an accident of history his father might have trodden a similar path at a different pace. He might have had to take that journey without his uncle. For good or ill.

There was something else Hilary often thought of: sixty years in politics, and in all that time, whether in or out of office, on the front bench or the back benches, both men had hung on their walls that Salvation Army hymn which their mother had sung to them and they to Hilary:

Standing by a purpose true,
Heeding God's commands,
Honour them, the faithful few!
All hail to Daniel's band!
Dare to be a Daniel,
Dare to stand alone,
Dare to have a purpose firm!
Dare to make it known.

~

The slap on his shoulder from the party's deputy leader, Tom Watson, brought Hilary Benn back from his reverie.

It was just a speech. The Budget deficit was still intolerably bad and growth was threatened by the global downturn, Russia was causing havoc in Ukraine, the threat from Daesh in Syria and Iraq remained, the migrant crisis would be worse this summer than in 2015, and there was the ongoing Euro-crisis and the fallout from the recent referendum's decisive Brexit vote with which to contend. Oratory could move minds but not facts. Inevitably, there would be a backlash. People who applauded today would become critics tomorrow. Thank God someone else read his Twitter feed.

He looked around the chamber. Ed and David Miliband to his left, two brothers also serving in Cabinet, opposite him Liam Fox and former Prime Minister William Hague. Among the deafening sounds, the face he most longed to see – that of the man who had cried proud tears when he made his maiden speech – was not in the public gallery.

He felt a gentle tap on his shoulder.

'President Clinton on the line for you, Prime Minister.'

He looked at his grim-faced PPS at first blankly, before pulling himself together.

'I'll be right there. Thanks, Jeremy.'

Chapter 5

What if the British government had decided to float the pound in 1952?

Ted Morris

Sterling's weakness was no more the cause of Britain's dismal post-war economic performance than Sarajevo was the cause of the First World War. But, like Sarajevo, it was the painful juncture at which a whole flock of complex troubles came home to roost.

Successive economic strategies foundered in spiralling crises of inflation and balance of payments deficits. Gold and dollar reserves drained remorselessly away, as governments sought to escape from desperately anaemic growth rates. And it was always the exchange rate that took the strain. In those days of fixed exchange rates, that meant a succession of sterling crises that humbled Chancellors from Dalton to Callaghan and led to one lurch after another down the inexorable slope to the humiliations of the 1970s and the bailout by the IMF. It was not a fixed exchange rate that caused boom and bust – as has been amply demonstrated in the era of floating rates – but the ultimate requirement for a government to defend a fixed rate which usually became the trigger for an urgent need to deflate an unsustainable boom.

The new world order of fixed exchange rates had come into being with the Bretton Woods agreements at the end of the Second World War. It lasted until 1972, but lingered on for sterling until the abolition of exchange controls in the first Budget of Mrs Thatcher's government in 1979. As the Chancellor, Geoffrey Howe, noted in that Budget speech, Britain's share of world trade had in 1954 been the same as France and Germany combined; by 1979 their combined share was three times that of the UK.[1] This was not a world order that had served Britain well, though her woes were largely of her own making.

This chapter tells the story of one point in this depressing tale where a different road could have been taken. It is the story of ROBOT – not, perhaps disappointingly, an Asimov short story, but a project name acronym formed from the three civil servants behind it: Leslie Rowan, George Bolton and Otto Clarke.

ROBOT was never implemented, and was a closely guarded secret at the time,[2] which may explain why the episode is not more widely known today given that it has been cited as our 'economic Suez'.[3] ROBOT is, however, a favourite episode for historians of Britain's post-war decline,[4] both because of the tantalising possibilities it sets out and because it was, as Professor Marquand puts it, 'one of the most passionately fought and politically charged Whitehall battles of the post-war period'.[5] Professor Hennessy regards the episode as 'a huge, retrospective and counterfactual temptation',[6] though none of the adherents on either side of the argument have structured their assessments in quite that form.[7] It is, however, a temptation to which, in these next pages, we will now succumb.

Background

The problems the British economy faced were not just that the exchange rate was fixed – with the rate of $2.80 to the pound set after devaluation in 1949 already arguably unsustainable by 1952 – but also the arcane mechanisms of the sterling area.

A legacy of the days before 1914, when Britain was the centre of the world's financial system, the sterling area comprised those countries whose currencies remained pegged to sterling. That area included all of the then Commonwealth countries except for Canada (a dollar economy) as well as a handful of other jurisdictions. It was the mechanism for preserving artificially the role of sterling as a world currency. The price paid by the UK was the obligation that went with being the sterling area's central banker, with the accumulated sterling balances held throughout the Commonwealth a continuing threat to the UK's dollar reserves. As Correlli Barnett points out, the Treasury and the Bank of England maintained, through the sterling area, an economic overstretch every bit as draining as the diplomatic and military commitments maintained by the Foreign Office and the chiefs of staff.[8] Between 1946 and 1951, the non-UK sterling area had run a net deficit of £300 million that the UK had been obliged to fund.[9] Half of Britain's trade at that time was with the sterling area – and indeed half the trade in the world was carried out in sterling – and the Commonwealth was seen as fundamental to holding on to what influence Britain had in the world. The sterling area seemed to pose an insoluble political and economic conundrum.

The obligations of the sterling area, combined with the continuing weaknesses of the British economy, led to continuous strains on the balance of payments, for which the reserves were ludicrously inadequate to cope. The additional burdens shouldered though rearmament for the Korean War were all but unbearable (and the hard choices that had resulted had riven the Labour Cabinet). The ensuing sterling crisis that erupted in September 1951 was one of the worst of the period.

These were the circumstances in which R. A. Butler arrived at the Treasury as Chancellor in October 1951. A surprise choice to some, he was the beneficiary of the early death of Oliver Stanley in 1950 and what Churchill saw as the excessively pro-City stance of Oliver Lyttelton (who was made Colonial Secretary instead). Butler was acutely aware of his lack of both formal economic training and of any independent political power base. These were both underlined by the unique arrangements put in place by Churchill: a second Treasury minister, Arthur Salter; a Treasury Advisory Committee with such senior figures as Lords Woolton and Swinton; and the powerful Lord Cherwell (formerly Professor Lindermann) occupying a free-ranging role as Paymaster-General and enjoying the Prime Minister's ear. Far from providing support to Butler, these figures undermined his standing and underlined that he was, at least initially, an unusually weak Chancellor, highly dependent upon the goodwill of his neighbour at No. 10.

Meeting Sir Edward Bridges, the immensely respected Permanent Secretary at the Treasury, and William Armstrong, the new Chancellor's principal private secretary, for lunch at the Athenaeum on his first day in office, Butler heard a lurid portrayal of 'blood draining from the system'[10] and of imminent financial collapse. The 48-year-old Butler at this stage was not the sure-footed Whitehall operator he was later to become, and had no basis to reject the assessment of the situation put forward by his most senior advisers. Emergency short-term measures in the November Budget – reducing and rescheduling the rearmament programme, cutting imports and raising interest rates – proved to be just about sufficient sticking plasters for the time being, but by February 1952 Butler's mood of despondency pushed him towards an uncharacteristic gamble.

It must have been a similar mixture of exhaustion and desperation that drove the originators of ROBOT. Its roots lay in the otherwise uninteresting conclusions of a report in early January 1952 that called upon the Treasury to draw up contingency plans in the event of the orthodox handling of the crisis proving inadequate. The resulting paper, drawn up by Otto Clarke, the fizzing intellect who was number two at the Overseas Finance Section of the Treasury, and addressed to his immediate superior Sir Leslie Rowan, was certainly anything but orthodox.

Clarke looked back at previous convertibility crises and identified a simple problem: if sterling were made convertible at what was considered too high a rate, then holders of sterling could simply swap into dollars – so holders of sterling within the sterling area would hold a Damocles Sword over Britain's precious reserves. His solution was to allow convertibility at a floating rate so that if there was excess supply the exchange rate would fall to the point at which supply and demand cancelled out.

There would be clear advantages. Britain had frittered away Marshall Aid in trying to maintain the exchange rate to no obvious lasting benefit (while the Germans used the money more wisely to retool their economy). The plan did not represent a narrowing of the Treasury's view of the role of sterling as a world currency. If anything, it was an attempt to regain the initiative and restore, or at least maintain, its role, which was seen as impossible if either the reserves ran out, so triggering the break-up of the sterling area, or if sterling simply limped on with its credibility undermined by the sterling balances.

Moreover, Clarke saw that a floating rate would unleash equilibrating pressures on the economy: a fall in sterling would force importers to manage costs or demand while still making exports more competitive. This contrasted with the current approach, with its unseen hand that merely left everything as the government's fault, balanced by artificial restrictions or fiscal measures. The pre-echoes of the 1980s are startling to any present-day reader.

Sterling floats on the currency markets today, and we take the workings of the market for granted. However, in 1952, this was revolutionary thinking, too much so even for Clarke, and probably structurally impossible given the complexities of the sterling area. For there, the structural problems were seen as so deeply rooted that a floating pound could plummet to a level that would create its own crisis and beyond which the equilibrating forces would not take effect because even essential imports would not be affordable. Clarke's answer was that the convertibility element would not be immediate. Instead, the sterling balances would be frozen and tight exchange controls maintained. Even with this safeguard, ROBOT was recognised as an enormous risk.

As it rumbled onward through Whitehall and the Bank of England, additional safeguards for ROBOT were proposed, notably in a paper by Sir George Bolton, Deputy Governor of the Bank of England. As well as adding the last elements of the eponymous acronym, Bolton's paper and the consequent evolution of the plan added significantly to its complexity. It is quite likely that many around the Cabinet table where it ended up being discussed did not fully understand the proposal.

Nevertheless, ROBOT moved relentlessly on. The situation appeared dire. Between June 1951 and February 1952, over $2 billion had been lost in protecting sterling. The reserves now stood at $1.8 billion and the further loss forecast for the first quarter of 1952 was $800 million.[11] The reserves would clearly be exhausted before long, and they were already far less than the sterling area balances, the equivalent of $7.2 billion, which were hanging over the reserves.[12]

So, despite the risks identified even by the authors, ROBOT was presented to ministers at 10 p.m. on 22 February. Butler set out a devastating summary of the unsustainability of the current position. Though he did not downplay the risks of ROBOT, the Chancellor made it clear that it was, in his view, the only way ahead.

ROBOT was gathering momentum and was to dominate three full Cabinet meetings on 28 and 29 February. The aim was to announce the scheme in the Budget, which was put back a week to 11 March to allow time to prepare.

From its inception, ROBOT provoked powerful adversaries. Even Clarke in his initial paper had talked about 'formidable difficulties' and 'terrific risks' (all that was lacking from the *Yes, Minister* playbook of unpersuasive Whitehall arguments would seem to have been to call for a 'brave decision'). Within the Treasury, his peer, Under Secretary E. R. Copleston, gloomily warned that it could result in the disintegration of the sterling area, the Commonwealth and of Europe, as well as being suicide for the government. Some critics focused on the country's obligations to the sterling area, where ROBOT amounted to a repudiation of Britain's commitments that left many feeling uneasy, even if they were otherwise sympathetic to the scheme. This amounted to a moral dimension that clearly weighed on Lord Cobbold, the Governor of the Bank of England, who wrote of the fiduciary responsibilities owed to overseas holders of sterling.[13] Conversely, Robert Hall, Director of the Cabinet Office Economic Section, focused on the risks to the UK economy: the likely impact on unemployment – which he saw rising from 400,000 to 1 million[14] – and the scheme as a potential trigger of sharp recession. (Devaluation would mean a rise in the sterling cost of imports, which would require deflationary measures to reduce import demand, and those in turn would lead to higher unemployment.)

But once open to Cabinet examination, the critics of ROBOT extended beyond the mandarins, notably to two men who, while hardly conventional politicians, were holders of political office. Sir Arthur Salter, as the second Treasury minister, carried weight when he questioned the potentially grave consequences across a whole range of foreign policy issues, the impact on unemployment and the difficulties even of enacting the measures with the government's thin majority in the Commons. At the second Cabinet meeting, on 25 February, Lord Cherwell submitted a paper – partly authored by Robert Hall – which emphasised the risks identified in the ROBOT paper itself and suggested that the government would be pilloried by world opinion if it took the measures proposed. Cherwell argued that there were 'no sufficient grounds for the violent reversal of policy' outlined by Butler[15] and proclaimed that ROBOT 'would lead to an appalling disaster'.

The key intervention, however, was by Anthony Eden, Foreign Secretary, heir apparent to Churchill and the clear number two in the government, and it was Robert Hall who was responsible for securing it. Eden was in Lisbon for a North Atlantic Council meeting and among his officials was Edwin Plowden, a close ally of Hall. A batch of briefings were sent to Lisbon: from the Prime Minister to Eden on the severity of the financial crisis, from Sir Edward Bridges seeming to imply that ROBOT was an inevitability; and – crucially – from Hall to Plowden setting out the case against ROBOT and asking Plowden to seek to persuade Eden. Eden was no economist and his main concerns were with the impact of the policy on Commonwealth relations; he duly dispatched a letter – drafted by Plowden – to Churchill conveying his anxieties. Plowden himself believes that Eden's voice on this occasion was instrumental in both stalling ROBOT's momentum and in changing Churchill's mind.

The idea of setting sterling free had been attractive to Churchill. It had been his decision as Chancellor in 1925 to return Britain to the gold standard, fixing sterling's exchange rate against gold. It was a decision he had reached only reluctantly and ever after regretted as the greatest mistake of his life, fixing sterling once again at an unviably high rate and leading directly as it did to the economic crisis faced by his Labour successor in the wake of the Wall Street Crash. The theme of freedom also fitted in closely with the philosophy of the new Conservative government in 1951, which was seeking to emerge from wartime controls. But that was only one side to the government's approach. In the 1951 election, the Conservatives had been elected with a majority of just seventeen – and indeed had secured fewer votes than Labour – and at least partly as a result had never sought to repudiate the welfare state framework created by its Labour predecessor. Churchill retained a consensual, cross-party approach in domestic politics as he pursued his central goal of a Great Power summit. At the age of seventy-eight, his priorities were the nuclear threat and the new Queen (the late King had died on 6 February), not sterling.

With a powerful alliance now formed against ROBOT, and without Churchill's active support, the scheme was now in effect dead in the water, though discussions continued in a desultory fashion. Oliver Lyttelton passed to Butler a note during Cabinet that summed up the defeat: 'This goes ill. The water looks cold to some of them. They prefer a genteel bankruptcy, force majeure being the plea. Micawber Salter.'[16]

As Edmund Dell mournfully put it, 'Never again would a British government contemplate the possibility of imposing its policy on its external economic environment. In 1952, for the last time, the thought was there that it might be attempted.'[17]

The counterfactual

Professor Marquand and Correlli Barnett both say that there is no way of telling what would have happened if ROBOT had been adopted[18] – but let us try.

Nigel Lawson believes that the best chance for ROBOT would have come under a different Chancellor, if the more experienced and pro-market Oliver Lyttelton had been in No. 11[19] instead of Butler.[20] Perhaps so. Possibly it might only have taken a more astute cultivation of Churchill by Butler, but then all sorts of counterfactuals for the period are driven by want of a clear lead by the enigmatic Rab. Perhaps the outcome might have been different if Hall's letter to Plowden had simply gone astray, so that Eden's decisive intervention never took place.

Let us assume, however, that the Cabinet merely reached a different decision.

Breakthrough to sunlit uplands

'So it seems we have a decision,' growled the Prime Minister at the end of the long and gruelling Cabinet meeting of 29 February. Turning to Lord Cherwell, he added, 'Frederick, I realise that you're not happy with this, but can I ask you to chair a Cabinet committee to coordinate implementation? This isn't going to be just a Treasury matter, you know.'

As he got up to leave, there came an intervention from the far end of the Cabinet table. At the age of fifty-seven, Harold Macmillan had come late to Cabinet office, taking on a high-profile commitment to build 400,000 new homes as Minister of Housing and Local Government. He realised this was his one chance to make a name for himself. He also realised that ROBOT meant the end of both that housing commitment and his prospects as minister. 'I'm afraid, Prime Minister, that I cannot accept this outcome. I will submit my formal resignation in the morning.'

Churchill was dismayed and distracted by this inauspicious start; Macmillan had been a close ally since well before the war. The Prime Minister glared at Butler: 'I hope to God this was the right decision. Now make it work.'

The following morning Cherwell met Eden, Butler, Lyttelton (Colonies), Lord Salisbury (Commonwealth Office),[21] Walter Monckton (Labour) and Peter Thorneycroft (president of the Board of Trade). The key decisions were made on timing. The Budget had already been pushed back a week to 11 March and now the government announced that it would take place on 8 April, providing another vital four weeks for preparation.[22] Frenetic diplomatic activity was half the picture: an OEEC[23] conference was called for mid-March in London and a meeting of Commonwealth Finance Ministers was arranged in Ottawa for the end of the month,[24] allowing Eden to lead a delegation to Washington in the days running up to it. This groundwork was critical, for what was being sought was a rebuilding of the world's financial structures at the same time as dealing with a financial crisis.

Churchill met Macmillan the same day. The Prime Minister was unable to dissuade him from his decision to resign, but put sufficient pressure on him – together with the carrot of a possible return to Cabinet – for Macmillan to mute his opposition to the scheme. This was key to ensuring that formal opposition, at least within the Conservative Party, did not spread more widely.

As they moved into April, the government could look back at a mixed diplomatic landscape. There had been some consternation within the Commonwealth. The January Finance Ministers' conference had publicly looked forward to sterling convertibility, although that was thought of only as a long-term goal; there had been the assumption of a continuing fixed rate. As expected, the freezing of the sterling balances raised hackles, though India, Pakistan and Ceylon already had agreements in place controlling dollar releases so the practical impact for them was limited. The outspoken Australian Treasurer Sir Arthur Fadden was particularly vocal and Eden did well to keep his cool at Fadden's talk of 'betrayal'; it was no surprise that in September both Australia and New Zealand chose to leave the sterling area. But, contrary to some predictions, the sterling area, let alone the Commonwealth, did not disintegrate – not least, of course, because the colonies – as opposed to the self-governing Commonwealth members – did not have a choice. And – an essential part of ROBOT – the sterling area members started to address their own budget imbalances.

In Europe, the outcome of the talks was less positive. The European Payments Union – a mechanism to allow non-dollar multilateral trade, a form of limited convertibility for otherwise inconvertible currencies – had only recently been set up. It was a nascent step in European cooperation that had been regarded as one of Eden's greatest achievements. Sterling had been a key part of the system, and it simply could not survive with one participant floating.[25] Cries of 'Perfidious Albion' from the French government were perhaps as inevitable as they were uncomfortably close to the truth, but fortunately most of the noise amounted to little more than letting off steam. Eden's concern that this would lead to Europe falling apart just as it was starting to come together proved unrealised. If anything, the implication that Britain could not be trusted did more to force the pace of France's reconciliation with Germany.

The US was, in all this, the dog that didn't bark. In part, this was because Truman was in the final year of his presidency. But, perhaps less encouragingly, it was also because Treasury Secretary Snyder and others in the administration simply felt that floating a convertible pound would not work, that it would hasten the demise of the sterling area and hence bring forward dollar hegemony. That seemed a reasonable price to pay for the inconvenience of having to put back together the Bretton Woods consensus.

When Butler stood up on 8 April to deliver his Budget to a packed House of Commons, the atmosphere was tense. Few Budgets had been as anticipated. The authors of ROBOT had been clear that floating sterling would have to be accompanied by strong deflationary measures, which meant a rise in interest rates to 4 per cent (from 2.5 per cent) and aggressive cuts in public expenditure.[26] Particularly difficult was the housing budget. It had been a symbolic government priority, but house building also had a substantial dollar cost. Butler dissembled with broad language to spare his former colleague embarrassment; the target of 400,000 new houses was dead in the water but Butler did enough to prevent Macmillan agitating more visibly against the Budget proposals.

These were the key measures for this Budget, but Butler knew that they would not be enough. Public spending would need to be substantially reduced over the next few years. This meant politically difficult targets for the welfare state and food subsidies as well as unsustainable defence and overseas commitments.[27] This last area was particularly difficult for the Conservatives, especially on the back benches, where Butler had never escaped his pre-war reputation as a 'man of Munich'. The Chancellor was able to maintain the commitment to the nuclear weapons programme, which would have been, in current parlance, a red line for Churchill and Eden. They accepted that the quid pro quo would have to be cuts to some of the conventional commitments of imperial overreach. Early to go were some of the bases in the Middle East and in Asia, as 'East of Suez' was abandoned, incidentally giving King Farouk of Egypt a valuable political victory at a difficult time and defusing a potential flashpoint in Anglo-Egyptian relations that might otherwise have had escalated rapidly out of control.[28]

It was not clear which Butler found the more difficult: the acidic, withering response of Attlee, who accused the Chancellor of reversing a decade of cross-party agreement, or the uproar from the Labour back benches. He was perhaps fortunate that the full implications of what he was proposing were not immediately apparent. The Conservative benches were noticeably quiet, a dangerous sign for any Chancellor, and particularly one reliant on a majority of just seventeen. Butler was relieved that there were only seven abstentions – Macmillan most prominent among them – on a critical opposition motion.[29]

As Butler had told the Cabinet in February: 'There would be a continuous process of change and readjustment, much of which would be painful.' That process began almost immediately.

Sterling formally became convertible as the London markets opened the day after the Budget and slumped almost immediately. Within a few weeks, it had fallen by around 15 per cent to $2.40, which had been the speculative rate it had been trading at in New York. It hit a low of $2.32 in June but then stayed in the range of $2.32 to $2.40 throughout the summer.

The impact on the economy from the Budget measures and the de facto devaluation was predictable. Inflation rose by some 2 per cent[30] by the end of the year, which was uncomfortable but not unmanageable, before falling back in 1953 as raw material prices fell. Unemployment started to rise from 400,000 and nearly doubled by the end of 1953, to the fury of the TUC and the Labour benches. The higher levels of unemployment did, however, weaken the unions' negotiating position and some of the anticipated strikes, especially in the skilled industries, failed to materialise as the country adjusted to the new realities.

In 1949, the economy had responded quickly to devaluation; combined with the tough Budget measures, that proved to be the case again. In 1952, the economy was of course far more balanced than it is today and it helped that steps taken in the November Budget were already working through, even though they were not yet evident in the forecasts. Lower defence spending soon allowed for the reallocation of limited resources towards an export drive, and export industries – shipbuilding, civil aviation and defence – started to lead the way towards recovery, benefiting from cheaper sterling. The Centurion Tank, de Havilland Comet and – later in the decade – Hawker Hunter provided the visible symbols of the export-led recovery.

Change in the economy had started but the early 1950s saw a difficult and acrimonious period of adjustment. There may not have been as many strikes as some had expected, but that was no indication that the unions were happy, and the higher unemployment carried with it social and political costs. And with the breakdown in consensus between Labour and the Conservatives, louder ideological voices made headway on both sides of the House.[31] For Labour, this was seen in the narrow victory of Aneurin Bevan – the authentic voice of socialist outrage – over Hugh Gaitskell for the Labour leadership. For the Conservatives, it was in the moves by some of the younger members, such as Iain Macleod and Enoch Powell, towards advocating a distinct Tory message, more than simply a party of financial austerity. Nobody talked now of Mr Butskell.

When Churchill suffered his stroke in 1953, the verdict on ROBOT was far from decided and the polls suggested that the public were not giving the government the benefit of the doubt. It came as no surprise when the elderly Prime Minister chose to step aside rather than preside over the continued grind of politically unpalatable measures. Eden was also seriously ill, suffering the effects of a botched operation, but the Cabinet was in no mood to trust the succession to Butler, the only conceivable alternative. Eden duly succeeded and Lord Salisbury minded the shop until his return.

By the end of 1954, the economy was more definitely responding to its medicine. Hesitant and patchy though the recovery was, it was there. Eden, now firmly in charge and in good health – who knows what more years waiting for the succession might have done for his nerves? – chose to wait until the last possible moment to allow the economic upturn to be as widely felt as possible, and called the election in early 1956. He was rewarded with a slightly increased majority, and Butler could move to the Foreign Office with his reputation intact and his position as heir-apparent cemented. ROBOT had, against the odds, proved a success.

But a success only so far. As Sir David Eccles took over at the Treasury in 1956, he recognised the challenges ahead. The government had diluted but not openly abandoned its 1951 commitment to full employment. Eccles knew that it was impossible to pursue both the goals of ROBOT and full employment: as Cherwell had said, 'letting the exchange rate take the strain' in reality could mean 1 million unemployed. The West German model showed the value of institutional structures that kept temptation away from politicians and ensured disciplined monetary policy.[32] Trying to maintain a balance without those structures would test the best of Chancellors.

The term ROBOT was of course never used by the government, and the role played by Leslie Rowan, George Bolton and Otto Clarke was never made public in their lifetimes. The credit was shared by Butler and his Cabinet colleagues – but that was the lot of civil servants.

Postscript

Could ROBOT really have been attempted? It is in many ways extraordinary that the proposal made as much progress as it did. Timing seems to have been key: ROBOT tapped into a rich vein of official despair and built up momentum from the presentation of Clarke's original paper on 25 January 1952, fuelled by the perceived need to act by the early March Budget.

ROBOT would have represented an extraordinary reversal of government policy of more than a decade, of both parties, that would have come completely out of the blue both to the domestic electorate and to Britain's partners around the world. Lord Salisbury's intervention at Cabinet may have been critical when he said that this may have been beyond what was practicable in a democratic country.[33]

ROBOT could have wrenched Britain out of its downward economic spiral and ended the depressing cycle of boom and bust that characterised economic policy in the 1950s and 1960s. As it was, every subsequent attempt to foster above-trend growth – Maudling's 'dash for growth' in 1963–64, Labour's National Plan in the mid-1960s, and the Barber boom of the early 1970s – took place without the natural balancing mechanism of a floating exchange rate. Each attempt ended in tears. We had to wait until 1979, and Mrs Thatcher, for a government prepared to try the harsh medicine that ROBOT would have involved – arguably a comparable policy measure, but she had the benefit of a generation that had seen economic policy fail and was therefore more prepared for the difficult steps that were taken.

Or ROBOT could have been disastrous, rupturing the post-war political consensus and putting the Conservatives out of office for a generation; as Salter and – when he eventually learned of the episode – Hugh Gaitskell, both thought.

As it turned out, and not for the first or last time, the doom-laden Treasury forecasts had overstated the extent of the crisis. For sure, the 1952 Budget included a sharp increase in interest rates and measures to reduce imports. But once those began to bite, and the trade balance improved, the crisis receded. In the final quarter of 1952, far from running out, the dollar reserves increased sharply and 1952 as a whole saw a balance of payments surplus. The Korean War ended in 1953 and defence spending was reduced. Disaster had been averted and the economy performed strongly throughout the next two years, ironically providing the basis of Butler's reputation as Chancellor.

We had muddled through – and, in each succeeding crisis, we would continue to muddle through. We had opted, in Lyttelton's phrase, for that 'genteel bankruptcy'. Sterling remained fixed at the increasingly overvalued $2.80 rate for fifteen long years, until devaluation in 1967. The consequences of that choice remain with us today.

Notes

1. Charles Moore, *Margaret Thatcher, Vol 1* (Penguin, 2013), p. 465.
2. Gaitskell, as shadow Chancellor, did not find out about it for two years.
3. Peter Hennessy, *Having it So Good: Britain in the Fifties* (Penguin, 2007), p. 199; Edmund Dell, *The Chancellors* (HarperCollins, 1996).
4. David Kynaston's *Family Britain, 1951–1957* (Bloomsbury, 2010) helpfully summarises the sources in a comprehensive note on p. 705.
5. David Marquand, *Britain Since 1918* (Weidenfeld & Nicolson, 2008), p. 152.
6. Hennessy, op. cit., p. 217.
7. Nigel Lawson, 'ROBOT and the fork in the road', *Times Literary Supplement*, 21 January 2005, perhaps comes closest to the format (and gives a good example of the passions ROBOT still evoked more than half a century on).
8. See Correlli Barnett, *The Lost Victory* (Macmillan, 1995), pp. 106–12 for an overview of the workings of the sterling area.
9. To put that in context, total UK central government income in 1951 was £4.6 billion.
10. R. A. Butler, *The Art of the Possible* (Hamish Hamilton, 1971), p. 157. Butler was to use the same phrase in a radio broadcast the following January, demonstrating that Bridges's words had made their impact.
11. Dell, op. cit., p. 173.
12. Hennessy, op. cit., p. 203: total sterling balances £3.43 billion, of which about £872 million were held outside the sterling area.

13. Memorandum by Cobbold, 13 February 1952, quoted in Correlli Barnett, *The Verdict of Peace* (Pan Books, 2002), p. 158. Others, such as Lionel Robbins, influential Professor of Economics at the LSE, shared this concern.
14. Barnett, *The Verdict of Peace*, p. 164.
15. Ibid., p. 172.
16. R. A. Butler's papers, as quoted in Anthony Howard, *RAB: The Life of R. A. Butler* (Papermac, 1988), p. 187.
17. Dell, op. cit., p. 194.
18. Marquand, op. cit., p. 153, and Barnett, *The Verdict of Peace*, p. 175.
19. Lawson, 'ROBOT and the fork in the road'.
20. Metaphorically speaking; Butler chose to live in his own home in nearby Smith Square while Chancellor.
21. In reality, Lord Ismay was Commonwealth Secretary until March. But work of this importance may have provoked bringing forward his replacement.
22. John Fforde, *The Bank of England and Public Policy 1941–1958* (Cambridge University Press, 1992), p. 450. With a close eye on operational realities, Fforde believes that the timing was critical and that combining the strategic changes of ROBOT with the Budget 'stepped over the line between the possibly right and the definitely wrong tactical way' of implementing the plan.
23. The Organisation for European Economic Co-operation, forerunner of the OECD and at this time essentially all of Western Europe.
24. Fforde, op. cit., p. 437. These were the proposals in Clarke's paper on 22 February.
25. Hennessy, op. cit., p. 203.
26. Dell, op. cit., p. 167. These were actual 1952 Budget measures.
27. Hennessy, op. cit., p. 217. Professor Hennessy points out that in reality 'education and health had lost out to guns and housing' in the early '50s; what the counterfactual suggests is that defence spending and housing would have been largely in the same position instead of being protected.
28. As indeed it did: the Suez Crisis.
29. Still a significant rebellion in those days. There were to be fifteen abstentions over Suez, though that was in the next parliament where the government's majority was more secure.
30. Taking Clarke's own estimate of the inflationary impact of devaluation. Raw material prices did fall in reality.
31. Hennessy, op. cit., p. 217; Professor Hennessy suggests this may have happened.
32. Barnett, *The Verdict of Peace*, p. 163. Correlli Barnett's view is that without an independent Bundesbank-style regime, the contradictory policy imperatives would have been unsustainable.
33. Ibid., p. 174. Correlli Barnett believes that ROBOT would have been too great a leap to make at that time.

Chapter 6

What if Britain had voted to leave the EEC in 1975?

Tim Oliver

On Thursday 5 June 1975, a Labour government put a choice to the British people: either they could leave the European Economic Community (EEC) or, as Labour Prime Minister Harold Wilson urged them to do, they could vote to stay on the new terms his government had recently negotiated. The British people's answer to the question: 'Do you think that the United Kingdom should remain part of the European Community (the Common Market)?' was a 67 per cent vote in favour. On a turnout of 65 per cent, the vote seemed a solid commitment to Britain remaining a part of the European project.

Yet European integration has remained one of the most divisive issues in British politics. It has split parties, provoked rows and defections, produced new political parties and helped to topple prime ministers. Divisions reached a new height when, on 23 June 2016, almost exactly forty-one years after the 1975 vote, another referendum saw the British vote by 52 per cent to 48 per cent to leave the European Union (EU, as the EEC has been known since 1992).

Relations between the UK and the rest of Europe have been difficult too, typified by opt-outs, vetoes and a domestic – and especially media – debate, prone to nationalism and lashing out. British politics has long struggled to come to terms with the UK's membership of an organisation that was shaped by others before the UK joined and which has become mixed up in anxieties about British decline, with sovereignty – and the EU's infringement of it – becoming something of a leitmotif of Eurosceptic arguments against UK membership. British politicians have also rarely seen much to gain from saying anything positive about the EU, instead blaming it for a range of the UK's own problems. While the EU's own weaknesses and flaws have not helped build support for it among the British people, after five decades of membership the British are some of the most ill-informed about the EU and, unsurprisingly, the most Eurosceptic.

Would, therefore, British politics have been better off had the British voted to leave in 1975? Shed of an awkward partner, would European integration have advanced further and faster? Would Britain have found a new role in the world and been spared the divisions and political poison that the question of Europe has so often produced? Or would the UK and the EU have found themselves tightly bound to each other, drawn together by the UK's need for some form of close economic and political relationship, and the EU's desire to manage its place as the central economic, social and political organisation of Europe? And would this in turn have caused many of the same tensions about sovereignty, interference and influence, with British politicians blaming the EU for a range of Britain's problems? Let us examine what would have happened if the 1975 referendum vote had gone the other way...

The EEC: an incomplete community

The morning of Friday 6 June 1975 was a sombre one for the leadership of the European Commission. A few years earlier, things had looked so promising, with the prospect that the European Economic Community's first enlargement would bring in four new members. The loss of Norway as a result of a rejection by referendum had already cast a shadow over the idea of enlargement. But Norway's loss was made up for by the inclusion of the UK, one of Europe's largest and most powerful states.

For Commission officials, the UK's membership – alongside that of Ireland and Denmark – worked as a useful means of counterbalancing France. Under General de Gaulle, France had been the *enfant terrible* of Europe in the 1960s, with the 1965–66 'empty chair crisis' – during which France boycotted European institutions – bringing the Community close to collapse. British membership, European officials hoped, would bring new life to the Community and allow the Commission to assert its political predominance. Instead, Britain's narrow 52 per cent vote in favour of withdrawal, just two years after it had joined, triggered not just unwanted exit negotiations but intense internal discussions over the direction the Community would now take. The outcome saw member state governments invest more thoroughly in relations with one another, with the effect that the EEC's central supranational institutions remained weak, limited both in scope and ambition. The status of France, in particular – French politicians smugly noted – was reinforced, as de Gaulle's warnings about Britain being insufficiently European proved to be all too accurate.

Commission officials, however, eventually rallied, with new ideas to pursue further integration, notably the tentative proposal in 1978 for a 'Single European Market'. The idea was aimed not just at reducing the Common Market's remaining economic barriers but also at putting in place strong common social rights. In the event, however, it was the Anglo-Saxon neoliberal economic agenda then sweeping the Western world that shaped the development of the Community, with West Germany, supported by the Netherlands, promoting market liberalisation. As always in EEC negotiations there was resistance, with each of the eight member states taking turns to be labelled an 'awkward partner'. France's willingness in particular to object, threaten vetoes and allow large-scale domestic protests against the plans led to a growing concern that Germany was growing too powerful and France too semi-detached. In response, West Germany, uneasy at losing French support for the Franco-German relationship that had helped it rebuild and reintegrate within the framework of European cooperation, offered budgetary and social protection concessions.

Notwithstanding the setback of June 1975, soon enough there were grounds for another ambitious project of enlargement, driven by political changes in the Mediterranean. Even the British government, now sitting back in the European Free Trade Association (EFTA), supported EEC membership for Greece, Portugal and Spain, recognising that trading links alone would be insufficient to support the political reform process in all three new southern European democracies; though some British politicians were growing increasingly wary of the EEC's growing market size and political power. This enlargement gave the EEC opportunities to build its position as the predominant organisation in European politics. Regional development funds, created as part of the failed proposal to help keep the UK in, were now deployed to assist the new members.

Inevitably, however, enlargement triggered bitter budgetary arguments – again mainly involving France – as European funds flowed south. West German concessions to France on social protection in the new Single European Market could only go so far before they rubbed up against West German, Dutch and Danish demands for open markets in the wake of the growing Western acceptance – championed by Margaret Thatcher in Britain and Ronald Reagan in the US – of privatisation and deregulation as the new model in place of Keynesian economics.

Internal EEC tensions reached a new high as the Cold War reached its denouement. The reunification of Germany and the applications for EEC membership from Sweden and Finland, followed by former Soviet bloc states in Eastern and Central Europe (strongly backed by a US keen to see the EEC complement the expansion of NATO) shifted Europe's centre eastwards. The EEC was renamed the European Union. In a reversal of its former position, France now became the member state keenest to talk of a new attempt at British membership, with Paris seeing this as a way to counterbalance the new united Germany and the shift of the EU towards the east.

Britain: inside the European kingdom but outside the castle

For Britain's political elite, the morning of Friday 6 June was also a sombre one. The U-turn so dramatically imposed by the referendum was a humiliation for Her Majesty's Government akin to the Suez debacle of 1956. Despite his taking something of a back seat in the campaign, the 52 per cent vote to withdraw led immediately to the resignation of Prime Minister Harold Wilson, a move that further weakened a Labour Party governing on a tiny majority.

Commentators blamed the slender majority for 'no' on a range of issues. Some argued that Wilson was to blame; his decision to allow Cabinet ministers to campaign on either side showing weakness and an inability to manage intra-party tensions. Others pointed to the impact the Scottish nationalists had wrought as a result of their campaign against EEC membership, based on the hope that an independent Scotland could one day imitate non-EEC Norway. The 'No' campaign had not put on a stellar performance, but it had faced a 'Yes' campaign that had been complacent and which had in practice struggled to present Harold Wilson's pre-referendum renegotiation of Britain's membership as offering a better deal than the one Ted Heath had taken Britain in on in 1973. Bad weather put off younger 'yes' voters, with older 'no' voters outnumbering them and winning the day.

The result left an already struggling Labour government stunned. But the leadership of the Conservative Party – then the more pro-European of the two main parties – was also damaged. Even in opposition, many Tories (though not all) saw the no vote as a personal defeat on an issue they considered central to Britain's future and security. Leaders of the victorious 'no' tendency in the Conservative Party, especially those who had campaigned vigorously on a message of sovereignty and a history of British independence in the face of European domination, made clear they would not rest on their laurels. They would watch carefully to ensure that a British exit meant Britain would not now find itself forced into a relationship that saw it become a member of the EEC 'by the back door'.

The no vote added to a sense that Britain lacked direction, racked as it was by high inflation, declining competitiveness, growing unemployment, industrial strikes and growing union militancy, constitutional uncertainty and political fragmentation (especially in Scotland), not to mention social changes that many saw as evidence of moral decline. A spending crisis in 1976 forced the government to seek a £2.3 billion loan from the International Monetary Fund, in turn leading some pro-Europeans to point to how, even outside the EEC, Britain's sovereignty was much less in reality than many of the 'out' campaigners had argued during the referendum campaign the year before.

Relations with the United States also reached a new low. Only a month before the referendum, Britain and the world had watched the fall of Saigon. Now the EEC, a creation that owed so much to the US's commitment to Europe in the post-war era, appeared incapable of enlarging, in large part because of the feelings of the citizens of America's closest ally. Commentators in the Soviet Union pointed gleefully to a US and Western Europe at loggerheads, with the British people supposedly showing a clear disdain for the free market capitalist club that was the EEC.

After only two and a half years as an EEC member, negotiations between the British and EEC teams were relatively straightforward, although they still took over a year for both sides to reach agreement on what would happen to shared projects and agreements. In June 1976, the UK officially withdrew from the EEC and reverted to membership of the European Free Trade Association. However, this was an organisation that had already failed to live up to its promise of trade liberalisation without the strictures of political integration, and which, having lost Denmark, now consisted only of Austria, Iceland, Liechtenstein, Norway, Portugal, Sweden and Switzerland. From here, Britain continued to face the economic challenges of the end of empire and a shift of trade towards Europe, though it also tried to invest in new efforts to expand trade with non-European markets.

Just as earlier such attempts had flatlined, so too did these run into trouble, as Britain's non-European trading partners always seemed more interested in the EEC than in EFTA. Similarly, Britain – along with the rest of EFTA – still had to think about European markets more than any other. As a result, and in no small part because of the slim referendum result, the issue of Europe remained unresolved. Pro-European and Eurosceptic beliefs continued to underlie political debate, as developments in the rest of Europe were inevitably shaping the future of the UK. For pro-Europeans, Britain's inability to secure its economic interests was a continual source of concern. The City of London regularly bemoaned the UK's inability to directly influence and access the EEC Single European Market, especially in the areas of services and capital.

For Eurosceptics, buoyed by the vote to withdraw, the growing power of the EEC, its expanding economic reach and the pressure on Britain to 'kowtow' were a continual source of excitement. The US's strong backing of the UK's EEC membership meant that Euroscepticism was also matched by a strain of anti-Americanism, reflecting uncertainty about Britain's position in the world, its political economy and its political and constitutional development. The experience of the Falklands War in 1982, however, left the British feeling relieved that they were not quite the declining power many in the UK and abroad had felt. The cooperation and support of the US, France and other European allies also helped to ease formal relations, but much of this assistance remained hidden from view, in no small part at the request of those allies.

Despite spending the 1970s as the 'sick man of Europe', life within the UK began to improve, in part thanks to Britain benefiting from the 1980s economic boom across the Western world. Britain's social and cultural life was affected by most of the same currents that affected Western Europe. Travel, sport, media (satellite TV especially) – even British food began to take on more European dimensions. An Anglo-French Channel Tunnel went ahead, albeit not without some difficulties; British funding for the project soon ran into problems and was only saved thanks to an injection of investment from Saudi Arabia. Mrs Thatcher's policy of privatisation saw European, US and international companies and investors buy up large swathes of the UK's utilities and infrastructure.

At the same time, thanks to pressure from France and some of the southern European states, by the mid-1980s the EEC had begun to take steps towards balancing the capitalism of the single market with a more social Europe. If this had happened earlier it could have helped the Labour Party to adopt a more settled position on Europe – but it came too late to avert the split that led to the formation of the Social Democratic Party, a divide built partly on animosity between pro-Europeans and Eurosceptics after the European referendum. Just as victory for the 'no' side had emboldened the right of the Conservative Party, so too did the referendum embolden Labour's left, which had portrayed the EEC as a free-market capitalist club that cared little for Europe's workers. The left's victory in a series of internal struggles allowed them to push Labour towards policies of unilateralism, withdrawal from NATO and increasingly far-left economic policies. The SDP's alliance with the Liberal Party kept alive a left-of-centre pro-Europeanism that drew widespread support, which, had it not been for Britain's distortionary electoral system, could have helped the new alliance replace Labour as the main opposition party.

A Conservative majority in the Commons could do little to settle some of the regional tensions the UK faced. In Scotland, the SNP found themselves on the back foot after a narrow rejection by the Scots of devolution in a referendum in 1976 and in the face of a Labour Party rebuilding itself. As with the EEC referendum, the outcome did not settle the issue, with Scottish nationalism remaining an effective if truncated force. The appeal of the EEC also slowly drew the SNP towards a position of supporting closer relations, with some arguing for Scottish independence within the EEC.

A vote that had split along sectarian lines in Northern Ireland had only added to the divisions between the Unionist and nationalist and Protestant and Catholic communities. The Irish government had decided that British withdrawal from the EEC would not change Ireland's commitment to membership. Since the UK–Irish common travel area remained in place, the problems this presented to the emerging Single European Market were a continual source of argument and debate in Ireland, the UK and the EEC. But, through its membership of the EEC, Ireland found a framework in which its international position was no longer overshadowed by the UK. It was able to utilise its access to the single European market and draw on EEC funding to develop its economy, and could count on the EEC's tacit support when expressing concerns about developments in Northern Ireland. This helped pave the way for an easing of Anglo-Irish relations, and, in 1988, the British and Irish governments reached a special agreement with the EEC that allowed the Community's regional development funds to be spent in Northern Ireland. The public justification that the funding would facilitate cross-border economic relations hid hopes in the UK, Ireland, EEC and the US that the money could lay the foundations for the early stages of a peace process. Loyalists, and some members of the Conservative Party, considered the policy an unwanted intrusion, but in the end Loyalist politicians did not turn down the much-needed cash.

In 1989, only a year before the disaster of the poll tax brought her premiership to an abrupt end, Mrs Thatcher delivered a speech at the College of Europe that brought to a head the ambivalent feelings that had been developing within the governing party about Britain's relations with an EEC that was growing in both size and power and, from their perspective, was headed in a direction that a growing number were suspicious of. The 'Bruges speech' made clear that Britain was determined to resist any attempt by the EEC to impose regulations and norms across the whole of Europe. As Mrs Thatcher put it: 'We have not successfully rolled back the frontiers of the state in Britain only to see them re-imposed at a European-wide level with a European super-state exercising a new dominance across the whole of Europe from Brussels.' The speech was a defining moment in relations between the UK and the EEC. London's financial services sector was a regular target of accusations (especially in France) that it was home to a casino capitalism that too often gambled with Britain's and Europe's economic stability – accusations that stoked fears among some Conservatives that the EEC would attempt to curb an industry in which the UK led the world, and upon which the UK Treasury increasingly depended for tax revenue. On top of this, a growing global and European economy in the 1990s saw the UK economy surge, bringing in an influx of migrants from around the world and especially from the rest of the EEC and the European Economic Area (EEA) – free movement that was guaranteed by an EEC–EEA agreement. Tensions began to build over immigration, with a start-up party called the UK First Party (UKFP) pushing for stronger controls on immigration and resistance to EEC meddling in UK affairs.

To appreciate why hostility to the EEC – whether from Mrs Thatcher or the UKFP – was on the rise, we need to go back to 1975 to understand how the EEC's place in European politics had grown and how UK–EEC relations had been changed by it.

Living awkwardly ever after

On Saturday 7 June 1975, Sir Michael Palliser, the first, and soon to be the last, British Permanent Representative to the EEC, met European Commission officials to begin negotiations for the withdrawal of the UK. It soon became clear that both sides held potentially irreconcilable positions. Britain hoped to open up the possibility of EFTA – with the UK in the lead – entering into relations with the EEC on a more or less equal footing with other EEC member states. But the EEC could not allow any new relationship to compromise its own process of political integration.

If Britain, or EFTA, wanted a relationship, they would have to accept that this entailed political rather than merely economic relations – something that the British people had just rejected and which victorious Conservative and Labour 'no' campaigners would watch for carefully.

But both sides faced a dilemma. There was no denying that the UK played a central role in Western European politics, especially through its security and transatlantic relations. Moreover, despite its label as the 'sick man of Europe', Britain's economy remained one of the world's largest. Other members of EFTA, and the EEC, also made clear their hopes for some new arrangement, something pushed for particularly by Ireland and Norway. The British withdrawal had also raised questions in Brussels. If the British could not feel at home in the EEC, politicians asked, did this bode well for possible future enlargements?

The exit deal negotiated in under a year left many questions unanswered. Britain reverted to the EFTA membership it had left in 1972. But channels remained open, with European Political Cooperation (EPC) – an attempt by EEC members to work together on foreign affairs – offering a clear conduit for British involvement, a connection taken up enthusiastically by a London keen to salvage some inside influence over the EEC.

In the mid-1980s, the Commission proposed the creation of a joint 'European Economic Area' (EEA) as a means of upgrading relations between the EEC and EFTA. Following some resistance from the European Court of Justice (ECJ) to the way in which shared decision-making could compromise the EEC's autonomy, the 1992 Maastricht Treaty paved the way for a formalised two-tier Europe, with the internal tier renamed the European Union. The EEA countries agreed to abide by all EU laws, including the free movement of people, goods, capital and services, in exchange for access to the Single Market. EEA members could, however, maintain their own policies in certain specified areas; Norway, for example, refused to contemplate any involvement in the Common Fisheries Policy (CFP). Following the ECJ's intervention, EEA members were granted some limited say in EU decision-making, with a voting system that would take into account their status. The new structure, however, clearly favoured the member states of the EU. While some EFTA members such as Austria and Sweden (Portugal having joined the EU in the 1980s as part of the southern enlargement that included Spain and Greece) opted for membership of the EU, others remained committed to a relationship through the EEA. Norway experienced another failed referendum on EU membership, opting instead for the EEA.

The outer ring of EEA members and an inner core of EU members were intended to be a means to balance the most important European geopolitical development: a reunited Germany. The inner core would take economic integration further through currency union. Reaching agreement was not without its difficulties, with the Danish people showing strong opposition to being included in the inner core; after a referendum, they opted to try to straddle the inner and outer tiers. Danish reservations, along with opinion polls showing doubts among other peoples in the EU, were seized upon by British Eurosceptics as a sign that the whole EU structure lacked democratic support. In one notable outburst in 1990, Thatcherite Conservative minister Nicholas Ridley described the proposed EU–EEA system as 'a German racket designed to take over the whole of Europe', and argued that giving up sovereignty to the EU and EEA was as bad as surrendering to Adolf Hitler. The EEA, he claimed, was nothing more than 'a colonial system, designed to pay tributes to Europe's German masters'. In a more subtle way, a young Brussels-based reporter for the *Daily Telegraph*, Boris Johnson, had gained a loyal following among Conservative politicians and supporters for his reports about supposedly silly EU laws forced onto the UK through the EEA, and EU and EEA inadequacies dragging down the UK.

It therefore came as no surprise that British agreement to the proposed EEA–EU deal – which the government saw as essential to the future of Britain's economy – faced tough opposition in the House of Commons, where some Conservative MPs, regretting the fall of Mrs Thatcher, increasingly considered her Bruges speech a prophetic warning of the EU's growing domination of Europe. They felt it had been a mistake for Britain to agree to participate in the free movement of peoples (albeit outside the Schengen passport-free area), and the fact that Britain, like other non-EU EEA members, was to pay contributions towards the shared EU budget provoked howls of protest.

The situation was not helped by the disintegration of Yugoslavia and the subsequent outflow of refugees to Western Europe, provoking calls for stronger border controls. Added to this, the failure of the EU, working with Britain, to handle the wars in the Balkans left a sour taste among some British politicians, who worried that the situation would undermine NATO and the US commitment to Europe; this partly explained the UK backing for the US in the Iraq War of 2003. On top of this, decisions by the European Court of Human Rights provoked a steady stream of headlines about European judges interfering in British democracy, even though it was distinct from both EU and EEA. The EEA court, established by the Maastricht Treaty to enforce relevant EU laws across the EEA, became a favourite focus of hatred by British Eurosceptics for its perceived infringements of parliamentary sovereignty.

While Europe in 2003 was far from united, British politicians could not help but notice that Eastern and Central European countries, and most other EFTA states, had opted, or were trying to opt, to join the inner core of the EU, leaving the UK a member of a dwindling outer tier group that – it was proposed – could soon include Turkey and Ukraine. Pressure began to build for a renegotiation of the UK's outer tier membership that would see an end to British contributions to the EU's budget and the free movement of EEA citizens and an assertion of the sovereignty of the British Parliament. This was especially true within a Conservative Party still struggling to come to terms with its divisions over Britain's relations with the rest of Europe; divisions that had been heightened by the way in which the Maastricht Treaty agreeing to the UK's involvement in the EEA had been forced through the House of Commons. While the economic costs of breaking links with the EEA and EU led many outside the Conservative Party to doubt the desirability of such a move, support for the proposal also drew on public unease at some EU/EEA policies, particularly free movement of people, and the fact that UK citizens were among the least well informed about the EU and EEA.

Referendum 2016: déjà vu for EU?

In 2016, a book of counterfactual history asked the question: 'What if Britain had voted to stay in the EEC in 1975?' To the book's editors the question seemed topical given the recent referendum result to end the UK's membership of the EEA and its links with the EU. The author of the chapter noted that relations inside the Union would probably have been fraught. British politics would more than likely have continued to struggle with its European question, while the rest of Europe would also have struggled with the British question. Both sides would have found themselves uneasy in managing their shared interests, whether in the Cold War or in the geopolitical fallout after its peaceful conclusion.

By 2016, the debate had reached a new level of intensity. The European question was again at the forefront of UK politics. As the predominant power of Europe, the EU had worked its way into almost every aspect of British politics – but British politicians and media had proved unwilling to explain these links or to talk positively of UK–EU relations. Instead they had preferred to turn the EU into an 'other' against which Britain defined itself. Things had only been made worse by economic crises in Greece and wars in the Middle East, which had highlighted inadequacies in both the Eurozone and the Schengen Agreement, leaving both under intense pressure.

Eurosceptics had for some time been urging the British people to demand their government negotiate a more distant relationship and so spurn cooperation with what for them was an inherently dysfunctional and flawed organisation. Facing intense pressure from his backbenchers, Prime Minister David Cameron attempted to secure a revised relationship. He did not attempt to jeopardise British access to the European Single Market, something the government still considered essential and which, polling showed, was one of the strongest reasons behind such public support as there was for close relations with the EU. He did, however, set out to cut Britain's contribution to the EU budget, restrict the free movement provisions of EEA membership and include within the EU–EEA agreement a provision stating the supremacy of the British Parliament.

Eurosceptics inevitably ridiculed the eventual agreement, but both Cameron and the EU's leaders reached a compromise of sorts, hoping that the British people would vote to maintain their part in the EEA and their links with the EU. Some in the UK and elsewhere in Europe hoped that the vote would, as David Cameron had told his European counterparts, 'settle the matter for a generation'. When the referendum saw a 50.5 per cent vote to leave the EEA, historians of UK–European relations felt vindicated in their less-than-optimistic assessments that the referendum could have done anything of the sort.

Chapter 7

What if Britain had lost the Falklands War?

Prime Minister Roy Jenkins (1984–94)

Peter Cuthbertson

How Roy Jenkins actually came to power in Britain is as remarkable as his decade in office. This is particularly true given that the Jenkins years represented the end of a brief counter-revolution aimed at reversing Britain's decline.

Margaret Thatcher is now remembered only for being the first woman Prime Minister and for the Falklands crisis. But we should also remember her for paving the way for someone who was, for better or worse, a truly transformative Prime Minister.

The chronology of the Falklands crisis is familiar to all students of recent British history. What began with the Argentine invasion of the Malvinas Islands (then known widely as the Falklands) ended just one month later. In a single attack in May, the Argentine cruiser *General Belgrano* and its convoy killed 907 British servicemen. Militarily, it was a heavy blow. Politically, it brought an end to Britain's hopes for repelling the invaders by force. Margaret Thatcher resigned rather than agree to a peace which recognised partial Argentine sovereignty over the islands.

In her resignation speech in Parliament, Thatcher mourned the loss of life but urged Parliament to go on fighting, warning that to recognise Argentina's invasion would embolden aggressors around the world.

Thatcher's successor, Francis Pym, politely ignored these warnings and spent the rest of the year negotiating a period of transitional rule by the United Nations.

It is difficult to see any way that Pym could have won the general election that followed. Given such a military humiliation, it was hardly surprising that the Conservative Party's poll ratings failed to recover once a new Prime Minister was appointed. The new leader made no difference.

It was Roy Jenkins who profited most from the Falklands crisis, although there is no evidence that he felt anything but horror as it unfolded. Re-elected to Parliament only a week before the invasion, Jenkins and his Liberal–SDP Alliance had already enjoyed poll ratings as high as 50 per cent in the preceding months. Jenkins had warned repeatedly of another Suez crisis, initially to much hostility.

Once Britain agreed to peace talks, Jenkins was vindicated over his warnings and returned to the theme with sustained attacks on Pym's new government, both in Parliament and in widely televised public meetings.

'The Conservatives have finally helped Britain to forget the Suez crisis – by engineering a new national humiliation that dwarfs Suez,' Jenkins told a London crowd. 'Indeed, they have made Sir Anthony Eden look like Alexander the Great.'

Pym called a snap election in February 1984, in which the Conservatives lost more than half their seats.

There is limited but compelling evidence that Britain's economy was actually – finally – recovering by the time Thatcher's brief premiership ended. Inflation was below 10 per cent and there were encouraging signs of growth.

But Pym himself quickly adopted a watered-down version of the Alliance programme – and faced very limited protest from his party's now cowed right wing. He abandoned Thatcher's monetarism and increased borrowing dramatically, with a view to cutting unemployment with a large programme of public works. Ultimately, this deference to its ideas only increased the public appetite for the Alliance. In 1984, an Alliance parliamentary majority was both an extraordinary upset and entirely unsurprising given the clear public mood.

In economic terms, the Jenkins government's rather agitated Keynesianism offers a fascinating case study in what *not* to do.

Jenkins's Chancellor, David Owen, immediately announced a new programme of borrowing, on top of Pym's. The borrowing supported a small reduction in Britain's National Insurance tax, but its overriding purpose was a major programme of capital expenditure. Owen pledged that the state would be in the vanguard of a modernisation of Britain's infrastructure. The government would identify and invest in major 'shovel-ready' projects in housing, energy and energy conservation, transport, hospitals, and the water and sewage systems. All this would support the Alliance's manifesto commitment of a reduction in unemployment by 1 million within two years.

In fact, by 1986 unemployment was noticeably higher than when Jenkins came to office. His first mistake was a failure to account for how the rest of the economy would react to his Keynesian experiment. Private-sector job creation and industrial investment fell sharply and failed to recover throughout Jenkins's decade in 10 Downing Street. There was no wider economic boost from the increased government spending: consumers simply saved more and spent less, rightly anticipating that taxes would rise in the future to repay the borrowing.

Jenkins's second mistake was his optimism about the ability of the British civil service to identify and implement suitable projects. British governments had always failed at picking winners, but Jenkins nonetheless made this central to his economic strategy. For all the money that was spent, the only success was the improved sewage systems. The housing projects were the butt of countless stand-up comedy one-liners. Hundreds of millions were spent installing quirky energy conservation schemes while the rest of the developed world simply took up double glazing.

Third was the mistaken belief that the state could move quickly. Some Keynesian economists theorised that even otherwise worthless investments would generate economic activity in the short to medium term – so long as they were indeed shovel-ready. But the civil service moved complacently slowly and the biggest projects required primary legislation to pass through Parliament. Every major job-creation project proposed by Jenkins and Owen also ran up against Britain's creaky planning system, which remained unreformed since the Attlee government's legislation forty years earlier. Local authority planning committees did all they could to prevent any incursion on the land they controlled, and even many Alliance MPs resisted stripping councillors of these powers.

Jenkins's fourth economic mistake was to provoke Britain's trade unions by trying to hold down wages during a public sector spending spree. In the face of declining real incomes, the union leaders again brought industrial chaos to the country as they attempted to divert the government's spending towards their members' wages and away from the programme of capital investment. The 1980s saw more working days lost to strikes than the 1970s. This industrial unrest further aggravated the delays, with some major projects beginning years later than originally timetabled.

Ultimately, the industrial unrest gave way to what Jenkins's supporters welcomed as an overriding principle of compromise. Formal, regular meetings took place in which industry, trade unions and consumer representatives, the unemployed and ethnic minority groups all had a major say in economic policy. Jenkins's critics described this accommodation as little more than formalised caving-in. No trade unions of any importance could now be defeated by elected governments. The prices and incomes policy was dead, and with efforts to control the money supply abandoned, inflation rose along with unemployment.

Britain entered a stagflationary period from which she has never since fully extracted herself. Unions would demand higher wage increases, anticipating higher inflation. This increased unemployment, tempting governments to be laxer with monetary policy – soon meaning even higher inflation.

Seeking a new way to control price rises, Jenkins twice took Britain into the European Community's Exchange Rate Mechanism, but each time industrial action against its disciplines soon forced a departure.

Britain entered the 1990s more backward in certain ways than she had been in the 1970s, and with over 4 million unemployed. Other advanced economies were giving control of their industries and utilities to the people: privatisation. But the nearest Britain came to privatising her nationalised industries was some oversight by an Efficiency Audit Commission that reported regularly to a House of Commons Select Committee.

Nor were Britain's greatest problems all economic. Roy Jenkins saw himself as a major social reformer, and the SDP MP Polly Toynbee won him over as she described Britain's prisoners as the next great progressive cause. She became Home Secretary in 1987 and quickly closed almost three-quarters of Britain's prisons, with the prisons budget largely diverted towards rehabilitation programmes.

Unfortunately for the law-abiding in Britain, the rehabilitation programmes worked out no better than the capital expenditure programmes. Crime had been steadily rising since the 1950s, but the crime wave of the 1980s was of an entirely different magnitude. There was an obvious risk to having tens of thousands more criminals on the streets rather than in prison. Britain became a dangerous place to be alone outside daylight hours – and in daylight in many areas.

Britain is famously the crime capital of the OECD. The greatest impact on quality of life has been seen in the rocketing of casual violence, and the effective destruction of secure property rights through everyday thefts and burglaries.

Sociologists note the curious emergence of two clear moral strains in Britain in the 1980s. Some people became much more religious in response to misery. Others saw greater opportunities in crime than in a stagnant economy with hardly any risk of prison – and seized those opportunities. Some parents admitted that they couldn't quite bring themselves to tell their children to live only on benefits and avoid the opportunities offered by crime.

No advanced nation had a tougher 1980s than Great Britain. It is reasonable to ask why there was no popular backlash.

First and most importantly, there already *had* been a backlash against these trends very recently: in 1979. Strange as it seems to present the three-year premiership of Margaret Thatcher as historically significant (her gender excepted), the 5 per cent swing from Labour to Conservative in 1979 represented a clear move to the right by British voters, however brief. Thatcher promised to take Britain on a free-market course and drive down taxes, inflation, immigration and strikes. It just didn't last very long, or end very well.

'What has Conservatism brought except military humiliation and mass unemployment?' Roy Jenkins first asked during the 1984 general election, in one of his fiercest speeches. In truth, he was tapping into a national anger with which his own sympathies were limited. He knew that Conservative governments had presided over more than the Suez and Falklands crises. But he also knew that the question would resonate, and it was a question he and many others repeated well into the 1990s, to the continuing discomfort of the Tories.

Second, the introduction of a more proportional electoral system soon led the Conservatives to split every bit as much as Labour had in 1981. But there was no equivalent to the Falklands crisis to allow either of the new right-of-centre parties to gain an electoral foothold in the way the Alliance had. So free-market conservatives and traditionalist nationalistic conservatives, who had previously been united in one party, now grappled for vote share without any great success.

Third, the Home Secretary's other major innovation was government regulation of the press and broadcast media. With the stated aim of defending the privacy of individuals and especially of ordinary members of the public, the Privacy Act fundamentally undermined the popular press. In the absence of a competitive print media, a dissatisfied general public was confused about who to blame.

In addition, the Act operated uniquely against right-of-centre politicians and commentators. It imposed major restrictions on what could legally be reported about individual behaviour, but it also included a public-interest exemption for hypocrisy. In practice this gave the press the opportunity to carry on reporting widely on adultery, sex scandals and drug and alcohol problems – as long as the individuals in question could be linked in some way to prior condemnation of these or similar behaviours.

Even those in the same political parties were quickly judged to be hypocritical by association, and the details of their personal lives exposed. The political right became known for living uniquely sordid lives. By contrast, while Roy Jenkins's extra-marital affairs were legendary and widely covered abroad, no British media outlet reported them during his time in office.

Fourth, those who read about Britain but fear visiting often fail to appreciate that some of the most influential people in the country really did do better than ever under Jenkins. Jenkins loved the establishment and the establishment loved him back. If Margaret Thatcher had worked towards a Britain in which ability was all, in Roy Jenkins's Britain the privileged professional was king. All major professions were carefully insulated from competition. The shop had never been so closed, which was an ongoing windfall for those in the professions. But, as the right-wing journalist Charles Moore argued in one column:

> So many people I speak to contrast the decline of their country with their own personal and family's prosperity. 'We can't prevent decline, but we can enjoy it,' one lofty cynic told me last month. Even as pure selfishness this seems short-sighted to me. Wealthy enough men in their thirties may be able to shield their children from the worst aspects of modern Britain. But their grandchildren? Especially those of their grandchildren who grow up without some or all of their advantages?

Finally, Great Britain had substantial outside help in the form of frequent and generous European Community subsidies. This drip-feed continues to this day and now probably makes the establishment complacent about the need for fundamental economic reforms. But it also certainly helped to mitigate Britain's problems in the 1980s and 1990s. A former president of the European Commission, Roy Jenkins felt entirely at home in Brussels, Paris, Bonn and Frankfurt, the world's leading financial centre. Jenkins used all his diplomatic clout in efforts to extract increasing subsidies from more productive EU countries – and rarely failed.

On the primacy of Europe, Jenkins was at one with his Foreign Secretary and Deputy Prime Minister, David Steel. But while relations with Brussels helped sustain the Jenkins project, it is difficult to identify any coherent foreign policy beyond it.

The Cold War was the major international conflict of the Jenkins era. But despite Foreign Office mandarins occasionally pushing the notion of Britain as a leading player, with the British Prime Minister joining Reagan and Gorbachev as one of the 'big three', Britain played no important role in the conflict's conclusion.

In particular, Jenkins's relationship with American President Ronald Reagan was dire. Reagan personally did little to hide his distress at the fall of Margaret Thatcher, but soon the State Department and Foreign Office were ready to forge a new relationship. Nothing came of these efforts, and the coolest of relationships was forged. In his memoirs, Jenkins admitted his contempt for Reagan's intellect as well as his politics.

So, while Britain remained a member of NATO and a nuclear power, and although Jenkins had a good working relationship with the Soviet leader Mikhail Gorbachev, his relationship with Reagan was sufficiently poor that Britain played no significant role in the end of the Cold War. Britain passively welcomed Reagan's moves in 1988, the last year of his presidency, to begin serious negotiations with Gorbachev. When the Berlin Wall finally fell in 1995, Britain was a spectator rather than a serious participant.

In the run-up to the 1989 general election, the Reform Conservative Party managed a brief poll lead, immediately following a highly controversial speech by their candidate Ann Widdecombe. Widdecombe pointed to how much of the country had already been lost, and suggested that religious freedom would be curbed if Roy Jenkins was re-elected. Many churches would be forced underground, she predicted, by intolerant legislation.

But the courts quickly ruled that she had committed a minor electoral offence. Britain's new secularism laws forbade appealing specifically to religious faith for votes. The embarrassed party hierarchy backed down and prevented her from standing. They made little progress in the election and Jenkins served another five years as Prime Minister of an Alliance/Labour coalition government.

The Reform Conservative Party re-entered government in 1994, a decade after its predecessor party had left office. But the party had to share power with the Alliance, and it now represented only a very weakened and fearful conservatism. That question – 'What has Conservatism brought except military humiliation and mass unemployment?' – still rang in Tory ears.

Above all, the written constitution and human rights laws introduced in the early 1990s transferred massive powers away from Parliament and to the courts. Senior judges seized on their new constitutional role with alacrity, and frequently prevented any democratic challenges to the left-liberal establishment status quo. Elected politicians now simply lacked the power to implement many conservative principles. Jenkins's policies were there to stay, whatever happened in the ballot box.

Two decades on, is it implausible to attribute even certain elements of the British national character to the Jenkins government?

It is a cliché that the British one meets abroad are much smarter than the ones who stay at home. But there is truth to this grim verdict: the 'Jenkins brain drain' has never really ended.

For all the crime and economic stagnation, there are millions of people happy to stay in Britain. But they are rarely the ones who wish to succeed or achieve big things in their lives. Seventeen of the world's twenty-five leading British-born businessmen have no business operations in their country of birth, and twenty-three of them have their global headquarters in other countries. In a typical year, Britain registers the fewest patents per head of any Western European country.

Likewise, the famed happy-go-lucky aspect of the British character, which is a relatively recent phenomenon in a people known two generations ago for their stiff upper lip. Could living for the moment simply be a rational response to life in a country that has now undergone more than thirty years of high inflation?

In 2015, Great Britain received another financial bailout from the European Union. As they came to Britain's aid, other EU member states noted haughtily that this was the country's fourth bailout since Britain first went to the International Monetary Fund in 1976. No one disputed that the British were visibly poorer than the German or Greek taxpayers who were footing the bill. But many asked why it was down to Britain's European neighbours once again to bail out Britain's coal mines and her notoriously useless nationalised telecommunications firm.

These complaints did nothing to stop the billions of euros making their way into Britain. But they underlined the central fact of Britain's history since 1945: other than by conquest, no other nation has ever fallen so far, so fast.

Looking back, it all seems inevitable. Even the coldest historians must feel an element of pity for the British, living their lives in a country undergoing an irreversible decline.

Much as my imagination sometimes runs wild, I do struggle to believe that the woman elected in 1979 could ever really have offered any hope of turning it all round.

Chapter 8

What if German reunification had never happened?

Michael Wuliger

On 28 August 1989, the Presidium of West Germany's ruling CDU party met for what was to be a routine session. The meeting turned out to be anything but routine, when Helmut Kohl, the party leader and Chancellor, told the assembled Christian Democrat grandees that he was going to sack Heiner Geißler, the General Secretary and informal number two of the party, for disloyalty. Geißler, it transpired, had planned to oust his boss at the next party congress in September; Kohl was to be replaced as CDU leader and Chancellor by Lothar Späth, the state premier of the south-western province of Baden-Württemberg.

The coup fell flat because, as the weekly news magazine *Der Spiegel* wrote gloatingly, Geißler and his co-conspirators – among them Rita Süssmuth, the Speaker of the Federal Parliament, Ernst Albrecht, state premier of the province of Lower Saxony, Employment Minister Norbert Blüm and Späth himself – were rank amateurs up against an old hand at intra-party intrigues. More importantly, they lacked guts: when push came to shove at the CDU party conference in September 1989, Späth lost his nerve and did not stand. Kohl continued as party leader and Chancellor for another nine years, reuniting Germany in 1990. Geißler, Späth and the rest of the cabal all lost their jobs in the years to come and were left out in the political wilderness.

However, the plot did not necessarily have to fail. If the conspirators had been a bit more adept at scheming (and if Späth had been a bit more courageous), they could have achieved their goal. At the time, Kohl was considered by many in his party, as well as the public, as yesterday's man. After seven years as Chancellor he seemed burnt out; an aura of stagnation surrounded his watch. Moreover, his increasingly autocratic ways had alienated many of his Cabinet ministers and MPs as well as important sections of the business, media and cultural elites, right up to the country's President, the Christian Democrat Richard von Weizsäcker, who had subtly but persistently criticised Kohl's policies and style of governing.

So let's assume Geißler's plan had succeeded.

~

At the CDU party congress in Bremen on 12 September 1989, Lothar Späth stood against Helmut Kohl and defeated him narrowly by 51.5 per cent to 48.5 per cent of the votes cast. Kohl immediately resigned as Chancellor. Three days later, Späth was sworn in as his successor. 'A badly needed breath of fresh air,' the influential *Frankfurter Allgemeine Zeitung* commented, voicing the general consensus of the country.

At fifty-one, Späth was eight years younger than Kohl. Where Kohl had exuded an air of stolidity, the new man radiated dynamism. He was trusted to get the economy back on track after years of slowing growth. As state premier of Baden-Württemberg – Germany's economic powerhouse, home to industrial giants such as Daimler-Benz, Porsche, Bosch and SAP – Späth knew about business, something that had never been Kohl's forte. In his first government policy statement to the Federal Parliament in Bonn, the new Chancellor placed special emphasis on the economy and announced reforms of West Germany's labour market and its bloated welfare system, measures that had been put on the back burner by his predecessor. When the first opinion polls showed the CDU's numbers significantly rising for the first time in years, even the many Kohl loyalists in the party grudgingly conceded that ousting the old man might not have been such a bad idea after all.

Three weeks after his election, Chancellor Späth travelled to Brussels to attend his first EU summit. In the past, Kohl had dominated these meetings of Europe's heads of government. Now France's François Mitterrand and Britain's Margaret Thatcher took the lead. Späth was the new kid on the block. As a provincial politician, he had little experience in international relations.

All of the summit's participants agreed that recent developments in the Soviet Union and Eastern Europe, where Communist dictatorships were manifestly eroding, called for a cautious approach. As welcome as the liberalisation of the Eastern Bloc was, any ensuing risk to the fragile geopolitical stability of the continent needed to be avoided. Margaret Thatcher used a metaphor: 'When the ice breaks there's the danger of ice floes.' To Späth, a long-time admirer of the Iron Lady, that made sense.

Thus it was that when, seven weeks later, on the night of 9 November 1989, the German Democratic Republic opened the Berlin Wall and tens of thousands of euphoric East Germans partied in the streets of West Berlin, Chancellor Späth, in his first televised statement, spoke of his and the whole country's joy at the Iron Curtain coming down and promised the GDR West Germany's full support for all steps leading to greater liberty for its citizens. He pointedly avoided, however, speaking of reunification. In fact, when asked at a press conference the day after whether the opening of the wall could lead to a united Germany, the Chancellor went to great pains to dismiss the whole notion. 'This is not the time to fantasise about what the long-term future may hold,' Späth said. 'Of course, we all wish for a new Europe without barbed-wire borders. But right now the task at hand is to encourage and to support the liberalising forces in the whole Eastern Bloc and the GDR in their course towards more democracy and a better life for their people.'

That was the line the Chancellor had agreed in telephone conversations with Mitterrand and Thatcher. Both the French socialist President and the British Conservative Prime Minister had politely but firmly warned that any mention of the R-word might severely trouble the European waters. It could provide Gorbachev's political enemies with ammunition at a time when the Soviet President's hold on power was looking increasingly fragile. Memories of the Second World War were still very much alive in the USSR. Poland, with its centuries-old experience of Teutonic aggression, would fear for its formerly German western provinces on the Oder-Neisse border, which West Germany had never formally relinquished. Even the

Federal Republic's friends and allies in Western Europe did not feel all that comfortable with the idea of a united Germany in their midst. 'Don't upset the apple cart,' Margaret Thatcher had urged Späth, for a moment flustering his interpreter before she came up with the appropriate German idiom: '*Mach' nicht die Pferde scheu*' – 'Don't frighten the horses'.

Not that Späth really needed much pressure. Unlike Kohl, an instinctive German nationalist for whom reunification was a genuine matter of the heart, his successor was a political pragmatist. Good relations with the Federal Republic's most important European partners counted for much more to him than what he considered – at least for the time being – unrealistic notions of national unity. Besides, Späth, a convinced European federalist, believed that the traditional nation-state was a thing of the past.

There was little criticism of this policy in the Federal Republic. Späth spoke for the majority of the country. Few West Germans really longed for a united fatherland, which most of them knew only from history books. The main opposition party, the Social Democrats, had long ago discarded reunification from their party platform. Though former Chancellor and party icon Willy Brandt declared when the Berlin Wall fell, 'now what belongs together will grow together', his decade-long right-hand man Egon Bahr, the SPD's foreign policy guru, was quick to characterise the idea of a united Germany as 'the Federal Republic's grand delusion'. Novelist Günter Grass invoked the memory of Auschwitz as a moral obstacle to reunification. The Green Party put up posters with the slogan: 'Don't talk of Germany. Talk about the weather.'

Späth's junior coalition partner, the liberal Free Democrats (FDP) under Foreign Minister Hans-Dietrich Genscher, also went along with the Chancellor. Though Genscher, himself a native of East Germany (he hailed from Halle in Saxony-Anhalt), had never lost his emotional attachment to his home province, he was realistic enough to know that West Germany could not act against the express will of its most important partners. Besides, as leader of a party that only represented 9 per cent of the voters, he was in no position to turn the tide.

Only Kohl grumbled from the sidelines. In a full-page interview with the conservative daily *Die Welt*, the former Chancellor insisted that 'this was the hour of reunification', and chided his successor as 'weak', 'short-sighted' and 'lacking in patriotism': 'Herr Späth, alas, is failing to, as Bismarck phrased it, grasp the coat of history.' Späth chose to ignore Kohl's carping, as did indeed most of his fellow citizens. There were, after all, compelling arguments against reunification besides the distrust of Germany's neighbours and allies. First and foremost, German unity would be an extremely expensive venture. 'It could cost us up to four trillion marks,' Finance Minister Theo Waigel had told the Cabinet at a meeting held immediately after the opening of the Berlin Wall. 'The GDR is an economic basket case.'

In 1989, East Germany, which in its propaganda had boasted of being the world's seventh largest industrial nation, was in fact on the brink of economic collapse. The country's infrastructure was in tatters. Whole blocks of buildings in cities like East Berlin, Leipzig and Dresden were literally falling to pieces. The machinery in many plants was ancient, some dating from the 1930s. What information technology the GDR had was pitifully lagging behind that of the West, the gap in computerisation widening year by year. Consumer goods, be they fresh fruit, spare parts for cars or underwear, were becoming increasingly scarce. Moreover, the country was completely dependent on loans from the West and heavily in debt. The GDR owed Western banks 49 billion marks and had to export manufactured goods below cost at crash prices just to acquire the foreign exchange needed to honour the annual interest and repayment rates. 'Our foreign debt has reached proportions that call in question our solvency,' Gerhard Schürer, head of the National Planning Board, had reported to the Central Committee of the ruling Socialist Unity Party (SED) in October 1989.

East Germany's widening economic crisis was one of the reasons – if not the main one – behind the wave of refugees fleeing socialism in the summer of 1989. At that time, one and a half million of the 17 million citizens of the GDR had officially applied for exit visas, even though such applications automatically ensured summons by the dreaded State Security Police and other reprisals, and in any case permission to emigrate was only rarely granted. Tens of thousands of discontents therefore used the summer holidays of 1989 to escape to the West via Hungary and Czechoslovakia.

The refugee crisis and the dire state of the economy cost East Germany's long-time ruler Erich Honecker his job. On 17 October 1989, the SED's politburo replaced him with his second-in-command Egon Krenz. Krenz immediately initiated a kind of East German *perestroika*. The secret police was put on a short leash. Censorship of the media was relaxed. Independent political groupings were legalised. And East Germans were granted freedom of movement.

Those measures, the GDR's new rulers hoped, would appease the population and stop the haemorrhage. However, the opposite happened. With no more risk of being shot by border guards, more and more East Germans now left their country for what they hoped would be a better life in the West. In November 1989 alone, 133,429 GDR citizens officially registered as refugees in the Federal Republic. Since West German law considered all Germans, including those from the GDR, as citizens of the Federal Republic, the refugees therefore automatically gained the right to draw welfare benefits. Soon local authorities in West Berlin and other cities near the border raised the alarm, warning that the influx from the East was overstraining their social security budgets. 'At this rate we will be broke by Christmas,' the Mayor of Bremerhaven told his city council. 'Our tax revenue this year is 128 million marks, 120 million of which is being spent on welfare.' The influx from the GDR also created a severe housing crisis. Youth hostels, army barracks, trade fair halls and, in Hamburg, even brothels were requisitioned to accommodate the new arrivals.

The public mood changed. The first wave of East Germans immediately after the opening of the wall had been welcomed euphorically with applause and champagne. They were treated to free rounds in pubs and, in not infrequent cases, to sexual favours. However, when the West Germans began to realise that their cousins from the other side of the Iron Curtain were not just day visitors but actually planned to stay, national enthusiasm rapidly ebbed. Shopkeepers and customers started complaining about idle East Germans loitering in malls and shopping promenades. City dwellers grumbled that the streets stank of the exhaust fumes of the GDR's Trabant two-stroke cars. Derisive jokes about 'Ossis', as the countrymen from the East were mockingly called, abounded, often targeting their seemingly insatiable appetite for exotic fruit such as bananas – 'How does an Ossi pregnancy test work? Shove a banana into the womb, withdraw it after one minute and look for bite marks.'

And the exodus continued. '*Wie viele noch?*' – 'How many more?' – screamed a banner headline in *BILD-Zeitung*, the tabloid with a circulation of 5 million. A cover of the weekly news magazine *Der Spiegel* depicted masses of scruffy GDR citizens pressing against a flighty barrier. The caption read '*Die Flut aus dem Osten*' – 'The deluge from the East'.

The East German immigrants were unhappy as well. The Federal Republic turned out to be anything but the land of milk and honey they had expected. To begin with, there were no jobs for them. Unemployment in West Germany stood at 8 per cent, with over 2 million people off the payroll. Even if there had been jobs, many Easterners lacked the necessary qualifications. Instead of instantly becoming prosperous citizens of '*Wirtschaftswunderland*' – the country of the economic miracle – as they had hoped, the Ossis found themselves in the role of poor and unwanted relations. For years they had longingly watched West German TV, dreaming that one day they too would own the cars, stereos and other consumer goods featured in the adverts. Now all they got were handouts from social security, mass accommodation in refugee shelters and contempt from their Western cousins.

Many Ossis were beginning to regret their flight. Some returned home. But going back to the East was no real option. The GDR's economy continued to plummet further. A 2-billion-mark emergency loan Chancellor Späth had quickly arranged on 15 November to stave off an immediate breakdown was soon burnt up. 'We desperately need at least 10 billion more immediately,' Krenz told the Chancellor on 12 December in one of their weekly phone calls. 'Otherwise, a catastrophe is inevitable. My economists tell me that just to keep afloat we would have to resort to Romanian-style austerity measures.'

'Meaning what?' Späth asked.

'Meaning that we'd be forced to ration food, power and heating – and winter is beginning,' Krenz answered. 'We would have to introduce a three-day working week. Overall, the standard of living would decline by 25 to 30 per cent – not in the long term but over the next few months.

Herr Bundeskanzler, I don't need to spell out what that could imply for the Federal Republic. If you think the 300,000 migrants you've taken in so far are a burden, figure out what 2 to 3 million more would mean.'

'Blackmail, pure and simple,' as Späth described the conversation to his Cabinet later that day. 'And I don't think 10 billion is the end of it. Next they'll want 20 billion, then 30... It's a bottomless pit.'

'Besides, I haven't got that kind of money in my budget,' Finance Minister Waigel added. 'Unless we raise taxes. Not a good idea just a year or so before the next elections.'

Minister of the Interior Wolfgang Schäuble raised his hand. 'We are not only facing a financial problem,' he said. 'The security services are reporting massive activity by extreme right-wing groups among discontented GDR refugees. Their propaganda is falling on fertile ground.' East Germans were unaccustomed to democracy. Unlike their cosmopolitan Western countrymen, they had no experience of living in a multi-ethnic society. Feeling let down by the West, many Ossis now reverted to traditional German xenophobia and authoritarianism. Led by the neo-Nazi National Democratic Party, thousands of East Germans held demonstrations in cities around the country. 'German jobs for German workers,' the protesters chanted, targeting the Federal Republic's 2 million Turkish 'guest workers'. 'If we don't get this under control there will be a potential threat to public safety and order,' Schäuble told his colleagues.

The potential threat became reality on New Year's Eve, when a mob of 2,000 discontented East German refugees, many of them drunk, marched on the Berlin district of Kreuzberg, home to 30,000 Turks. There the Ossis, shouting '*Deutschland den Deutschen*' – 'Germany for the Germans' – were met by an equal number of Anatolian toughs. Fistfights broke out immediately. Soon baseball bats, broken bottles and knives came into play. By the time the first police units arrived, cars were burning and shop windows had been smashed. The hopelessly outnumbered police officers were unable to quell the rioting and had to withdraw after they were attacked by both mobs. Only after heavily armed reinforcements had been sent in and water cannons were deployed was the unrest brought to an end, leaving seven dead and 187 seriously injured.

'Civil War in Kreuzberg' was the title of West Germany's main TV news programme, *Tagesschau*, chosen for its special edition the day after. A record number of viewers watched in shock as the scenes from Berlin's bloody New Year's Eve were broadcast. They heard Hans Mommsen, one of the country's foremost historians, evoke the spectre of the Weimar Republic, Germany's ill-fated first attempt at democracy between 1919 and 1933. 'We in the Federal Republic have enjoyed forty years of liberty, peace and prosperity,' the professor said. 'This, the most fortunate era in our national history, could now be over.'

In Bonn, the Cabinet met for a hastily convened emergency session. 'What a way to begin the 1990s,' Interior Minister Schäuble, known for his sarcasm, joked. But the mood around the table was not conducive to levity. 'This is a national emergency,' Chancellor Späth told his colleagues. 'The country's very stability is at risk. The one thing our people cannot abide is political insecurity. They turn ugly when their tranquillity is threatened. Then there's the economic aspect: any more events like last night's, indeed like those of the last few months, and we can kiss the recovery goodbye. Besides – not that this is my primary concern right now – this could cost us the next election. Ladies and gentlemen, we all know what the root cause of this whole mess is. It's high time to act.'

Three hours later, the Chancellor addressed the nation on TV. 'Fellow citizens of the Federal Republic,' a sombre Lothar Späth said from his office, a German flag to his right, the European Union banner to his left, 'our hearts are heavy tonight. What happened in Berlin has shaken us all. Our thoughts are with the victims and their families. But grief alone is not sufficient as an answer. Events such as last night's must never – I repeat, never – recur in our country. As Chancellor my foremost duty is to protect the security of the Federal Republic and the well-being of its citizens. Tough measures are unavoidable if we want to safeguard law and order in our streets and secure our welfare state against further abuse. I have therefore ordered that with immediate effect the border to the GDR be closed until further notice. Immigrants from East Germany will no longer be admitted.'

The Wall was up again.

Author's note

The events pictured here are obviously fictitious. However, I have based them on documented facts.

Lothar Späth, who died in March 2016, was definitely a reunification sceptic. As late as June 1990, in an interview with *Der Spiegel*, he criticised Helmut Kohl's reunification policy as 'hasty', calling it a case of 'precipitate labour'. (Ironically, if Späth had succeeded Kohl, his career as Chancellor could well have ended in January 1991, when a corruption scandal in his home region of Baden-Württemberg emerged. Späth then had to resign as state premier over evidence that he had allowed the electronics company Standard Elektrik Lorenz to pay for his holidays.)

The Schürer memorandum was presented to East Germany's ruling SED's politburo on 30 October 1989. It spelled out the dire state of the country's economy, warning of the GDR's imminent insolvency. Reducing the standard of living by some 25 per cent was one of the possible consequences the memorandum listed.

The quotes by Egon Bahr and Günther Grass are authentic. So is the Green Party's slogan, '*Alle reden von Deutschland. Wir reden vom Wetter.*'

Approximately 340,000 people – 2.1 per cent of East Germany's total population – emigrated to West Germany from the GDR in 1989. In November 1989 alone the number was 133,429. After Kohl announced his ten-point plan for reunification on 28 November 1989, and when speedy reunification became imminent in the months to follow, the numbers receded significantly. By June 1990, they had fallen to around 10,000.

The housing and welfare crisis due to East German immigration and the increasingly negative attitudes of West Germans towards Ossis were widely reported in the German press. The city of Hamburg really did requisition brothels to house the immigrants, though only ones that were no longer in use. No sex workers or punters were harmed by the measure.

The total cost of reunification in the end amounted to 4 trillion marks. To shoulder the burden, taxes were raised. In June 1991, a 'solidarity levy' of 7.5 per cent of income and corporate tax was introduced as a temporary measure, designed to last one year. Twenty-five years later, Germans are still paying this 'temporary' levy (albeit now reduced to 5.5 per cent).

Even before official reunification on 3 October 1990, the Kohl government introduced a full economic currency and welfare union with the GDR on 18 May 1990. This meant that the West German welfare system (including pensions) was fully transferred to the East. As a result, West Germany's already depleted welfare funds were quickly drained. This was one of the factors that necessitated the painful cuts in the welfare system introduced by Social Democratic Chancellor Gerhard Schröder's 'Agenda 2010' in 2003.

Kohl's reunification also forced the pace towards the euro, and further European integration, as laid down in the Maastricht Treaty of 1992. According to the former chairman of the German Bundesbank, Karl Otto Pöhl, and France's former Foreign Minister, Hubert Védrine, monetary union and an increasingly federal structure of the EU at the fastest speed possible was the price exacted by Mitterrand from Kohl for his reluctant consent to reunification. Had Späth been Chancellor, without reunification, Maastricht and the euro would have come far later, if at all.

Chapter 9

What if Britain had joined the euro?

Chris Huhne[1]

For anyone who spends any time on the Continent, one of the oddities of the British political debate is the implicit assumption that the euro is a disaster and that British membership would have been a cataclysm for the economy because Britain is so exceptional and different.

Neither is true, as this chapter will show. The euro has certainly faced more than its fair share of challenges, which partly reflect design failures of the automobile, and partly failures of its drivers. But the British have consistently under-estimated the political will to make the European project work. The euro is no exception, even if, as in other areas of pan-European endeavour, it usually takes a crisis to spur political decisions that should have been taken with more foresight and leisure.

There is no sustained majority in any euro area country to leave it, even where the pain inflicted by the recent recession has been as severe as it has been in Greece (as Alexis Tsipras's referendum in 2014 showed). In theory, all recent EU members are obliged to join the euro at some point, but in reality it is difficult to meet, and therefore easy to flunk, the debt and inflation criteria for membership. Nevertheless, the euro area continues to attract new members that are keen to join the system. The initial eleven members on 1 January 1999 were Germany, France, Italy, Spain, Belgium, Netherlands, Luxembourg, Portugal, Ireland, Finland and Austria. Greece joined in 2001 – arguably the biggest mistake made by the euro system. Since then, seven further countries have joined fully, namely Cyprus, Slovenia, Slovakia, Estonia, Lithuania, Latvia and Malta. Four sovereign states have treaty arrangements to adopt the euro without representation on the European Central Bank, but can issue their own coins: Monaco, Andorra, San Marino and the Vatican. Two countries – Kosovo and Montenegro – have unilaterally adopted the euro.

What would have happened if Britain had joined? Much would have depended on the foresight of British policy-makers in dealing with specific issues. By making mortgage borrowing cheaper during the boom years – and probably lengthening British mortgages – the euro would have precipitated sooner the arguments about the problems in the British housing market, to which we will turn. There are fixes for Britain's housing problems now, and it is as true today as it was in 1997 that interest rates and the exchange rate are an implausible fix for a broken property market.

But what about the big adjustments to economic shocks – which, it can be argued, require the flexibility in interest rates and the exchange rate that are denied to euro members? As it happens, Britain outside the euro suffered one of the worst shocks in Europe precisely because of our dependence on financial services, and the 2007–08 global crisis that began with Lehman Brothers in New York. The fall in British GDP – in the economy's output – was unusually severe by historical standards.

Yet I will argue that the response of the economy to that shock shows that we did not need either a separate exchange rate or a separate interest rate, and that the British economy was surprisingly well placed to adopt a single currency because of the flexibility of its labour market. Indeed, the hard evidence from the history of the recession and the recovery is that Britain was better placed to join and remain a member of the euro area than any of the existing members except Germany.

But could Britain really have joined the euro? Never mind the economics – to which we will return – was it politically possible? Many serious folk thought so, and many business leaders thought we would pay dearly if we did not. As part of the rebranding of New Labour, both Tony Blair and Gordon Brown were determined to be the most pro-European administration since that of Edward Heath, and they succeeded. Given what we know about the Granita deal in 1994, is it so hard to imagine that Brown might have concurred with an enthusiastic Blair on euro membership?

Maybe Brown could have extracted a written promise from Blair to vacate the premiership after the 2001 general election, which he would then have taken care to store away safely. He might also have insisted on a referendum on joining the euro in addition to the famous 'five tests'.

When, after the 1997 election, the new Chancellor surprised the City by announcing the independence of the Bank of England – a policy that he had refused to embrace during the election campaign, even when challenged to do so – he could also have explicitly stated that the new rules would be compatible with the euro system (as they were). In the full flush of Labour's honeymoon period, and with the support of the Liberal Democrats and Europhile Tories like former Chancellor Ken Clarke, British adoption of the euro in an autumn referendum in 1997 might have been approved resoundingly.

Such a referendum would have dealt with the issue that Gordon Brown and his special adviser Ed Balls had long thought to be among the most problematic about euro membership for Britain: the relative lack of political consensus. Although it was true that other countries also possessed leading politicians and parties that were sceptical about the euro, such as Jean-Marie le Pen and the Front National, not to mention the Parti Communiste Français, in France, Britain was self-evidently less united about the European project, let alone an important leap into monetary union. The euro required commitment in bad times as well as good, and Britain's Eurosceptics had proved over many years that they would use any problem – real or imagined – to denigrate their bogey. Even a crushing referendum result could not have destroyed Euroscepticism in Britain, any more than the 1975 referendum did. But it would have meant that there was a clearly expressed national will to take part in and make a success of the project. At least it would have bought decades to make the euro work (and indeed might have staved off the prospect of a referendum on EU membership).

So entry was plausible, but what would have happened next would have been in large measure down to the imagination and resourcefulness of the British economic policy-makers. Within the Treasury, Ed Balls had inherited a Eurosceptic streak from his father, and had long been distrustful of euro membership, but he would have been under instructions to use the Treasury machine to fashion work-arounds for the loss of both the exchange rate and the separate setting of interest rates. Brown might also have set the Treasury another test: how could London become as dominant a financial centre in the euro area as New York is in the dollar area? Brown was sceptical about the City's boosterish claims to be the world's leading international financial centre, because the key word was 'international'. On certain measures, including foreign exchange, London led on international business. But Brown knew that the scale and depth of the New York bond and equity markets dwarfed anything London could offer. If London could become the centre of bond and stock markets in the euro area, it would mean a new supercharge to City prosperity.

The one issue that hardly surfaced publicly – but which would eventually test the euro system close to destruction – was what would happen in the event of a banking failure such as hit Lehman Brothers in the United States in 2008.[2] On this issue, the central banks – not least the European Central Bank – were at their most reassuring up until and during the crisis. They told any sceptical questioner (including the rating agencies, which repeatedly asked) that they had war-gamed a banking failure, and that there were clear plans for dealing with the problems, including any that stretched internationally across the whole system.

The sceptics should have been put on the alert by the classic public sector response to any probing after detail: we cannot go into that because it would scare the markets – but trust us, we have it sorted. The inadequacy of this complacent response was only revealed much later. Joining the euro would have made no difference to the single most important cause of the 2007–08 global crisis and the recession. No one in Europe could imagine that sub-prime mortgage loans in Florida would bring down banks in Britain and Ireland; but British influence might have made a difference to the euro system's preparations for bank support.

Brown would have set up a commission to look at the entry rate for sterling into the system. If the rate were too low, rising import prices would stoke inflationary pressures and earnings. If the rate was too high, British economic history provided plenty of warnings of the impact on the economy's key trading sectors, notably manufacturing. It was the orthodox determination to lock sterling back into its pre-First World War parity with gold that had caused the 1920s to be such a lost economic decade in the UK. As Sir Winston Churchill, the Chancellor of the Exchequer responsible for that fateful decision, said in his epitaph on the period: 'I would rather have finance less proud and industry more content.' Brown, too, wanted industry content. The sensible rate at the time – a compromise and a judgement made by an independent commission of leading international economists[3] – was about €1.33 to the pound sterling, down from the €1.52 average rate in 1999. This was the exchange rate that could, with some official guidance to the markets, have been locked in.

What would that have meant for the UK's trading sectors? The average exchange rate since 2000 has in fact been surprisingly similar at €1.35, but there has been substantial volatility around the average: the peak of sterling early in the history of the euro-system, when some very silly predictions were being made about its demise, was €1.75. The low point was €1.02. It is hard to argue that the extremities of this range were helpful in policy adjustment, and it certainly added to costs for traders and investors in trying to hedge and deal with the uncertainty. The impact of a fixed rate would almost certainly have been positive for both investment and the output of trading sectors like manufacturing and tourism. The exchange rate did, though, fall sharply in the wake of the financial crisis – from €1.46 in 2007 to €1.12 in 2009. However, the drop had much less impact on trade than had been expected, and the rate gradually recovered. The drop will, though, have had some impact in deterring imports (by increasing their price, and also reducing real incomes) and by providing incentives for exporters. Nevertheless, the exchange rate would have been lower during the boom and higher during the recovery. That would have exacerbated the cycle to some degree.

What of interest rates? They would have had to align with what the European Central Bank thought was an appropriate interest rate for the whole area, not just Britain. In recent years, that would not have made much difference, but it would certainly have involved cuts in short-term interest rates in Britain after 1999 if we had joined the euro at the outset. Since we do not know what euro interest rates would have been if the

European Central Bank had also been taking account of monetary conditions in Britain – which would have formed a substantial share of the Eurozone economy – the difference between sterling and euro interest rates as they actually happened will certainly overstate what would have happened. Even so, the differences are not large. In the entire period from January 1999 to November 2008, British three-month interbank interest rates exceeded euro three-month interbank rates by 1.63 percentage points. Since that time, the rates have tracked together, with a UK excess of just 0.13 percentage points. Moreover, the timing of interest rate changes was the same: the peak sterling interest rates were in the same quarter as the peak euro interest rates, and the trough of interest rates also coincided.

In the period of the upswing and boom, what would have been the economic impact of UK short-term interest rates about 1.5 percentage points lower than they actually were? Clearly, they would have benefited corporations and others with short-term borrowing, helping businesses finance working capital and investment. They might also have increased investment overall, perhaps with some benefit to productivity. However, lower short-term interest rates would also have fed through to mortgage interest rates, and would have encouraged an even sharper increase in house prices. As it was, house prices in England and Wales increased by 159 per cent between January 1999 (the start of the euro) and the peak in November 2007. By common consent, a lower path of mortgage rates would have seen an even more rapid ascent in prices, though possibly with an earlier peak and fall. Such an enormous upswing in house prices – the most important source of wealth for most UK households – would inevitably have increased consumers' feel-good factor through the 'wealth effect' and would have boosted demand. There might, as a result, have been more pressure on the available resources in the economy, leading to some upwards pressure on prices.

This point, however, can be overstated, because there are strict limits on the extent to which national policy instruments (like short-term interest rates) could and should be used to influence even an important market like the housing market. The housing market is irredeemably cyclical, not just in the UK but worldwide. There were similar booms and busts in house prices in the United States and also in euro area countries, notably Ireland and Spain. The sensible response – and one increasingly being contemplated by financial policy-makers – is to use policy instruments that directly target the housing market when it begins to look frothy (and hence poses a risk to the loan quality of lending institutions). An obvious instrument is variable capital requirements. By insisting that mortgage lenders increase the amount of their own capital that they have to set aside to offset the risk of losses on their mortgage portfolio, mortgage lending becomes more expensive for them, and mortgage interest rates rise, even though other short-term interest rates do not.

An even better policy response to deal with the extraordinary long-run trend increase in property prices in the UK is to work on supply rather than demand: easier planning rules, shorter planning determination, and the imposition of an ongoing annual cost on landholders who under-use or abandon their land would all help to increase supply. All these instruments are available now outside the euro area, and would equally be available within it. One thing is for sure: after yet another 27 per cent run-up in English and Welsh house prices between their trough in April 2007 and the end of 2015, having a separate currency with a separate interest rate does not solve the crises of home ownership or homelessness.

What of the view that the housing market and the dependence on financial services meant that the UK suffered a particularly severe shock in the global financial crisis of 2007–08? The fall in output in Britain was large by historic standards, but only a little bigger than the fall in the euro area economies, and the timing was the same. From the quarterly peak in the first quarter of 2008 to the quarterly trough in the second quarter of 2009, the OECD (expenditure) data show that GDP fell by 5.6 per cent in the euro area compared with 5.9 per cent in Britain. Not surprisingly, interest rates came tumbling down in both economies until they each reached the same 1.25 per cent in the second quarter of 2009. Neither central bank covered itself in glory. Both acted too slowly in response to the crisis.

So the reality was that monetary independence for Britain did not lead to substantially different policy outcomes. Later in the crisis, the Bank of England was quicker to use unconventional methods to reinforce the impact of low interest rates (the so-called quantitative easing, or money creation through buying bonds). But that also begs the question of whether the dynamics of the euro system would have been different had the Bank of England's Governor been a member of the European Central Bank's rate-setting council. The answer is almost certainly yes, for two reasons. First, the European Central Bank would have been even more aware of the systemic fragility of the financial system, thanks to the Bank of England's presence, and second, the UK would have lined up with – but have had greater credibility than – the central banks of France and Italy in seeking more monetary support in the face of the challenges to the real economy.

It is clear, though, that monetary policy could take matters only so far, whether in London or Frankfurt. Output fell very sharply and in surprising parallel on both sides of the Channel. The biggest surprise, though, was the unprecedented reaction of the UK labour market. Until the 2007–09 recession, it had been an article of faith among most British economists that the labour market was slow to react to shocks, and that this provided an important reason for having a separate exchange rate in times of stress. After all, if your labour costs were 'sticky', so that they did not react to a serious recession, then it was a particular advantage to be able to reduce all the costs of the economy (compared to other economies) by letting the exchange rate fall. That is the classic case for having a separate exchange rate, particularly in economic areas that have different characteristics, or which suffer different shocks.

The surprise in Britain in 2008–09 was that, for the first time in the entire post-war period, the labour market adjusted remarkably quickly – and went on doing so during the recovery. In previous recessions, even when they were very severe, employees had refused to forgo pay rises in line with inflation, or even real increases in pay. As a result, businesses had to cut their costs by sacking some of their employees. Those dismissed were usually those who had joined the firm most recently, which often meant the young. Since the most variable part of national output is usually manufacturing production, and since manufacturing is particularly important in the Midlands and the north, unemployment also tended to be relatively concentrated geographically. The social costs of this phenomenon – young people not acquiring the discipline of work, and towns particularly hard hit by unemployment – were very high.

The big difference in the 2008–09 recession can be seen in Table 1, which shows that the fall in output (GDP) from peak to trough quarter was not very different to the fall in output in the most extreme post-war recession in 1979–81, though substantially greater than in the next most severe recession, in 1990–91. Yet, the increase in unemployment (taking the internationally standard measure, again from trough to peak) was much more moderate than in either of those recessions. Indeed, a simple calculation showing the ratio of the rise in unemployment to the fall in output shows that the rise in unemployment was just half of what would previously have been expected. What was going on?

TABLE 1: A DIFFERENT TYPE OF RECESSION[4]

	Output *% change*	Jobless rise *% points*	Jobless rise *per % fall in output*
1979–81	-5.6	6.7	1.2
1990–91	-2.2	3.8	1.7
2008–09	-6	3.4	0.6

All recessions inflict pain and hardship, and 2008–09 was no exception. But the difference compared with previous episodes of the post-war period was that the pain was spread much more evenly across the workforce than before. Employees agreed to pay freezes, and even sometimes to pay cuts, to ensure that their businesses could survive the recession. As a result, the impact on pay was far more severe than it had ever been, as can be seen in Figure 1. In effect, the long-term liberalisation of the labour market, and the decline of trade union power, meant that all employees shared the hardship of adjustment. In my view, this outcome of the recession is far preferable to the previous type of adjustment, through unemployment. Of course, that adjustment of pay might have had to go harder and faster if Britain had been in the euro, because the exchange rate could not have dropped. However, it is difficult, given the new evidence of flexibility, to argue that such an outcome was improbable.

FIGURE 1: REAL INCOME GROWTH VANISHES[5]

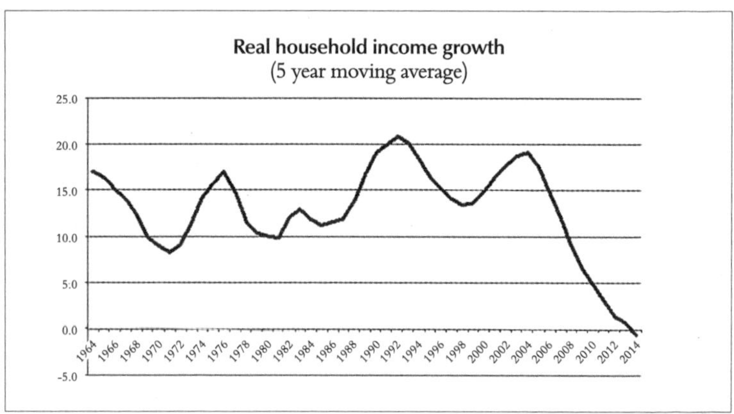

This unprecedented pay flexibility was to have many other political and social ramifications, but it was essentially the outcome of a largely bipartisan consensus that it would be wrong to re-regulate the labour market after the Thatcher reforms. Although the Labour government of 1997–2010 did undertake some re-regulation – for example, shortening the period during which an employer could dismiss a new employee without fear of triggering a claim for unfair dismissal – the essential consensus remained in place. Ironically, the first serious break in that consensus came with former Chancellor George Osborne's announcement in 2015 that he wanted effectively to raise the minimum wage by substantially more than previously contemplated and rename it the living wage. A number of labour market economists are concerned that this may reintroduce a rigidity into the market, the adverse consequences of which will only become fully apparent in the next downturn.

Another measure of the flexibility of the British labour market is provided by the developed country research club, the Organisation for

Economic Co-operation and Development. It pulls together various indicators of employment protection which show that the UK, despite our membership of the European Union, has one of the most flexible labour markets in the world. The attached table ranks countries by just one of these measures: the ease with which employers can dismiss employees. This is important because if regulation makes it very difficult to dismiss some of the workforce, employees also have very little incentive to accept pay flexibility if the business is threatened. (It is possible to rank countries instead by the number of permanent workers or temporary employment, but on all measures the message is the same in showing the UK as remarkably unregulated.)

Table 2 shows that only in the United States and Canada is it (marginally) easier to dismiss employees, and by other measures too the UK is remarkably free from heavy-handed regulation. Indeed, the next least regulated EU country is Hungary, in ninth place, followed by fellow Anglosphere EU member Ireland. By comparison, the other big EU member states are far more regulated: Spain ranks 28th and comes in last in this premiership league, while Germany is 52nd, France 55th and Italy 56th. Germany compensates for its lowly position on this measure with great flexibility in temporary employment contracts, and a remarkable history of low wage cost growth.

Why is this labour market flexibility in the UK not better known? Indeed, why are the facts so at odds with the perception among many Eurosceptic British people that the EU has imposed massive regulatory burdens on the British employer, particularly in the labour market? Of course, the Thatcher–Blair consensus was one that neither side had much interest in broadcasting, for evident reasons of their domestic political base. Nor in general are politicians likely to be vocal in claiming to voters: 'Look how brilliantly we've managed to reduce your income growth.' Indeed, most of the period since the recent downturn has seen repeated tussles about the hardships visited on family budgets. As Secretary of State for Energy and Climate Change, I became particularly aware of this issue because of the collateral damage visited on any governmental addition to energy bills, one of the biggest items of household spending.

TABLE 2: EMPLOYMENT PROTECTION LEGISLATION[6]

Country	Permanent workers 2015	Temporary employment 2015	Individual dismissal 2015
United States	1.2	0.3	0.5
Canada	1.5	0.2	0.9
United Kingdom	1.6	0.5	1.2
Barbados	1.7	0.2	1.4
Guatemala	1	2.3	1.4
Nicaragua	1.4	1	1.4
New Zealand	1	0.9	1.4
Switzerland	2.1	1.4	1.5
Hungary	2.1	2	1.5
Ireland	2.1	1.2	1.5
Australia	1.9	1	1.6
Jamaica	1.6	0.4	1.6
Japan	2.1	1.3	1.6
Peru	2.2	2.9	1.6
Saudi Arabia	1.2	3.5	1.6
Colombia	2.3	2.3	1.7
Costa Rica	1.2	3	1.7
Estonia	2.1	3	1.7
El Salvador	1.2	2.3	1.7
Serbia	2.2	n.a.	1.7
Brazil	1.8	4.1	1.8
Slovak Republic	2.3	2.4	1.8
Mexico	2.6	2.3	1.9
FYROM	2.3	3.5	1.9
Paraguay	1.8	1.7	1.9
Uruguay	2	4.5	1.9
Dominican Republic	1.4	2.1	2
Spain	2.3	3.2	2

But the consequence contains a delicious irony: the British economy, because of the flexibility of its labour market, was probably one of the European economies best equipped not just to survive euro membership, but to prosper from it. Of all the major European economies except Germany, Britain stood in least need of a separate exchange rate, because it was capable of rapid adjustment of competitiveness and costs through domestic flexibility – as was clearly demonstrated in the recession.

The debate about the impact of the euro on trade and investment creation continues, so I will not look at the overall advantages of the system. However, it seems to be that there would have been two other economic consequences of British euro membership that are worth flagging up.

First, euro membership would, over time, have increased further the financial business conducted in the City of London. This is essentially because the euro area financial system is evolving slowly in the same way as the US financial system. In the euro area, bank loans account for more than 70 per cent of total lending to households and non-financial businesses, whereas in the US bank loans account for less than half this figure.[7] In the last thirty-five years, the US has become a much less bank-oriented and much more market-oriented financial system. Businesses have access to cheaper capital by directly placing their loans – bonds – with investors, and cutting out the banking middle-man. However, that type of 'disintermediation' particularly benefits from a large currency area where investors are able to diversify their risk. That trend is happening already in the euro area, and it is also bound to benefit those financial centres where bonds and equities are placed and traded, which will particularly be London.

Some of this was happening in any case, with Britain outside the euro but inside the European Union. But there will be substantial regulatory and political resistance to having important financial markets formally out of the reach of the central bank that has to manage their consequences (there has already been litigation on this issue). If Britain had adopted the euro, a further consequence would have been that the Bank of England would have become the single most influential central bank in the euro system, whether or not the system was actually based in London. The exact parallel is with the New York Federal Reserve Bank in the US Federal Reserve

System (which meets in Washington). The president of the New York Fed is a permanent member – indeed, the deputy chair – of the Federal Open Markets Committee that sets rates, whereas other presidents rotate. The New York Fed, as the part of the system with its feet in the financial marketplace, is always the most influential of the constituent parts of the system, and never more so than during a financial crisis. The Bundesbank would have had a real counterweight in the Bank of England.

Second, if Britain had been in the euro, the Bank of England would have had extraordinary influence over the euro system's response to recession by virtue of its special status as the central bank in the most important financial centre. I suspect that this would have meant a more radical and far-reaching euro system response, using unconventional measures earlier on and with greater enthusiasm. I also suspect that the euro system would have had to face up to the issues of bank support in a crisis, and not sweep them under the carpet (as it is still doing by failing adequately to address the recommendations of the 'Five Presidents' report in July 2015).

Would the euro area have avoided other mistakes if Britain had been at the table? Greece should never have been allowed to join when it did, not least because its government did so on a false prospectus that hid the full extent of its liabilities. (The only parallel case in recent economic history was Hungary, whose Communist government before 1989 kept two sets of accounts, one for the IMF and the markets, and a private one which showed its real indebtedness.) Indeed, it would have been better if all the 'Club Med' had been in the anteroom while the system proved itself, but that might have been hard once the Portuguese were seen to have met the entry criteria and once the French and Germans had bent those criteria in application to themselves. Nor is it likely that the British would have championed some fiscal redistribution within the system, because rich member states are not prone to such generosity. Those issues are certainly material to the overall success of the euro system – in particular to its weaker members – but are less important for British membership precisely because of the flexibility of the labour market. The euro would probably continue to have been dominated by the uncomfortably pre-Keynesian ideas of Germany's policy-makers.

What of the politics? There would still have been a global financial crash following the failure of Lehman Brothers and the sub-prime bond market in 2008. That would still have involved massive economic and financial losses in the UK, exactly as it did outside the euro. The UK taxpayer would still have had to pick up the bill. It would have involved just as much pain for household budgets. But would the euro have been blamed for the problems? Would there have been a fracturing of support that would have made membership very difficult for the Bank of England and the government? Possibly, but it would have been impossible politically to join the euro without a positive result in a referendum on adopting the euro, as both the Labour Party and the Liberal Democrats had made clear that there should be a referendum on any extension of Brussels's powers. Had that referendum been decisive, as it would probably have been in the slipstream of Labour's 1997 victory, it is hard to see how Eurosceptics could have made much of the inevitable hardships visited by a clearly global financial crisis and recession. The 2016 referendum would have been avoided.

British adoption of the euro is now so far off Britain's political agenda that discussion of it seems mildly eccentric, but, in retrospect – and looking at the EU referendum result in 2016 – the succession of decisions to become semi-detached from the European mainstream (the Eurozone and the Schengen passport-free area) may come to be seen as the beginning of the way out altogether. The interim economic judgement, however, seems clear. First, London and Britain would have stood to benefit particularly from the new growth of market-oriented financial services, as New York has done in the US. Second, the flexibility of the British labour market would have made our membership easier than that of most other joiners. Third, there is no reason to suppose that the costs of the financial crisis would have been any greater in the euro than outside, although the political handling might have been more complex. Fourth, the euro should not be counted a material factor in the mess that is the UK housing market. That needs sorting out by UK domestic measures – both on the demand and the supply side.

Britain could have made a go of the euro, and that might even have saved British EU membership and increased the chances of Eurozone success.

Indeed, Britain could have been a disproportionate beneficiary, as it has been from most other measures of globalisation that reduce the costs of cross-border trade and investment, such as the EU single market. The euro would have been a better currency for British influence, which might have counter-balanced Germany's economic primitivism. But the fundamentals of the global financial crisis would not have changed. There would still have been sore-headed victims. The problems of a minority left behind from the benefits of globalisation would have continued. The essential problem of modern economics – how to combine prosperity with equity – would have remained unresolved.

Notes

1. I would like to thank Graham Hacche and Professor David Howarth for commenting on an earlier draft of this chapter. Errors of fact and interpretation remain my own.
2. See James Forder and Christopher Huhne, *Both Sides of the Coin: The Arguments For and Against the Euro and European Monetary Union* (Profile, 1999 and 2001).
3. See Independent Commission report, 'Britain's adoption of the Euro', Liberal Democrats, September 2000.
4. Source: author's calculations from ONS data.
5. Source: author's calculations from ONS data.
6. Source: OECD.
7. See Celine Choulet and Yelena Shulyatyeva, 'History and major causes of US banking disintermediation', *Ecoconjuncure*, BNP Paribas, January 2016.

Chapter 10

What if Primakov, not Putin, had become Russian President in 2000?

Tina Burrett

Without Yevgeny Primakov, there would be no Putinism. The former Russian Prime Minister and grand spymaster, who died in June 2015, pioneered many of Putin's trademark policies, notably countering US hegemony internationally and strengthening state authority domestically.[1]

Putin's politics, and his path to power, parallel Primakov's. Although a generation apart, both men were veterans of the Soviet security services, and both served as Prime Minister to Russian President Boris Yeltsin. Putin's appointment to the premiership owed much to Primakov – or, rather, to attempts by Yeltsin's inner circle to avert a Primakov presidency.

Primakov's successful efforts while Prime Minister (1998–99) to stabilise the Russian economy in the wake of financial crisis made him the most popular politician in the country, well placed to win the presidential elections scheduled for June 2000. But his anti-corruption crusades and well-known disdain for the results of privatisation troubled the oligarchs around Yeltsin, dubbed 'The Family'. Promising to put 90,000 businessmen in prison if elected President, Primakov's brand of anti-oligarchic, patriotic populism appealed to ordinary Russians impoverished by a decade of economic chaos. The Family needed an alternative to Primakov who could match his popular appeal. Enter Vladimir Putin, promoted as a younger, more dynamic – albeit less refined and intellectual – rival to Primakov. Backed by the might of the Family-controlled media, the replica soon replaced the original in public popularity. But Putin proved an unwilling puppet and more like Primakov than the Family had envisioned. Ironically,

Putin pursued many policies initiated during Primakov's premiership, including depriving obstructive oligarchs of their wealth and freedom.

More than an alternative to Putin, Primakov is the political godfather of Putinism.[2] Yet, undoubtedly, a Primakov presidency would have differed from Putin's. Primakov's greater political experience and superior intellect would have made him a better coalition-builder at home and a more successful diplomat overseas. Unlike Putin, despite his long career, Primakov was never personally or professional tainted by corruption. As President, Primakov's integrity could have helped Russia to change course after the errors of the Yeltsin era to become a more law-governed and genuinely pluralist society.

Primakov's path to power

Before entering politics, Primakov enjoyed a distinguished career as a Soviet academic specialising in the Middle East. Fluent in Arabic, he served as a foreign correspondent and then headed two top Soviet think tanks, the Institute of Oriental Studies and the Institute of World Economy and International Relations. He first came into active politics in the late 1980s as an adviser to Mikhail Gorbachev, who, in 1990, appointed him to the Presidential Council, which was struggling to contain secessionist demands from Soviet republics, including Primakov's native Ukraine. In August 1991, when a coup by KGB and Communist Party hardliners temporarily displaced Gorbachev, Primakov stayed loyal to the Soviet leader. Once back in the Kremlin, Gorbachev attempted to curb the power of the security services by appointing civilian loyalists to senior positions within the KGB; Primakov was installed as head of foreign intelligence. Four months later, when the Soviet Union collapsed, Yeltsin kept him in post as boss of the newly formed Foreign Intelligence Service (SVR). Although an outsider, during his four years at the top of the SVR, Primakov was well respected by the intelligence community, in part owing to a shared concern over US expansionism in the former Soviet sphere of influence.

During the Yeltsin era, Russia's foreign policy elite was divided between liberal pro-Westernisers and pragmatic nationalists.[3] Both groups hoped to integrate Russia into Western-dominated international security and economic organisations, but differed in their approach to achieving their aims. The nationalist camp, which included Primakov, feared that dependence on Western loans and too much deference to the US on foreign policy would weaken Russia's negotiating position. In the intra-elite debates, Primakov opposed NATO's eastwards expansion and argued forcefully against capitulation to Washington's preference for a unipolar global order. To restore Russia's great power status, Primakov advocated restraint in relations with the West in favour of strategic alliances with India and China. His vision of a multipolar world is today the backbone of Putin's foreign policy.

Following the collapse of the USSR, Yeltsin initially embraced the Westernisers' approach, placing maintaining good relations with the US at the heart of his foreign policy. When it became clear that the olive branch extended to Washington was not bearing fruit, Yeltsin changed tack. In 1996, just prior to seeking re-election, he replaced his pro-Western Foreign Minister Andrei Kozyrev with Primakov. It was clear to Primakov that the friendship proffered by the US was not on equal terms. Under his direction, Russia's foreign policy quickly came to emphasise the need for a multipolar order. In the future, Moscow would pursue its own interests, even if they contradicted those of Washington.

When financial crisis hit in 1998, Yeltsin again turned to Primakov. After Russia's debt default in September, Yeltsin first attempted to reinstate Viktor Chernomyrdin as Prime Minister, but the state Duma blocked his appointment. Primakov, a politician of the centre-left and advocate of a greater role for the state in the economy, was chosen as a compromise figure acceptable to the Communist majority in Parliament. As premier, Primakov was credited with cushioning the impact of Russia's financial crisis by forcing controversial tax reforms and successfully leading difficult bailout negotiations with the IMF. But his appointment did not please everyone. During his tenure, Primakov fought bitterly with the Yeltsin Family, who had been running the country as their personal fiefdom during the ailing Yeltsin's frequent stays in hospital. Primakov's efforts to restore government control over policy-making put him on a collision cause with the Family's unofficial patriarch, Boris Berezovsky.[4]

Putin would later drive the oligarch into exile for similarly trying to frustrate a restoration of state power following Putin's election to the presidency in 2000.

Primakov out, Putin in

In May 1999, at the behest of Berezovsky and others in his entourage, Yeltsin fired Primakov, ostensibly over the slow pace of economic recovery. In reality, those close to Yeltsin feared losing power to the popular Primakov; they worried that he was using the premiership to build a power base from which to bid for the presidency. Primakov's refusal to sack Communist Party ministers from his government – including Deputy Prime Minister Yuri Maslyukov – while Communist deputies in Parliament prepared unsuccessful impeachment proceedings against Yeltsin was seen as evidence of his presidential ambitions.[5]

However, in convincing Yeltsin to sack Primakov, the Family had made a tactical error. Outside government, Primakov was free to enter politics on his own terms. He did so by forming a political party, Fatherland–All Russia, with the then Mayor of Moscow Yury Luzhkov, to contest the December 1999 Duma elections. Initially, the party surged ahead in public opinion polls. But Berezovsky and the Yeltsin Family did everything in their power to undermine Fatherland. The oligarch's TV channel, ORT – with the widest audience reach in Russia – engaged in a propaganda campaign against Primakov and his political allies.[6] Luzhkov accused ORT's star political presenter Sergey Dorenko of a dirty-tricks campaign against Fatherland, including, for example, allegations of Primakov's involvement in an assassination attempt against Georgian President Eduard Shevardnadze.[7] In the last month of the Duma campaign, Luzhkov successfully sued Dorenko for defamation, but it was not until after the election that he was allowed the right to reply on Dorenko's programme.[8]

State broadcaster RTR was also drafted into the campaign against Primakov. News reports on the channel emphasised his working relations with the Communist Party, implying that, as President, Primakov would take Russia back to Soviet-style repression and a planned economy. At the same time as demonising Primakov and Fatherland, ORT and RTR lauded the Kremlin-backed Unity Party, which was created as a vehicle to build support for the new Prime Minister, Vladimir Putin.

Ultimately, Fatherland lost the election to Unity, convincing Primakov to withdraw from the presidential race scheduled for the following year. Ahead of voting in the December 1999 Duma elections, Putin's popularity was boosted by his successful direction of the second war in Chechnya, which began with the Chechen invasion of Dagestan on 7 August 1999. It was the outbreak of war that prompted Yeltsin to promote the little-known Putin – then head of the Security Council – to the role of Prime Minister just two days after the Chechen incursion. Unlike in the First Chechen War of 1994–96, the Russian public supported military action by their government. In September 1999, the horror of the war was brought home to Russian civilians by the bombing of apartment blocks in Moscow, Bunaisk and Volgodonsk that killed over 300 people. As Prime Minister, Putin was well placed to capitalise on the patriotic emotions engendered by the Chechen conflict, and jingoistic coverage of the war by ORT and RTR helped Putin build his public image as a shrewd commander and strong leader.

Prior to his appointment as premier, Putin was a relatively unknown figure outside the political elite. After graduating in 1975, the young Putin joined the KGB. Between 1985 and 1990 he was stationed in Dresden, East Germany. Following the coup against Gorbachev in August 1991, he resigned from the security services and went to work for his former professor, Anatoly Sobchak, then Mayor of Leningrad. When Sobchak failed to win re-election in 1996, Putin moved to Moscow, initially serving in the uninspiringly titled Presidential Property Management Department. He moved steadily through the ranks of the presidential administration until in July 1998 Yeltsin appointed him head of the Federal Security Services (FSB), a successor agency of the KGB.

On appointing Putin Prime Minister on 9 August 1999, Yeltsin announced that he wanted Putin as his presidential successor. Without the second war in Chechnya and the propaganda services provided by the Berezovsky-owned media, Yeltsin would not have got his wish and Putin would not have been elected President in March 2000. When he took office as Prime Minister in August 1999, only 2 per cent of Russian voters identified Putin as their choice to replace Yeltsin.[9] Prior to August, Putin had failed to register any voter support at all – but his obscurity was an advantage, allowing Putin to create his public persona from scratch. Television coverage showing Putin planning tough action against Chechen terrorists, inspecting troops and taking part in martial arts competitions transformed him from a rather colourless state security officer into the strong leader Russians desired.[10]

If he were to have any chance of winning the presidency, Primakov needed to oust Berezovsky from Yeltsin's inner circle before the President settled on Putin as his preferred successor, in August 1999. A missed opportunity arose in March, when Yeltsin sacked Berezovsky as Secretary of the Commonwealth of Independent States (CIS), seeking to distance himself from the oligarch, who had become an emblem of corruption. This was the moment for Primakov – then still Prime Minister – to extend an olive branch to Yeltsin, with whom his relations had always been ambiguous.

Yeltsin had never fully trusted Primakov. In the constitutional stand-off between the President and the state Duma in October 1993, Primakov declined to publicly support Yeltsin's use of military force to end Parliament's putsch. To win Yeltsin's support for his presidential bid and ensure Berezovsky's permanent banishment from the corridors of power required Primakov to guarantee the President protection from prosecution in retirement; Putin's loyalty in helping his former boss Anatoly Sobchak flee the country to evade corruption charges is a key reason Yeltsin handpicked him as his successor.[11] If Primakov had spoken out against the Communist-dominated Parliament's plans to impeach Yeltsin in spring 1999, he could have convinced the President to anoint him instead of Putin as his successor – but Primakov's silence compounded Yeltsin's distrust of his premier. After settling on Putin as his successor, Yeltsin brought Berezovsky back into the fold to provide PR support for his protégé.

Even if Yeltsin had thrown his support behind Primakov, could the left-leaning seventy-year-old have won the March 2000 presidential election? The fact that 81 per cent of Russians were against his resignation as Prime Minister in May 1999 suggests that victory was within his grasp.[12] No doubt the Berezovsky media would have thrown mud, but Primakov could have relied on support for his candidacy from the state-owned media. Primakov's centre-left inclination would have undermined the appeal of Communist candidate Gennady Zyuganov, who was Putin's main presidential opponent in 2000. Despite his leftist tendencies, Primakov's pragmatic handling of the 1998 financial crisis had won him backers among Russia's industrialists and entrepreneurs; in responding to the crisis, Primakov's government had met the demands of business leaders halfway. For all his rhetoric, as Prime Minister Primakov did not do battle with the oligarchs; he did not, for example, follow Parliament's decree that oligarch Anatoly Chubais be removed from the leadership of the national electricity monopoly UES.[13] Primakov could also have relied on support from Russia's influential regional leaders, many of whom were gathered under the Fatherland–All Russia banner. By mobilising voter turnout and providing access to local media, these regional leaders would have been effective campaign lieutenants if Primakov had run for President.

So Primakov had a real chance. The rest of the chapter imagines how Russia today might have been different if Primakov, not Putin, had taken the helm in 2000.

Media freedom

Russia today has one of the most repressive media environments in the world. His own success in the 2000 presidential election convinced Putin of the power of the media over public opinion; such a powerful tool could not be left in the hands of the oligarchs. During the Yeltsin era the oligarchs had used their control over the media as a tool to extort favours from the President. When the government's economic decisions went against the interests of the oligarchs, Yeltsin's ministers found themselves the victims of negative news stories.

Although media-owning oligarchs Boris Berezovsky and Vladimir Gusinsky backed Putin's 2000 presidential campaign, after the election they quickly proved unreliable partners. The first test of Putin's leadership, and the loyalty of the media barons to his administration, came with the sinking of the *Kursk* submarine on 12 August 2000. The dramatic nature of the accident ensured that the story dominated the media for several days.

As it became apparent that offers of international rescue assistance had been accepted too late to save the stranded sailors, media indignation became focused on Putin; news reports in the Berezovsky and Gusinsky media were especially critical of the President,[14] drawing unflattering comparisons between Putin's secretive handling of the disaster and the conduct of his Soviet predecessors.[15] Symbolically, the *Kursk* disaster allowed Putin's opponents to question his election promises to restore Russia's national pride and international standing.[16] Negative media coverage threatened to undermine the President's authority by weakening the public support on which it was based. The *Kursk* incident taught Putin that to retain popular confidence and achieve his ambitions to restore the power and prestige of the state, he must strip the oligarchs of their media empires.

Legal loopholes and the oligarchs' murky financial dealings provided Putin with useful tools to restructure the media sector, and prosecutions were launched against Berezovsky and Gusinsky, forcing both into exile. In their place, the media became financially beholden to entities close to the Kremlin, with negative consequences for press freedom. Although under the influence of the oligarchs Russia's media had fallen far short of the fourth-estate ideal, they had at least provided audiences with a form of pluralism, however imperfect. By the end of Putin's first presidential term in March 2004, all Russia's main television channels and much of its print media had been brought under either direct or indirect state control.[17] On Putin's watch, harassment and violence against journalists in Russia has increased dramatically. New security laws passed in the face of the ongoing terrorist threat place draconian restrictions on what, when and where journalists can report. By 2015, Russia had slid to 152 out of 180 countries on the Reporters Without Borders World Press Freedom Index.[18] In the same year, the Committee to Protect Journalists ranked Russia the tenth most dangerous country in the world in which to be a journalist.[19]

Would Russia's media freedom have been similarly curtailed under a Primakov presidency? It seems unlikely. Primakov himself was a journalist in the early part of his career, between 1956 and 1970 working for Soviet radio and as Middle East correspondent for the newspaper *Pravda*.

As Russian premier, he demonstrated a willingness to work with political opponents from a variety of ideological positions. Unlike Putin, when Primakov took office as Prime Minister he already possessed a well-established political record and reputation. Primakov would have come to the presidency with greater political experience, a wider network, and a more intellectually coherent programme of reform. A creation of the media and temperamentally thin-skinned, Putin was more politically and personally vulnerable to media criticism than Primakov would have been as President.

Yet a more pluralist media environment under Primakov could have allowed a return to the 'information wars' of the 1990s, when the oligarchs leveraged their media influence to extract concessions from the Kremlin. For Russia's media to function as a public watchdog, rather than as the oligarchs' attack dog, necessitated changes in ownership. Primakov's past conduct suggests that he would have used proper legal procedures rather than threats to remove Berezovsky, who he genuinely regarded as corrupt.

As a man of culture, who wrote poetry in his spare time, Primakov exhibited a respect for free expression rare among ex-KGB spymasters. It is unlikely that as President he would have brought the media to heel as Putin has done. An open media is a two-way channel of communication between rulers and ruled, allowing leaders to better understand and respond to their citizens' needs. Freedom of debate improves the quality of public policy, information openness leads to greater innovation and investment. A freer media under Primakov would not only have improved Russia's information environment but may also have enhanced its economic performance.

A freer media may also have allowed Russia to experience its first truly free elections, which have become increasingly stage-managed during Putin's presidency. Genuine electoral competition is necessary to renew political leadership, but in today's Russia political opposition is stifled. Policy is stagnating, but no alternative to the Putin regime is in sight. Identifying a credible successor would have been an unavoidable issue for Primakov, who was already seventy years old in 2000.

Chechnya

Although the Russian military won a swift and decisive victory in the battle phase of the second war in Chechnya, the continuing Chechen insurgency, which includes terrorist attacks on Russia's major cities, is Putin's greatest failure as President. Two large-scale hostage-takings by Chechen separatists, the 2002 Moscow theatre crisis and the 2004 Beslan school siege, resulted in the deaths of hundreds of civilians, in the latter case many of them children. The exact number of casualties in the conflict is unknown, with estimates varying wildly. In 2007, Amnesty International reported at least 25,000 civilian casualties, with another 5,000 missing.[20] Both sides in the conflict have carried out blatant, ongoing human rights abuses, including torture and kidnapping. In 2006, Human Rights Watch issued a report concluding that the use of torture in Chechnya was so widespread and systematic that it constituted a crime against humanity.[21]

Under a Primakov presidency, some of the human tragedy in Chechnya could have been avoided. As Prime Minister in March 1999, Primakov prevented his government from being drawn back into military action in Chechnya following the kidnapping in Grozny of Russia's senior envoy Major General Gennady Shpigun. The abduction, committed by rebel Chechen field commanders, aimed to undermine relations between Moscow and moderate Chechen President Aslan Maskhadov. But Primakov declined to take the bait, stating categorically that he would not let the incident reignite war.[22]

As Foreign Minister in 1996, Primakov had supported Yeltsin in negotiating a truce with the Chechen separatists that ended the First Chechen War. In September 2002, he called on Putin to begin similar ceasefire negotiations with rebel leaders. Primakov argued that US operations in Afghanistan had cut off the rebels' financial support from abroad, making it an opportune time to extract concessions from the separatist commanders who were signalling their willingness to negotiate.[23] Putin, who built his reputation on uncompromising action in Chechnya, did not heed Primakov's advice. In negotiating a settlement with Chechen leaders as President, Primakov could have prevented the province becoming a training and recruitment ground for international jihadists, thus limiting terrorism in Russia and beyond.

The economy

During Russia's financial crisis in 1998, Primakov led negotiations with the IMF to unfreeze a promised $US22.6 billion loan after Russia defaulted on its debts, forcing a devaluation of the rouble. Prime Minister Primakov became Russia's top economic negotiator after President Yeltsin was hospitalised with pneumonia at the peak of the financial chaos.

In navigating the politics and economics of the crisis, Primakov faced an almost impossible mission. On one side, the Russian Parliament demanded that he reassert state control over wide sectors of the economy, spend more on welfare and pay back wage arrears, while on the other, the IMF insisted on urgent fiscal reform, including tight spending cuts. But Primakov proved equal to the task. Against the odds, he managed to negotiate a deal with the IMF and began pushing the necessary legislation through the Duma to meet the IMF's conditions. Inflation was brought under control and the fall in the value of the rouble halted.[24] Tax cuts were introduced, aimed at curbing rampant tax evasion, a policy later adopted by Putin.[25] VAT cuts, against IMF advice, made Primakov hugely popular with Russian voters and with conservative forces in the Duma. Before he could introduce further economic reforms, however, Yeltsin fired him, officially due to the slow pace of economic recovery, but more likely due to the premier's fast-growing popularity.

Russia recovered from the 1998 financial crash surprisingly quickly. This was due partly to a rapid rise in world oil prices from 1999 to 2000, giving Russia a large trade surplus; partly to domestic industries benefiting from devaluation, which caused a sharp increase in the price of imports; and partly to Primakov's tax cuts allowing businesses to pay off wage arrears, boosting consumer demand for goods produced by domestic industries. Although Putin did little to kickstart Russia's economic recovery, as President from January 2000 he was given all the credit. High growth, falling unemployment and improving living standards sustained his approval ratings at an enviable 70 per cent for most of his first two terms as President.[26]

Whoever succeeded President Yeltsin was destined to benefit from such a positive economic backdrop. If Primakov had become President, he would have actually deserved the credit he received for improving Russia's economic fortunes. High approval ratings bolstered by a strong economic performance would have given Primakov the political capital to take on the oligarchs who had prevented him from making more radical reforms when battling to save the economy from disaster while Prime Minister in 1998.

In the early years of his presidency, Putin built on Russia's economic recovery with a series of market reforms, including, most impressively, the tax reforms that replaced a progressive personal income tax with a flat-rate tax of 13 per cent from 2001. Corporation taxes and social security contributions were also cut, reducing costs for struggling small- and medium-sized businesses, and deregulation further boosted a business environment in Russia that had been depressed by high volumes of red tape. In 2003, however, Putin's economic reforms came to a crashing halt with the state takeover of oil giant Yukos, Russia's most successful company. Putin wanted to neutralise the firm's main owner, Mikhail Khodorkovsky, who had become his most outspoken critic, and the President's cronies coveted the company's lucrative assets. A successful legal case was engineered to throw Khodorkovsky in jail and to renationalise Yukos.

This was just the first in a wave of renationalisations. In most cases, the motivation was 'rent-seeking': large financial kickbacks for the Kremlin insiders who took senior positions within the newly acquired state enterprises. Primakov made no secret of his support for renationalisation, nor of his dislike of the oligarchs, but his rationale was ideological, whereas Putin's choice of companies to plunder has been mostly political, allowing him to pick off opponents by separating them from their financial assets. Primakov's motivation may have been more honourable, but under his presidency renationalisation would still likely have occurred, even though it has contributed to stagnation in Russia's energy, banking and manufacturing sectors. The forcible confiscation of private businesses has scared off foreign investment, which remained low despite the economic boom of 2000–2007.[27]

Foreign policy

Despite renationalisation, corruption, and repression, Russia's economy continued to grow rapidly during Putin's first two terms, boosted by skyrocketing oil and commodity prices. A booming economy gave Putin the confidence to assert an independent foreign policy, often counter to US interests.

In distancing Russia from the West in favour of a more diverse foreign policy, Putin had channelled Primakov.[28] As Foreign Minister from 1996, Primakov made no secret of his hostility to US hegemony, setting about expanding Russian influence over former Soviet republics and promoting an alliance with China and India to counter US encroachment in central Asia. He also re-established ties with former Soviet allies in the Middle East, such as Iraq, Egypt and Syria, countries in which Primakov had spent time as a journalist in the 1960s. As Prime Minister, Primakov openly supported Slobodan Milošević's Serbia, opposing the US over independence for Kosovo. In March 1999, he ordered his plane to turn around over the Atlantic en route to the US after he learned that NATO had started bombing Serbia – a manoeuvre that became known as the 'Primakov Loop'.

As President, Putin initially turned away from the 'Primakov Doctrine', attempting to integrate Russia with the West. Following the attacks on the US on 11 September 2001, Putin offered Washington broad support for anti-terrorist operations in Afghanistan. At this time, he believed that Russian national interests were best served by a foreign policy that prioritised modernisation and economic growth, rather than counterbalancing US power.

Following the 'coloured revolutions', however, that brought power to pro-Western governments in Georgia (2003) and Ukraine (2004) – the latter with the assistance of US NGOs – Putin began to abandon his strategy of integrating with the West. A commitment by NATO to eventual membership for Georgia and Ukraine in 2008, and US deployment of missile defences in Poland and the Czech Republic in 2007, convinced Putin that Russia would not be accepted into the Western club on equal terms. The US ignored Russian protestations about the eastward expansion of NATO because Washington assumed that – as had been the case under Yeltsin – Russia would continue to tolerate this encroachment.[29] But, buoyed by a strong economy and growing anti-Americanism among Russian voters, Putin was ready and able to defend Russian interests.[30] Despite inferior economic and military assets, Putin was able to frustrate US policy aims and uphold Russian interests in Georgia (2008), Syria (2013) and Ukraine (2014).[31]

Primakov may have been even more effective than Putin in countering US foreign policy. His superior negotiating skills may have allowed him to build a stronger coalition against the 2003 US-led war in Iraq. Primakov was personally acquainted with both Saddam Hussein and his Foreign Minister Tariq Aziz, whom he had met in Iraq in 1969 while a correspondent for *Pravda*. In February 2003, Putin sent Primakov to see the Iraqi President with the message to step down in order to avert war.[32] As a mere envoy, Primakov was unable to convince Saddam to listen, but as President, he could have been more persuasive. At the very least, President Primakov may have persuaded the Iraqi leader to fully cooperate with UN weapons inspections, denying the US and its allies their pretext for war. Primakov previously had some success in convincing Saddam not to expel the UN Special Commission in 1997, when the US was preparing a new attack on Iraq.[33] During his time in Iraq in the 1960s, Primakov had also cultivated relationships with Kurdish leaders, links which would have enabled him as President to play an effective role in negotiating a post-conflict settlement between Iraq's different communities, perhaps helping to prevent some of the sectarian violence that followed the collapse of the Ba'athist regime.

In the context of Putin's new assertiveness in dealing with the West, Russia has pivoted to Asia. Deteriorating relations with the West on multiple issues – including Syria, missile defence, Edward Snowden, anti-homosexual laws and Ukraine – leaves Russia with few choices but to look to the East. Added to this, the 2008 global financial crisis revealed the West's economic vulnerability.[34] In seeking to strengthen ties with China, India, and other emerging political and economic centres in Asia, Putin is again following a path forged by Primakov. In 2011, Putin outlined plans for a Eurasian Economic Union between Russia and its former Soviet neighbours, an idea first explored by Primakov and his central Asian counterparts in the late 1990s. Putin has also pursued the strategic partnership with China advocated by Primakov; since 2000, all border disputes between Moscow and Beijing have been resolved, and bilateral relations have advanced through the Shanghai Cooperation Organisation. Bilateral trade has grown enormously; in 2010, China became Russia's largest trading partner, with bilateral trade reaching US$55.4 billion.[35]

If Primakov rather than Putin had become President in 2000, Russian foreign policy would have moved away from the West earlier. But this does not mean that there would not have been differences. As Foreign Minister, Primakov was a tough but pragmatic advocate of Russia's interests. Although he opposed NATO's expansion into the former Eastern Bloc, he negotiated the Foundation Act between Russia and NATO, signed in May 1997, that officially ended Cold War hostilities.

Putin lacks Primakov's nuanced understanding of international diplomacy, and in his third term is taking an extreme anti-Western stance that is now harming Russia's interests. As one of his last public acts, in January 2015 Primakov urged Putin to wind down the Ukraine conflict and ease tensions with the West. In supporting separatist militias in Eastern Ukraine, he argued, Putin is playing into US hands by driving a wedge between the EU and Russia, a division which allows Washington to keep Europe under its influence. Primakov called on Putin to recalibrate Russia's international relations with the US in areas of common interest, in order to counter the growing economic dependence on China. In May 2014, Western sanctions against Russia over the Crimean conflict allowed China to bargain for a thirty-year gas deal at a lower price than Moscow had wanted to concede.[36] It is hard to imagine that Primakov would have allowed Russia to become as isolated as it is now under Putin. During the Kosovo crisis, Foreign Minister Primakov put special effort into wooing the French and German governments. This was shrewd diplomacy. Primakov calculated that the chances of a settlement acceptable to Moscow would be enhanced if he could build a sympathetic coalition within NATO, rather than by dealing exclusively with the US.[37]

The West may be fortunate that Primakov did not become President, as his foreign policy would have been more effective than Putin's.

Similar policies, different politics

President Primakov's policies would have been very similar to those pursued by President Putin, but the politics would have been somewhat different.

Russia would probably have parted company with the West in the foreign policy sphere earlier under Primakov. Domestic politics may have been less corrupt and repressive, but also less stable in the short term. During the more pluralist Yeltsin years, Russia's political and economic elites waged destabilising information wars against government policies that threatened their interests. The result was a weakened state and a weary citizenry. Putin's turn to authoritarianism has decreased the ferocity of inter-elite conflict. Elite actors refusing to accommodate Putin, such as media moguls Boris Berezovsky and Vladimir Gusinsky, have been the targets of criminal proceedings; their fates confirmed to other oligarchs the prudence of cooperating with Putin. In the long term, by suppressing political opposition, Putin has undermined the means of renewal and eventual replacement of political leadership at the top of the Russian state. There is quite literally no alternative to Putin. Opposition groups that do remain are a ragbag of nationalists, Communists and others held together only by the slogan 'Russia without Putin!'[38] Rather than strengthening state power as he intended, Putin has built a political system that hinges on his personal authority.

Primakov was less likely than Putin to have built a polity based on his own personality, for two main reasons. First, he was less personally afflicted with authoritarian tendencies. If he had been more willing to take on the Yeltsin Family in 1999, he might have destroyed Berezovsky before the oligarch was able to unleash his media attack dogs, ending the chances of a Primakov presidency. Second, in 1999 Primakov was already seventy years old, while Putin was a youthful forty-seven. The ageing Primakov would not have lasted in office as long as Putin has, giving him less time to personalise power. At best, it is unlikely that Primakov would have remained President beyond the March 2008 presidential election, when Putin's second term came to an end. His graceful exit from the premiership in 1999 demonstrates that Primakov knew not to outstay his welcome. The same cannot be said of Putin.

If Yevgeny Primakov had become Russian President in 2000, Russia today would not look radically different. The direction the country took, after Yeltsin gave up power on the eve of the new millennium, had little to do with Putin personally. The state that Putin inherited from Yeltsin was weak and fragmented. On the domestic front, regional governors had established personal fiefdoms that overtly rebuffed central authority, while several national republics talked of secession. Russia's oligarchs plundered the nation's wealth with little respect for the rule of law. Internationally, Russia felt humiliated by the loss of its Soviet Empire and by NATO's military interventions in Serbia and Kosovo.

In this climate, someone with a conservative-nationalist world view was fated to lead the Russian Federation. But, for Russia, better it had been Primakov than Putin.

Notes

1. Yevgeny Primakov, *Mir bez Rossii* [*World Without Russia*] (Rossiyskaya Gazeta, 2009).
2. Kyamran Agayev, 'Sostoyavshiysya krestnyy otets putinizma' [Godfather of Putinism], *Kasparov.ru*, 27 June 2015; http://www.kasparov.ru/material.php?id=558DC48DD303A.
3. Andrei Tsygankov, *Russia's Foreign Policy: Change and Continuity in National Identity* (Rowman & Littlefield, 2013, third edition).
4. Henry E. Hale, *Why Not Parties in Russia? Democracy, Federalism and the State* (Cambridge University Press, 2005).
5. David Hoffman, 'Citing Economy, Yeltsin Fires Premier', *Washington Post*, 13 May 1999.
6. Ivan Zassoursky, *Mass-Media Vtoroy Respubliki* [The Mass Media of the Second Republic] (Izd-vo Moskovskogo Universiteta, 1999).
7. 'Election Commission Turns Attention to Press', *Radio Free Europe/Radio Liberty*, 1 November 1999; http://www.rferl.org/newsline/1999/11/1-rus/rus-011199.html.
8. 'Monitoring the Media Coverage of the December 1999 Duma Elections in Russia: Preliminary Results', *European Institute for the Media*, December 1999, p. 39.
9. VCIOM nationwide surveys. See www.russiavotes.org.
10. Laura Belin, 'Russian Media Empires VI', *RFE/RL*, July 2000; http://www.rferl.org/specials/russia/ media6.
11. Karen Dawisha, *Putin's Kleptocracy: Who Owns Russia?* (Simon & Schuster, 2014), p. 154.
12. G. L. Kerman, 'Smena Kabineta: Predvaritel'nye Politicheskie Itogi' [Cabinet Changes: Preliminary Policy Results], *Public Opinion Foundation*, May 1999; http://bd.fom.ru/report/cat/pow_gov/ government_primakov/0904901.
13. Sergei Glazyev, 'Primakov Government in Retrospect', *Executive Intelligence Review*, 11 June 1999.
14. Jonathan Steele, 'Fury Over Putin's Secrets and Lies', *The Guardian*, 22 August 2000.

15. Helen Womack, 'Media: The New Russian Journalism Finds Old Soviet Habits Die Hard', *The Independent*, 22 August 2000.
16. Richard Sakwa, *Putin: Russia's Choice* (Routledge, 2004), p. 83.
17. Tina Burrett, *Television and Presidential Power in Putin's Russia* (BASEES/Routledge Series on Russian and East European Studies, 2011).
18. '2015 World Press Freedom Index', Reporters Without Borders; http://www.index.rsf.org.
19. 'Getting Away With Murder', *Committee to Protect Journalists*, 8 October 2015; http://cpj.org/reports/2015/10/impunity-index-getting-away-with-murder.php
20. 'Amnesty International Issues Reports on Disappearances', *Jamestown Foundation*, 24 May 2007.
21. 'Widespread Torture in the Chechen Republic: Human Rights Watch Briefing Paper for the 37 Session of the UN Committee Against Torture', Human Rights Watch, 13 November 2006; http://www.hrw.org/legacy/background/eca/chechnya1106/.
22. 'World Europe: Russia Keen to Avoid New Chechnya War', BBC News, 10 March 1999; http://news.bbc.co.uk/2/hi/europe/294415.stm.
23. Eric Engleman, 'Primakov Urges Talks with Chechen Rebels', *Moscow Times*, 11 September 2002.
24. Thomas Graham, 'World Without Russia', Carnegie Endowment for International Peace, 9 June 1999.
25. Thomas Remington, 'Putin, the Duma and Political Parties', in Dale Herspring (ed.), *Putin's Russia: Past Imperfect, Future Uncertain* (Rowman & Littlefield, 2003).
26. For presidential approval ratings see http://www.russiavotes.org.
27. Anders Aslund, 'An Assessment of Putin's Economic Policy', Peterson Institute for International Economics, July 2008.
28. Marlène Laruelle, *Russian Eurasianism: An Ideology of Empire* (Woodrow Wilson Center Press and John Hopkins University Press, 2008).
29. George Breslauer, 'Observations on Russia's Foreign Relations Under Putin', *Post-Soviet Affairs* 25 (2009).
30. Richard Sakwa, '"New Cold War" or Twenty Years' Crisis? Russia and International Politics', *International Affairs* 84 (2008).
31. Tina Burrett, 'Russia's Competing Nationalisms and Relations with Asia', in Jeff Kingston (ed.), *Asian Nationalisms Reconsidered* (Routledge, 2015).
32. Evgeny Primakov, *Vstrechi na Perekrestkakh* [*Encounters at the Crossroads*] (Tsentrpoligraf, 2015).
33. Alexei Kupriyanov and Natalia Rozhkova, '"Petlya Primakova" Zamknulas' ["The Primakov Loop" Withdrawn], Lenta.ru, 26 June 2015; https://lenta.ru/articles/2015/06/26/primakov_kariera.
34. Andrei Tsygankov, 'Russia in the Post-Western World: The End of the Normalization Paradigm?', *Post-Soviet Affairs* 25 (2009).

35. Russian Federation Federal State Statistics Service; http://www.gks.ru/bgd/regl/b13_12/Iss www.exe/stg/ d02/26-06.htm.
36. Alec Luhn and Terry Macallister, 'Russia Signs 30-Year Deal Worth $400bn to Deliver Gas to China', *The Guardian*, 21 May 2014.
37. Martin Smith and Paul Latawski, *The Kosovo Crisis and the Evolution of a Post-Cold War European Security* (Oxford University Press, 2013).
38. Ivan Krastev and Stephen Holmes, 'Putinism Under Siege: An Autopsy of Managed Democracy', *Journal of Democracy* 23 (July 2012).

Chapter 11

What if the Iraq War had split the Labour Party?

Andrew Stone

Tony Benn's diary, Sunday 25 January 2004

I went to the founding convention of the Respect Party at Friends Meeting House in Euston.[1] I'm old enough not to be overly sanguine about such events – but I did find myself being quite impressed. There was the SWP there of course, as well as the Socialist Alliance and a few other sects, but also a number of Muslims and lots of comrades from the Stop the War Coalition and CND. Bob Crow spoke from the RMT, the environmentalist George Monbiot from *The Guardian*, Tommy Sheridan of the SSP and George Galloway.

I was in two minds about going, and certainly about speaking at it – people have been kicked out of the Labour Party for much less (as Galloway helpfully pointed out to me). But John Rees persuaded me to say a few words. I must admit I did sit on the fence a bit – I talked about the need for unity and cooperation, which is about as uncontroversial as you can get until you actually talk about practicalities. I left out my usual list of the eleven socialist parties this time – I guess most of them must have been represented there – and focused on wider issues of democracy and peace.

Colin Powell, the American Secretary of State, has said that he doubts whether weapons of mass destruction will ever be found in Iraq, so I joked that searches are being made to see if there is any truth in our

> Prime Minister, and so far no evidence has been found. That was a bit naughty really, I know I shouldn't personalise these things.
>
> If I am expelled I'm not sure that I would challenge it – I'm afraid to say that the Labour Party is a shell now – Blair has degutted it completely. It has had right-wing leaders before, but never have they been so autocratic, or conference been so stage-managed or the unions so cowed. I do worry that if I were to leave it would cause problems for Hilary or Nita.[2] Maybe I'm a foolish old man thinking that it matters what I do at this point. But I've always believed that you must act as if you can make a change, however small...

The break-up

In the days following the launch of Respect, Tony Benn attended a series of meetings with its leading figures, as well as his colleagues in the Socialist Campaign Group and Labour Against the War. Having spent half a century in Parliament representing Labour, he now set about fomenting its most damaging split since the formation of the SDP in 1981. With the zeal of the new convert, the energetic 78-year-old began trying to convince the small band of left-wing Labour comrades of the need to build a new socialist party in its place.

He met with initial scepticism. Seasoned campaigners such as Jeremy Corbyn and Diane Abbott didn't need persuading to oppose Tony Blair or New Labour more generally – they had plenty of experience of doing so. But they found it hard to imagine that this opposition would be more effective outside the structures of what was still the biggest and most electorally successful social democratic party that the country had seen.

However, Benn's timing was propitious. The conference was sandwiched within a series of bellwether events. On 23 January, David Kay of the US Iraq Survey Group resigned over the failure to discover the weapons of mass destruction that had supposedly been the *casus belli* of the previous year's invasion. On the 27th, the Labour Party executive decided to expel the RMT union – one of the founders of the party in 1900 – because some of its Scottish branches were affiliating to Tommy Sheridan's Scottish

Socialist Party. On the same day, a Parliamentary Labour Party revolt against top-up tuition fees was defeated by five votes after the rebellion was abandoned by its leader Nick Brown, an ally of the Chancellor. And on the 28th, the Hutton report into the death of Ministry of Defence scientist and Iraq whistle-blower David Kelly was released and was widely condemned as a 'whitewash', finding Blair and his chief advisers largely blameless, while forcing the resignation of BBC journalist Andrew Gilligan, its chairman Gavyn Davies, and its Director-General Greg Dyke.

The combination of these events in such a concentrated period provided the context in which Benn began to win over some of his colleagues. He argued that these examples showed how corrupted New Labour had become by power, how it was turning on the workers and dismantling the achievements of Hardie and Attlee. It had waged war based on lies and yet it was only critics of the war that seemed to be paying the price. 'If not now, when?' Benn asked rhetorically, if not very originally.

Slowly a trickle of his comrades began to be persuaded. Stoke MP Mark Fisher was the first to choose to go, followed by Paul Flynn, then Jeremy Corbyn and John McDonnell, Neil Gerrard, Lynne Jones and Ronnie Campbell. Combined with George Galloway, this gave the nascent Respect Party eight MPs – more than long-established nationalist parties such as the SNP and Sinn Féin. None were likely to be promoted to high office under New Labour, but they were still taking a substantial risk. It was very possible that they would all lose their seats and their livelihoods at the next election. No doubt this was one consideration of the notable left-wingers such as Diane Abbott and Michael Meacher, who attended these discussions but decided to remain in the party. Meanwhile London Mayor 'Red Ken' Livingstone had just been readmitted after his success standing as an independent in 2000. Whatever his sympathies with the rebels, he judged that it would seem perverse to leave again so quickly.

Of course, such discussions could not take place without them coming to the attention of the whips. Yet the Whips' Office was on this occasion uncharacteristically indecisive. Having taken a hard line with Galloway in the hope that it would drive other critics into line, they feared exacerbating the rebellion by taking repressive measures against less obnoxious personalities. So they used all their skills – and those of Downing Street's Director of Communications, David Hill – to keep the press ignorant. Meanwhile, they began intimating to the rebels that there might be a policy concession here, a constituency boon there, maybe a select committee chairmanship down the line ... all of which only confirmed the defectors in their belief that this protest was the most effective stand that they could take.

And so, on Saturday 7 February 2004, as a poll emerged showing 51 per cent support for Blair's immediate resignation,[3] Respect unveiled its new recruits at a small but stunned news conference. Mark Fisher was to be its initial parliamentary leader, thanks to his brief ministerial experience, though he stressed the collegiate nature of the grouping. 'Clearly we will not be forming the next government,' admitted Jeremy Corbyn, 'but we will be offering the electorate a chance to vote against the war and the lies told to justify it. More than that, we will propose a positive vision for Britain based on solidarity, egalitarianism and mutual respect. We urge our fellow Labour members and representatives to stay true to the principles that first inspired you, and to join with us to fight for them.'

The shake-up

Despite the inevitably hostile press coverage they encountered, this was a message that struck a chord with a significant layer of the labour movement. Labour's membership dropped by 30,000 in the space of a few weeks, and most of them joined Respect, along with around 20,000 more from the anti-war movement. Both the right-wing press and the Labour leadership presented this as a marriage of the hard left, though many of the 'Trots and tankies' were too young to grasp the Cold War nomenclature. In truth, groups such as the SWP became marginal numerically. If they did tend to 'punch above their weight' due to tight organisation and political experience, this was held in check by the political profile and authority of the MPs. And though Tony Benn couldn't be persuaded to stand again for Parliament – 'I'm too busy to retire from activism,' he joked – his role as honorary president brought gravitas and charm to the new party.

Meanwhile, RMT general secretary and tabloid bête-noire Bob Crow was convincing his members to affiliate to Respect. Over the coming year they were joined by the FBU, PCS, CWU and BFAWU, giving the party the support of – and influence over – strategically important workers in transport, communications, the civil service and fire service, as well as providing an important source of revenue. They also gained the benefit of credible and popular speakers such as Mark Serwotka and Andy Gilchrist into the bargain. The left in larger unions were also vocal in support, and even Unison, with a track record of witch-hunting socialist office-holders, found a third of its conference backing Respect.

In April, the exposure of appalling abuse by American guards in Abu Ghraib prison, alongside the continuing deterioration of what was euphemistically described as 'the security situation' in Iraq, provided more fuel to the Respect bandwagon. A speaking tour pulled large crowds and 5,000 more recruits. Though a wounded post-Hutton BBC provided few platforms, the commercial radio and TV stations were much more generous, if only to provide more vigorous opposition than Howard's lacklustre Conservatives. The Tories' initial support for the war – and continuing concern for maintaining Britain's international status – meant that they were unable to capitalise on Blair's foreign policy woes. The Liberal Democrats, who had achieved dramatic success at the Brent East by-election the previous summer, continued to achieve good poll ratings. But while Charles Kennedy had gained plaudits for his Hyde Park speech on the eve of the invasion, his party's subsequent policy of reluctant support for the British troops put a cap on its gains, particularly once a more consistently anti-war party was seen as a credible option.

Respect were beginning to gain that credibility. By June, Stop the War convenor Lindsey German had been elected to the Greater London Assembly as a top-up member. Respect showed further electoral potential in two by-elections the following month. Labour narrowly lost the previously safe seat of Leicester South to the Liberal Democrats, while Respect's Yvonne Ridley (the journalist who had briefly been held hostage by the Taliban) beat the Conservatives to third place with 20 per cent of the vote. In Birmingham Hodge Hill Respect's national secretary John Rees, a parachuted-in candidate, managed 12 per cent, which was also sufficient to enable a Lib Dem victory.[4] No. 10 began to view Respect as their own Referendum Party.

At Labour's September conference the leadership lost a series of votes on rail renationalisation, council housing, Iraq and trade union rights, as the remaining left and union affiliates united to punish the leadership and try to win back their departed comrades. 'Triangulation' began to take on a new complexion now that there was also a left-wing pole of attraction. Meanwhile, outside the Brighton conference hall, a mass protest backed by Respect almost drowned out proceedings. As Blair proclaimed that 'so many things that used to divide our country bitterly now unite it in healthy consensus', some wag in the audience shouted, 'Yeah, we all think you should go!' Thrown out by security onto the street, when her exploits became known to the crowd she was held aloft and carried in tribute around the waterfront. In the hall, Blair rushed to finish his speech, received perfunctory and dutiful applause and retreated under heavy guard to commiserate.

The take-up

At the general election in May 2005, Respect did not yet have the strength of finances or organisation to stand in every constituency. After sharp internal debate they decided on a half-way house somewhere between the two positions of 'stand everywhere' and 'stand only where we can win', and contested ninety seats in England and Wales. They decided against posting candidates in Scotland; despite Tommy Sheridan's removal as leader, the SSP still had an established record, though in the event they slumped to just 43,500 votes as a result of internecine fighting.

Respect's stated strategy was to avoid challenging left-wingers within Labour and the Greens, and to stand candidates with a credible local base wherever possible. Standing George Galloway in Bethnal Green and Bow was one of several exceptions to this rule, though his victory seemed to bear out its wisdom. Respect did very well to retain six of its defectors' seats – previously healthy majorities meant that only Paul Flynn and John McDonnell lost out. They also achieved the historic election of Salma Yaqoob, the first female Muslim MP, in Birmingham Sparkbrook and

Small Heath. And in a number of other seats they came second or third. The impact was not straightforward – sometimes they cut Labour's vote sufficiently for them to lose, other times they minimised the Lib Dems' opportunity to soak up protest votes. They also seemed to convince new, often younger voters to come to the polls, and psephologists speculated that the 64.4 per cent turnout (a 5 per cent rise on 2001) would have been lower without their influence.

The ultimate result was that Labour got home with a majority of just thirty-four. This was far less than the 100-seat majority that Blair's advisers felt was necessary for him to stay in power for a full third term. A downcast Prime Minister, suffering from intense back pain and increasingly tired and depressed, won a historic third term with a historically low 33.8 per cent of the vote and widespread questioning of his legitimacy. 'Blair limps back,' declared *The Times*.

At a meeting of the PLP on 11 May, Blair was excoriated by a number of his own MPs for how hard he had made the campaign. As Brownites circled for the kill, Blair struggled to break out of his despondency. It informed his decision not to risk tainting London's Olympic bid with his personal lobbying. Crucial votes were thus lost to the French; 'Chirac was haughty, but at least he was there,' commented one unimpressed IOC delegate. When the crowds in Trafalgar Square heard that Paris had won the vote, there was anger as well as disappointment. 'Mr Blair styles himself as a great statesman,' commented the *Daily Telegraph*, 'but a statesman would not have hesitated to have entered the fray.'

What might have been a prolonged inquest was driven from the papers the following day by the horrendous terrorist attacks in London that killed fifty-two civilians and injured 700 others on three Tube trains and a bus. Blair, always appreciating a crisis, was temporarily roused from his slump, flying back from the G8 summit in Gleneagles to manage the security response and to make speeches denouncing the atrocities. A measured response by Respect likewise condemned terrorism but pointed out that the anti-war movement had warned that such dangers would increase with every new invasion. This predictably outraged much of the press, though it failed to generate the same level of antipathy in the general public.

Blair had by now become fixated on the manner of his leaving, and although the thought of being dragged out by his party like Thatcher repelled him, neither did he want to appear as a 'quitter' in the UK's hour of need. He thus continued to bat back enquiries as to his own exit strategy as persistently as those asked of the occupation forces in Iraq. He soldiered on until the local elections of May 2006, where Labour was pushed into third place, provoking renewed fury and desperation within the party. Blair's response, a reshuffle, demoted his previous ally Geoff Hoon, who could not be dissuaded from then resigning from the government entirely. He did so with a Molotov cocktail of a statement that revealed, contrary to the impression given by the Hutton report, Blair's close involvement in the decision to release David Kelly's name to the press. The whole tragic saga was thus revived once more. It was one of the few decisions for which Blair appeared to feel genuine remorse, rather than the faux-sympathetic front he habitually used to brush off critics. Its reappearance, at a time when the police were starting to look into allegations that one of his key supporters, Lord Levy, had promised peerages in exchange for loans, convinced him of the need finally to name the date of his departure – 27 September 2006, the penultimate day of Labour's Manchester conference. The conference agenda was adjusted so that Blair could give his farewells, then leave the last day for his successor.

There was rarely any doubt as to who that would be. David Miliband, Alan Johnson and John Reid all considered putting their hats in the ring, but feared that they would not just be defeated, but annihilated. Michael Meacher, who stood to pull Labour to the left, seemed to prove their point. Despite his argument that a coronation would be in no one's interest, he mustered just six nominations, meaning that the crown was Brown's automatically.

The make-up

One of Blair's major regrets was that he had been unable to see the peace process in Northern Ireland through to its conclusion. As he left Downing Street, the Stormont Assembly remained suspended. Though progress was made over the winter of 2006/07, and new elections took place for the Assembly in March, the installation of a DUP/Sinn Féin executive was stalled for a further six months. In a grimly ironic twist, the barrier to progress was that neither side could agree how to sit around a table in a reconciliation photograph. Sinn Féin wanted Gerry Adams to be beside the DUP First Minister to show that he would be integral to the new executive, but the DUP insisted that their leader, Ian Paisley, should sit opposite his old enemies, to show that he was still prepared to be 'Doctor No'. When Brown was informed of this he released an expletive-filled rant of exasperation, word of which got back to Ulster and impressed nobody. In his frustration he also silenced the Director-General of the Northern Ireland office, Robert Hannigan, whose simple solution – that Paisley and Adams sit at the apex of a diamond-shaped table – might just have worked.[5]

Northern Ireland thus threatened briefly to return from the brink of resolution to the long years of conflict, with its parties in turmoil and low-level violence beginning to re-emerge among some of their supporters. Fortunately one of Brown's uncharacteristically insightful promotions in his first reshuffle had been the appointment of Ed Miliband to the Northern Ireland Office. Always a Brownite, he nonetheless had a reputation of being a reasonable listener; the Blairites had given him the backhanded compliment of dubbing him 'the Emissary from Planet Fuck'.[6] The experience of attempting to bridge two warring groups stood him in good stead, and eventually, in September 2007, power-sharing resumed in Stormont.

Meanwhile, Respect had reorganised its own governance within its collective officers group. A delegate conference elected Salma Yaqoob and Jeremy Corbyn as leader and deputy leader respectively. George Galloway was defeated for the latter post despite being on the slate with Yaqoob. He was still licking his wounds that winter when he was approached to take part in *Celebrity Big Brother*. Yaqoob was informed of his intention to do so and vetoed it, claiming that it would open him up to ridicule and leave his constituents unrepresented. Her judgement was apparently vindicated when Galloway's replacement, Robert Kilroy-Silk, was widely mocked for a task that involved dressing in Lycra and impersonating a cat. A preening Galloway considered resigning from the party, but was prevailed upon to stay with the argument that to lose two parties in barely two years could be considered careless and would surely end his political career. He focused instead on other media engagements and international solidarity work, some of which would later attract controversy for its connection with repressive regimes. He was ultimately expelled from the party in August 2012 when he suggested that the rape accusations against WikiLeaks founder Julian Assange amounted to nothing more than 'bad sexual etiquette'.

Respect's steady growth was far from Brown's only problem, but he did experience a small initial bounce in support, which convinced some that he should call an early election, perhaps in May 2007. This would have given him a personal mandate and possibly an increased majority. A range of reasons would be proffered by his supporters as to why this never happened, among them that Brown considered the Labour Party to have been given a parliamentary mandate rather than Blair a presidential one. However, the key reason was Brown's default political caution, and as the world economy began to suffer the blowback of years of bad credit, possible election dates began to recede into the middle distance. The country ultimately went to the polls on 6 May 2010. The last time a government had served a full term – John Major's, between 1992 and 1997 – did not invite an auspicious comparison.

Although the UK had formally come out of the great recession by autumn 2009, its impacts were becoming very apparent on living standards, with wages and jobs both under pressure. Respect had found a growing audience, at the anti-capitalist protests that would later become the Occupy movement, and trade union conferences, for its calls for political control of the banks and nationalisation of firms that were shedding jobs. It began to popularise slogans about creating 1 million climate jobs, a plan originated by the Campaign against Climate Change, which took centre stage at 'the Wave' mass demonstration coinciding with the 2009 Copenhagen climate talks. Respect had been raising the profile of the talks and protest for months through speaking tours and stunts, so could not be accused of 'hijacking' the issue. Their seriousness about this led a number of left Greens to defect to the party, among whom Natalie Bennett would go on to be a Respect candidate at the 2010 election. This prompted Green leader Caroline Lucas to negotiate an electoral 'non-aggression pact' that served to benefit both parties.

Respect nonetheless expanded the number of seats it contested to 213, including thirty-five in Scotland. The Scottish left had not recovered from the SSP's break-up, and most serious elements of it thus joined the new Scottish Respect in 2008 (Welsh affiliates similarly rebranded themselves soon afterwards). Its progress was stunted by the SNP successfully positioning itself as akin to 'Old Labour', though its record at the head of a minority government in Holyrood began to undermine this claim.

The worst moment of Brown's campaign was the so-called 'dinosaurgate', when he was recorded in his car calling lifelong Labour voter Gillian Duffy 'a dinosaur' after she questioned why he wouldn't stand up for working people, unlike Respect, who were saying they would. Though it pained much of the media to give Respect any free publicity, the chance to show Brown squirming seemed too good an opportunity to miss. They were also aware that Respect were likely to cost Labour seats again, and so it proved. Though the left-wingers only increased their own tally to twelve – albeit including some important talents like North Ayrshire's Katy Clark and the re-elected John McDonnell – they split the Labour vote in many areas, reducing Brown's total to just 231 seats. The Conservatives were not the only beneficiaries of the collapse in the Labour vote, but still emerged with an eight-seat majority. Their leader David Cameron briefly considered a coalition to ensure a more stable government, but his backbenchers refused to accept anyone other than the Unionists as allies, and that arrangement remained unofficial.

The wake-up

Gordon Brown thus offered his resignation to the Queen, having served – unelected – for almost four years. David Cameron, his Chancellor George Osborne and Business Minister Oliver Letwin formed what became known as 'the troika' at the head of the new government, pushing an extreme austerity agenda that shocked even some of their natural supporters. They promised to rid the public sector of 1 million jobs as part of £95 billion of spending cuts, with reductions in departmental spending of an average of 24 per cent. The NHS would begin to charge for some 'non-essential' services and was to be opened up to large-scale privatisation. The government endorsed the Browne Review proposals to remove entirely the cap on tuition fees, prompting Liberal Democrat leader Nick Clegg to denounce 'an immoral tax on learning and aspiration'. A new Trade Union Bill was prepared to impose 60 per cent ballot turnout thresholds and even tighter restrictions on picketing.

The students reacted first. On 10 November they massed around Parliament, with a large breakaway group occupying Conservative headquarters in Milbank. The police made ninety-six arrests, and twenty-three protestors required hospital treatment. London Mayor Ken Livingstone (elected for a third term in 2008 with the help of Respect second preferences) condemned what he said was a police over-reaction. New Labour leader David Miliband, who had defeated his brother due to the denuding of the party's affiliates, rebuked Livingstone for his comments, but a range of trade unionists, particularly from the education unions, gave their support, and mobilised in large numbers for future protests. When the police tried to 'kettle' the next mobilisation they found themselves lectured on civil liberties from within the cordon by high-profile academics, with a series of these 'kettle lectures' going viral on social media. With sufficient Conservative MPs fearing for their slender majorities, the government pulled back from the fees increase, claiming that they had only intended to consult on the Browne Review.

In March, the TUC March for the Alternative was huge, and David Miliband attracted criticism from within his own ranks for refusing to address it. 'We cannot be seen to be beholden to the unions,' he told the PLP.

'It's not like they created us or anything, is it?' heckled Dennis Skinner.

Tony Benn was among several Respect speakers with no such reservations, and the trickle of new union affiliations continued.

Failing to take heed of the growing discontent, the government pushed ahead with its Trade Union Bill. Before it could have its second reading, the death of Mark Duggan at the hands of the police in Tottenham led to several days of sustained rioting across most major cities. Though the trade unions stood apart from the rioting itself, and some condemned it as vigorously as the government, once it died down both they and Respect made connections between cuts to youth services, the growth of inequality and the resulting social explosion.

An echo of the same mood was evident in the pressure for coordinated strike action over the government's pensions reforms. A well-supported strike on 30 June 2011 by the civil service union PCS, alongside education unions NUT, UCU and ATL, was a prelude to a much broader action on 2 November by twenty-five unions, involving around 3 million workers. Activists had pressured leaders to call an earlier date than the floated 30 November[7] to allow follow-up action before Christmas – a rolling programme involving most of the November group of unions. It also pre-empted the third reading of the Trade Union Bill. This proved to be a good strategy, as it encouraged a minor rebellion of Conservative backbenchers, led by David Davis. They marshalled a civil libertarian argument laced with pragmatism, and Cameron lost the vote by four. There were widespread street celebrations and unions began to recruit in large numbers for the first time in thirty years. Seeking to re-establish his authority, Cameron repeated the strategy of Edward Heath in 1974 and called an election on the question of who ruled – him or the unions? Like his predecessor, to ask the question was to answer it.

The country went to the polls on the unseasonal date of 9 February 2012. Cameron was advised that his ageing voter base would not fare well in the cold, but he was pig-headed in his determination. With temperatures hovering around freezing, and snow flurries in London and elsewhere, turnout was just 60 per cent, despite the inflamed passions. Though the Conservatives had a small plurality in the new parliament – 278 seats to Labour's 272 – the Liberal Democrats participated in only the most cursory of negotiations for a coalition with a party they accused of being divisive and illiberal. By contrast, David Miliband offered key constitutional reforms to produce an elected House of Lords and a referendum on the voting system. Together they could just about muster a majority, though they would often rely on the goodwill of Respect's gradually swelling group, which now reached seventeen MPs.

The four-year fixed-term parliament expired in April 2016 (February was considered an inappropriate month to repeat, despite a commission into the prospects of electronic voting), and the UK took part in its first general election under the single transferable vote system. Miliband and Clegg had long since lost their initial bonhomie, and were counting the political cost of three years of 'humanitarian intervention' in Syria. They were facing an emboldened trade union movement that was increasingly alienated from the Labour Party. UKIP had come third in the 2014 European elections and were seeking to exploit a spike in xenophobia around the Syrian refugee crisis, though Respect's position of anti-racist solidarity also gained it friends. The Conservatives under Theresa May had yet to recover their sense of direction, with one-nation Tories distressed by her pronouncements on human rights, welfare and immigration, and the Europhobic wing feeling betrayed that she would not endorse EU withdrawal without a referendum. Meanwhile, Boris Johnson wrote scathing (if somewhat rambling) editorials about his former colleagues in between appearances as Ian Hislop's replacement on *Have I Got News for You*. The long-awaited Scottish independence referendum due for that summer promised an agonising baptism for whatever multi-party coalition could be cobbled together out of the most fractured Parliament in British history. And senior military figures began to discuss in darkened rooms the circumstances in which a 'state of emergency' would be necessary...

Notes

1. In reality, Benn did not attend the meeting, but discussed it over lunch with Tommy Sheridan MSP.
2. Hilary Benn, Tony Benn's son, was Secretary of State for International Development at this time. Nita Clarke, Tony Benn's daughter-in-law, worked as an adviser to Tony Blair.
3. *Independent on Sunday*, 7 February 2004.
4. In reality, Labour did lose Leicester South to the Liberal Democrats, whose vote share rose by 17 per cent while Respect gained 13 per cent, but hung on to Birmingham Hodge Hill by 2 per cent.
5. This was in fact what was agreed – see Andrew Rawnsley, *The End of the Party* (Penguin, 2010), p. 430.
6. Ibid., p. 362.
7. When it was actually called.

Chapter 12

What if Tony Blair had sacked Gordon Brown in 2004?

Paul Richards

When the political relationship between Tony Blair and Gordon Brown was finally killed, there were no witnesses. It took place at about 9 p.m. on Wednesday 6 October 2004, the week after the Labour Party conference, at a private meeting in the Prime Minister's flat above 11 Downing Street. Four-year-old Leo Blair's toys, including wooden trains and a brown teddy bear, littered the floor. From outside the window came the muffled sound of the cars and buses on Whitehall.

According to those waiting nervously downstairs, including Sally Morgan and David Hill, the meeting lasted all of seven minutes, and then, according to one eyewitness, the Chancellor of the Exchequer tore down the stairs three at a time, scooped up his aides, and swept out of the building from the famous front entrance and into his waiting Rover Sterling.

Blair himself, still in his shirtsleeves in his flat, is said to have assumed the ashen-grey pallor of one who has witnessed a murder. In his autobiography *My Journey: A Prime Minister's Story 1997–2008*, published in 2009 after the Labour victory in that year's general election, Blair wrote:

> Sacking Gordon was the hardest thing I've ever had to do. It was like ending a marriage. But by 2003, it was a marriage that had turned bad. Whatever love there had been was soured by years of infidelity. Worse, by then, we disagreed on the fundamental direction of strategy and policy. I was New Labour. He wasn't. It was as simple as that. If sacking Gordon was hard, then the prospect of not sacking him was even harder.

Their relationship had started twenty years earlier when the two new Labour MPs shared an office and began earnestly to discuss how to bring Labour back to life as a party of government. They became entwined as political partners in crime throughout the 1980s and into the 1990s. First under Neil Kinnock, then under John Smith, they were integral to the modernisation of the Labour Party, which led to the electoral earthquake of 1997, when Labour won 418 seats on a 10.2 per cent national swing from Tories to Labour.

But, even in the early days, Blair recognised that Brown had traditional Old Labour instincts that held back his ability to think and act in New Labour ways. In Blair's published diaries, *The Making of a Leader*, covering the early 1980s, the reader can sense that one half of the double act is losing faith in the other's ability to fully modernise Labour and reach beyond its traditional borders.

In May 1992, after Labour lost its fourth general election in a row, the party elected John Smith to replace Neil Kinnock as leader. But the *Sunday Times*, on the weekend of Smith's election, ran a cover story in its magazine section on the 'Leader Labour Missed'; it was Tony Blair, not Gordon Brown. After May 1992, as shadow Home Secretary, Blair outgrew his friend. Blair recalls in *My Journey* that during the period from May 1992 to May 1994:

> It was like I was waking each day feeling stronger, more certain. Each encounter with my own party, the other party, the media, the public, would be like another layer of steel bolted onto an already well-fortified casing. I could see the opportunity to take hold of the Labour Party, rework it into an electoral machine capable of winning over the people.

When John Smith succumbed to a heart attack on 12 May 1994, aged just fifty-five, it was to Tony Blair that Labour turned. Any suggestion that it should be Gordon Brown was soon squashed. The contemporary accounts suggest a longer-term series of meetings in May 1993, which culminated in a 'deal' of sorts, promising Brown a prominent role in domestic policy, but no definite promise of a handover.

By the middle of 1994, Tony Blair was the obvious choice. Labour's long period in exile and the shock of losing the 1992 election, despite dumping unpopular policies such as opposition to Trident, focused the minds of Labour members. Blair won the leadership contest, beating Margaret Beckett and John Prescott in the trade unionists, members and MPs sections, with 57 per cent of the vote overall.

Within a few months Labour membership surged to 400,000. Labour's standing shot up in the polls, remaining in double figures. In one poll, on 9 January 1995, according to Gallup in the *Daily Telegraph*, Labour's lead was an astonishing 43.5 points over the Tories, with Labour on 62 per cent and the Tories on 18.5 per cent.

Blair's success in the 1997 election has been well documented and analysed both in the UK and by political parties across the globe. It remains the high-water mark of Labour success. It was a victory won with some simple insights: that progressive politics must be wedded to a wide electoral appeal; that economic competence is central; that political leaders must be attractive and credible; that Labour should place its values in a modern setting, rather than echo policies of a bygone age.

By removing the dead weight of unilateralism, anti-Europeanism, commitments to costly renationalisation of utility, energy and telecommunications companies, and the whiff of anti-Western, and even pro-IRA, sentiment that hung around corners of the left, Kinnock, Blair, Brown and the rest of the modernisers saved the Labour Party. Aside from a small group of refuseniks organised around the Campaign Group of MPs, who clung to the Bennite programme that had been so decisively rejected in 1983, these political truths were adopted with alacrity by the mainstream of the Labour Party.

Philip Gould, New Labour's strategist and pollster, set out the ambition for the party in a memorandum, *The Unfinished Revolution*, in April 1995. He wrote:

> Labour has not to just win the next election: it must win a working majority; it must have a project and policies that will transform Britain over an eight-year period ... it must become a party of sufficient

> structural and ideological coherence to support Labour in government without splitting and without sabotage.

It was clear from the first months after the 1997 election that the presence of Gordon Brown would be a brake on the government's ambitions. It was not quite sabotage, but it wasn't exactly enthusiastic support either. Brown created a coterie of acolytes within Parliament and government, and operated an informal whipping system among his own group. On contentious issues, Brown would hold government policy hostage within the Treasury and refuse to release it without concessions. Blair records in his memoirs that the Terrorism Act 2000, the Criminal Justice Act 2000, the Postal Services Act 2000, the Health and Social Care Act 2001 and the Police Reform Act 2002 were all subject to 'the Brown treatment'.

Gordon Brown created a government within a government, a parliamentary clique and a cadre of friendly journalists, which was mobilised to hold back the Blairites' enthusiasm and to create a significant obstacle to Blair himself. Brown's mastery over the Treasury, and his command of the House of Commons, was tempered by his own sense of entitlement to the top job. But, as Blair wrote in *My Journey*: 'Was it reasonable for him to block measures simply because I would not yield to him the position of Prime Minister? Of course not.'

The final straw for Tony Blair was the vote in January 2004 on tuition fees, which saw the government's majority of 166 fall to just five. It was the closest Blair came to resigning as Prime Minister, and it had little to do with reform of student finances. It had much to do with prominent Brown supporters, including Nick Brown and George Mudie, organising a rebellion and holding the Prime Minister to ransom.

The day after the knife-edge vote, the Hutton Report into the build-up to the Iraq invasion was published, which put Blair in the clear of any wrong-doing, but did nothing to placate his critics, who dismissed it as 'whitewash'. The following day, at a *Guardian* conference on public services at the Grove conference centre near Watford, instead of retreat or consolidation, Blair dialled up his rhetoric on public service reform. Addressing the need to drive up standards, he acknowledged the role of extra investment, spreading best practice, and government initiatives. But the main driver, he told his audience, was 'choice and contestability based not on wealth but on one's equal status as a citizen'. This was not the 'marketisation' feared by 'part of the progressive left' but instead 'continuous improvement through giving power to people [and] greater choice, greater voice and more personalised services'.

Throughout 2004, with the weight of Iraq on his shoulders and the constant battle with Brown (characterised by now as the 'TB–GBs'), Blair had considered resignation. But, by the summer, he had resolved to see his public service revolution through. This merely increased Brown's resolve to pile pressure on his rival. At the Labour Party conference in autumn 2004 in Brighton, Brown's speech was a naked appeal to the hall, not the country, with its references to the 1945 Labour government. He ended with an exhortation of 'values far beyond those of contracts, markets and exchange', which was then spun to the media as an attack on pro-public service reformers such as Charles Clarke, Alan Milburn and Blair himself.

Blair and Brown met behind the scenes and held a tense negotiation. Blair pleaded with Brown to support his agenda and stop destabilising the government. Brown, it is reported, replied, 'There is nothing that you could ever say to me now that I could ever believe.' Blair countered, not in his speech or in person, but in a surprise media interview with Andrew Marr for the BBC in which he announced that he intended to serve a full term after 2005, that he had bought a new house on Connaught Square, and also that he had an irregular heart beat and would be undergoing a heart procedure. This was also the moment that Blair decided to rid himself of his turbulent priest.

The fateful meeting in the Blairs' flat at which the Prime Minister sacked his Chancellor was not the result of a temporary moment of frustration, nor a building sense of annoyance. It was the culmination of a carefully worked-out plan. Three of Blair's closest allies – Peter Mandelson, the No. 10 'blue skies thinker' John Birt and chief of staff Jonathan Powell – were sanctioned by Blair to devise a plan to remove Brown. They code-named it, with a keen sense of irony, 'Operation Teddy Bear'.

Peter Mandelson recalls in his memoir *The Third Man*:

> The name 'Teddy Bear' was chosen so as not to give away the slightest hint of its true meaning. It began with the premise that we had to face up to the fact that Gordon wanted Tony out. Barring the prospect of the two of them coming to a co-existence pact, things would surely get worse.

The plan was to divide Gordon Brown's mighty Treasury into two separate government departments. One department would be the Ministry of Finance, with its Finance Secretary dealing with the macro-economic situation, including taxation, international markets, financial services and the banks. The second department was the Ministry of Economics, responsible for government expenditure. This was modelled on the set-up in the United States and many other developed economies.

This significant change to the 'machinery of government' is of course what happened in late September 2004, with Alan Milburn appointed as Financial Secretary and James Purnell as Economics Secretary. The move was bold, and can be credited with underpinning the government's ability to deliver rapid and lasting public service reform. It was also utterly unacceptable to Gordon Brown, who believed, rightly, that the move was designed partly to clip his wings or force his resignation.

Although no witnesses exist to the meeting where Blair showed Brown his plan, we know that Blair had briefing papers ready, including an organogram showing how the new arrangement would work. It was this that caused Brown to terminate the meeting so precipitately and bolt down the Downing Street staircase. Not since Michael Heseltine walked out of the Thatcher Cabinet in 1985 has such a high-ranking minister made such a dramatic exit from No. 10.

Brown formally resigned at 9 a.m. the following morning, making a short statement to a throng of cameras outside the Treasury entrance on Horse Guards Road, before catching a train to Dunfermline.

The sacking of a Chancellor, even when presented as a resignation, is a seismic event in the life of a government. There followed seventy-two hours of media ferment, with briefing and counter-briefing spewed across the pages of the newspapers and internet. For some of the hard-core Brown supporters it spurred open dissent and criticism of the Prime Minister. Jackie Ashley in *The Guardian* called it the 'greatest betrayal since Judas'. For Kevin Maguire in the *Mirror* it was 'the final victory for Islington Labour'. Four Brown-supporting junior ministers resigned. But a reshuffle immediately followed, with the promotions of Alan Milburn and James Purnell to the two new economy jobs, and eye-catching moves up for David Miliband, Alan Johnson, Ruth Kelly, John Hutton, Hazel Blears, Jacqui Smith and Tessa Jowell. This soon occupied the minds and pens of political journalists. When someone goes overboard from the ship of state, it continues to steam ahead while the waters close over their heads, no matter how furiously they wave and shout.

No sooner had the excitement over the raft of new government appointments died down than it mounted again at the prospect of a general election. After Christmas 2004, it was clear that Blair wanted an election in the spring, fought on a radical, unencumbered New Labour manifesto.

Labour won the election held on 5 May 2005, with a much reduced majority of sixty, and just 35.1 per cent of the popular vote. Charles Kennedy led the Liberal Democrats to a record sixty-four seats, with an anti-war pitch that attracted those opposed to Britain's engagement in Iraq. The Tories' lacklustre campaign, masterminded by Lynton Crosby, failed to break through. Labour beat the Tories by ninety-three seats in England. With a majority of sixty, and without Gordon Brown breathing down his neck, Tony Blair launched into a ferocious programme of reform and modernisation of Britain's public services.

Gordon Brown retired from politics at the 2005 general election and secured a number of positions on the world stage. He became a UN special envoy for global education. He established the Gordon Brown Foundation to tackle and eradicate malaria. He also accepted a lucrative advisory role with JP Morgan, earning him a reputed £2 million a year.

Yet, the impulses that had driven Brown since he was a student remained strong within him. Whenever his speeches strayed into British domestic policy, journalists pored over them for signs of criticism of the Blair government. They were seldom disappointed. In December 2005, in an address to the Smith Institute, he famously stated: 'I knew John Smith, I worked with John Smith, John Smith was my friend. He would have looked at this government, and dared not call it "Labour".'

Like Ted Heath, Brown found it hard to cast off the impression that he was engaged in one long sulk.

The period from 2003 to 2008 is hailed as one of the most tumultuous periods of reform in British history. The Labour government unleashed wave after wave of reforms to the NHS, to schools, to prisons, to university finances, and to the central machinery of government. The nature of such reforms is that what seems radical and controversial at the time often appears commonplace once implemented. The ban on smoking in public places, the police community support officers on our streets, the ID cards we all carry in our wallets: these were all the cause of great debate at the time of their introduction.

While many historians inevitably focus on the invasion of Iraq in 2003, supported by the British government and British forces, the domestic agenda of the Blair government bears close study. With schools, for example, the Education Secretary David Miliband brought in legislation to free schools from local authority control, allowing teachers and parents greater latitude in how they were run. These 'free schools', similar in design to Labour's academy school programme, proved popular with parents. They were state schools, however, funded from taxation; and comprehensive schools, because they were not allowed to select pupils by exams or by charging. Over 200 were established in Labour's third term, and are today a recognised part of the local education ecology in most towns and cities. Pupils' standards of literacy and numeracy have steadily improved.

In the NHS, waiting lists and waiting times were dramatically reduced by the use of private sector suppliers. These Independent Sector Treatment Centres allowed NHS patients treatment within days, not months or years, for routine operations such as cataracts or hip and knee replacements. The NHS was restructured to allow local hospitals to become Foundation Trusts along the lines of mutual or cooperative organisations, with direct patient, staff and public engagement. The Health Secretary, Tessa Jowell, toughed out some fierce resistance to change from the BMA, but after five years in the job she could be satisfied with record numbers of operations, falling death rates from cancer and coronary heart disease, and public satisfaction ratings at record highs. Investment and reform proved a winning combination.

Standing in Downing Street alongside his new Home Secretary, Hazel Blears, on the morning after his third election victory in 2005, Tony Blair announced a new programme to tackle anti-social behaviour. Anchored in the work of sociologist Richard Sennett, the Respect Agenda included new powers for the police and local authorities to tackle noisy neighbours, street gangs, drugs, prostitution and out-of-control dogs. There was an award scheme, 'Taking a Stand', for citizens prepared to stand up to anti-social behaviour. Crucially, millions were spent on 'family intervention projects' across the country, which sought to bring order into the chaotic lives of the most problematic families. This investment was designed to save the taxpayer down the line, by pre-empting the need for multi-agency support and the involvement of the criminal justice system. Blair put civil servant Louise Casey in charge of the programme, which became a huge success. The acronym ASBO, which is today an everyday term, began with the Respect Agenda. Independent analysis suggests that not only did the Respect Agenda restore order in many estates and inner-city areas, it also helped to shore up Labour's electoral support in the 2009 general election, directly contributing to Labour holding several seats such as Basildon, Harlow, Corby, Hastings and North Warwickshire.

When the global financial crash came in 2008, with billions wiped off stock exchanges and the collapse of Lehman Brothers, the Labour government was robust enough to weather the storm. The Department for Finance, with Alan Milburn at its head, acted decisively to prevent a run on the banks and secure institutions, such as Northern Rock, which were on the brink.

In 2008, as he always planned, Blair announced his intention to retire as Prime Minister. In his introduction to the 2005 manifesto, he had written: 'So now I face my last election as leader of my party and Prime Minister of our country.' He announced the timetable for his departure and the orderly transition to his successor at the Trimdon Colliery Labour Club, his political base in the heart of his constituency. Few failed to notice that his chosen successor was present in the audience.

Blair told the crowd, many with tears running down their faces:

> I was, and remain, as a person and as a Prime Minister, an optimist. Politics may be the art of the possible – but at least in life, give the impossible a go. So of course the vision is painted in the colours of the rainbow, and the reality is sketched in the duller tones of black, white and grey.
>
> But I ask you to accept one thing. Hand on heart, I did what I thought was right. I may have been wrong. That is your call. But believe one thing if nothing else. I did what I thought was right for our country.

There were three candidates in the June 2008 Labour leadership contest, and six for deputy leader, a post made available when Blair's deputy John Prescott stood down. A new deputy leader was elected after four rounds of eliminations, the former postman and union leader Alan Johnson seeing off challenges from Harriet Harman, Jon Cruddas, Peter Hain, Hilary Benn and Hazel Blears.

A clear winner in the leadership contest emerged after the hard left's kamikaze candidate, Jeremy Corbyn, won just 10 per cent of the vote across the three sections. As Corbyn wrote in his column in *Morning Star* afterwards: 'It was just my turn.' In the run-off, the transfers from Corbyn saw the winner over the line.

Labour's victory in the 2009 general election remains one of the gravity-defying moments of British politics. The campaign was fought on a combination of a strong record and a new face at the top. This combination of strength and freshness proved a winning combination. The government's handling of the global financial crisis proved an asset, and the uncertainty created by the crash stoked a popular reluctance to take a risk on the untried and untested David Cameron. Labour's campaign slogan – 'No time for a novice' – sealed Cameron's fate.

Private polling by Deborah Mattinson, the party's pollster, showed that Labour beat the Tories among C2 voters in thirty key marginal seats on the twin hot-button issues of economic competence and trust in the leader. The result was every bit as shocking as John Major's victory in 1992, or Ted Heath's in 1970. Labour's majority was down to twenty-seven, a far cry from the glory days of 1997 or 2001; but it was a majority, and the victory over David Cameron's Tories was sweet for the new Labour Prime Minister.

On Friday 18 June 2009, after the trip to the palace, the new Prime Minister entered Downing Street, leader of a Labour Party that had been elected for a fourth time. Pausing to check her hair and make-up in a compact mirror in the entrance of No. 10 (there being no mirror above the fireplace), she strode out to the podium to announce her intention to serve as a New Labour Prime Minister, carrying on the Blair revolution to new heights.

The lobby reporters, corralled behind their metal barrier, respectfully called out 'Prime Minister', but the shouts from the photographers from the newspapers were far less formal: 'Tessa, Tessa – over here, Tessa.'

Author's note

I hope readers will recognise this as a piece of creative writing, with every event after autumn 2004, and some before that date, a work of fiction. There are, however, some kernels of truth. 'Operation Teddy Bear' was a genuine proposal, cooked up by John Birt, Jonathan Powell and Peter Mandelson, to split the Treasury into two separate departments, with Gordon Brown as the much-denuded Finance Minister. Mandelson (genuinely) writes:

> Tony agonised over Teddy Bear for several weeks. With barely a year left until we would again be in election campaign mode, he knew that his decision might determine the fate of his second term, and very possibly his record as Prime Minister. He outlined the plan to Gordon, who responded with a flat 'no'. Tony decided his position was just too weak for him to impose it. It was a fateful moment.

Blair has always maintained that he never wanted to sack Brown, preferring him inside the tent pissing out, to use Lyndon Johnson's delightful phrase. The complexity of their relationship, and the genuine bonds between the two men, no matter how strained, ensured that Blair would never move against Brown. The reason, as he explained in his (real) autobiography, *My Journey*, was neither obligation to past services nor friendship, but:

> It was that I still disagreed with the premise that his absence from government was better than his presence within it ... The answer to the question, would 'life have been easier if he was removed?' seems so clear; however, the answer assumes that had he been sacked, everything else would have remained the same: i.e. it would have been the same world, minus Gordon. That's not how politics works.

Tony Blair's diaries of the period 1983 to 1985 remain, alas, unpublished.

The rest, with Blair being forced into an early announcement of his date of departure, and retirement, and Brown leading Labour to defeat and the loss of ninety-one seats, is history.

Tony Blair remains the only person to lead Labour to three successive terms of office, and the only person since 1966 to win a working parliamentary majority for Labour.

Chapter 13

What if Chris Huhne had beaten Nick Clegg to the Lib Dem leadership in 2007?

Mark Pack

Sitting squat and unloved on a north London industrial estate is a dull rectangular building. Its red-brick facade is topped by ugly green corrugations and only punctuated by a small number of characterless windows. Yet, for all the life-sapping mediocrity of the building's exterior, inside it, among piles of paper and envelopes, the hopes and dreams of many are made and broken. For this is home to Electoral Reform Ballot Services, the contractor of choice for elections of all sorts, from secretary of a small niche hobby group through to national political leaders hoping to be the next Prime Minister.

On 18 December 2007, it was the location of the Liberal Democrat leadership election count. Following Menzies Campbell's resignation on 15 October, Nick Clegg and Chris Huhne had been battling it out for the leadership of the party. Both were relative novices. The pair had been close friends and fellow MEPs; both were elected to Parliament for the first time in 2005. Strains in their friendship had surfaced when Chris Huhne had a tilt at the party leadership in 2006 after Charles Kennedy stood down; Menzies Campbell had won, while Nick Clegg had sat the contest out. A year and a half later, Clegg and Huhne were direct opponents.

Aside from a brief would-be entrance to the race by Birmingham MP John Hemming – who quickly found that not enough colleagues were willing to nominate him – it had been a bruising and often ill-tempered two-horse race, with little sign of their past friendship. Clegg started as the favourite and initially appeared to be out in front by quite some margin. But during the race it was Huhne who appeared to be making up ground, performing better in the one major TV debate and picking up the majority of the declarations online from activists who said, 'I was undecided, but now...'

YouGov's record at polling party leadership races was still in its infancy, so no one put too much weight on its one poll, which gave Clegg a clear but not crushing twelve-point lead (56 per cent/44 per cent). Moreover, that YouGov poll had recorded half of the party's members as having not yet voted.

Telephone canvass returns for both leadership campaigns also seemed to show a steady uptick in Huhne's support. Huhne's camp were convinced that the race was just like a traditional parliamentary by-election of the Liberal Democrat heyday, with a huge swing in support to their man in the last few days.

So there were nerves and hopes all around as the two campaign teams assembled in the pedestrian surroundings of the count, where the postal votes from tens of thousands of party members would be processed.

At the previous leadership election count, updates on how it was looking were leaked and used by some enterprising members to place highly profitable last-minute bets. As a result, this time a tight technology quarantine was imposed. The representatives of each leadership campaign had to hand over all their phones before being led into a sealed environment to watch the count itself play out.

A big lead for Clegg in the early ballot papers was steadily cut back as later and later postal ballots were opened. Nerves among the Clegg team, and hopes among the Huhne team, rose as it was clear that Huhne was leading strongly among party members who had voted late. The more recent the date stamp on the envelopes being opened, the more Clegg's lead over Huhne was being cut.

Looming alongside all of this was the legacy of a postal strike, resulting in a mini-mountain of 1,300 or so postal votes that had been put to one side for arriving after the deadline.

As the pre-deadline votes were all finally tallied, and the Returning Officer and his staff double-checked the data and the calculations, it was clear to everyone that Clegg was just ahead. So what to do about those late votes? The two leadership camps were informally sounded out: would they be happy for the late votes to be counted? If so, they would be, but if there was no agreement, they would not.

The Clegg camp, of course, said no. The rules had a deadline. Those votes had missed it. They shouldn't count and their man should be leader.

~

So far, this is what happened. The result was duly announced. Clegg beat Huhne by 20,988 to 20,477, a margin of just 511 votes (1.2 per cent). Well-sourced reports suggest that those late votes would have tipped the contest to Huhne if they had been counted. So the result could have been very different if the Huhne camp had known just one detail of the party's history...

~

18 December 2007, Electoral Reform Ballot Services

The two leadership camps were informally sounded out: would they be happy for the late votes to be counted? If so, they would be, but if there was no agreement, they would not.

The Clegg camp, of course, said no. The rules had a deadline. Those votes had missed it. They shouldn't count and their man should be leader.

The Huhne camp, however, had other ideas, and one of its members nervously ran their fingers along the folded handwritten note they had written the night before. It had been triggered by a phone call from a supporter, wishing them luck at the count and adding, 'I'm sure you know this already, but just in case the count is close...' No one in the Huhne camp had previously known what they had been told. Hence the note, sitting like a 'get out of jail free' card in their pocket with details of a largely undocumented and mostly forgotten incident from the party's past.

With the voting so close and the uncounted votes likely to tip Huhne into the lead, now was the time to play it.

Yes, the Huhne camp agreed – it was important to stick by the party's rules.

Yes, they agreed – the rules should not be changed, especially just for this one occasion.

But, yes, too – surely that also means that we should stick with the previous precedent for what to do when there is a postal strike?

Cue puzzled looks among the Clegg camp, caught unawares and wondering what postal strike this was all about. Puzzlement, followed by dread, as the details of a parliamentary candidate selection contest from several years previously were laid out. A party election that had been disrupted by a postal strike. A party election in which it was ruled that if members had posted their votes in good time then they should not be disenfranchised by a postal strike outside their control. All ruled, adjudged, counted, done and dusted. Precedent was clear. Count those late votes.

The Clegg camp objected, demanding details and arguing over the reliability of one partisan verbal account. The Huhne camp teased every drop of self-confident assertion it could from that one late-night phone call. Party officials retreated to a room outside the technology quarantine to hunt out urgently by phone and email anyone involved in that Westminster selection they could find.

Piece by piece, fragmented recollections were slotted together into a clear picture. The caller had been right. The precedent was there. But would the Clegg camp agree to follow precedence to a Huhne victory?

Wanting to minimise any lasting damage to the party over who 'really' won the contest, the Returning Officer, party chief executive Chris Rennard, wanted an outcome there and then that all sides would publicly agree to. He feared the damage that a protracted appeals process would do to the party. So he drafted a statement to be released alongside the result:

> A postal strike resulted in disruption in the delivery of some postal ballot papers for the Liberal Democrat leadership election. The spirit behind our rules is very clear – that party members get to choose our leader and if a problem occurs with their voting which is wholly out of their control, they should not lose their democratic rights as a result.

> This is also the principle the party followed during a previous contest which was disrupted by a postal strike. As with that precedent, this count has been conducted on the basis of including all postal votes which were posted in time to be received if there had not been a postal strike.

Reading out his proposed statement, Rennard added:

> If anyone wishes to appeal this ruling, we will cancel today's press conference, issue a holding statement that the result is being appealed and convene a full hearing of the party's Appeals Panel tomorrow afternoon when its members have had time to gather from around the country for a meeting.

That twist of timing had Clegg's camp muttering, 'Don't they have phone numbers?', but they knew what was being done. The motivation may have been to protect the party, but Clegg was being set up. He either had to agree with the ruling or face a blizzard of damaging publicity about trying to disqualify the votes of genuine party members. He would be forever the tainted bad loser, facing angry questions from party members about why he did not want their vote to count.

After only the briefest of pauses, Nick Clegg reluctantly nodded and said, 'Let's count those last votes and get this over with.'

18 December 2007, Liberal Democrat press conference

'Look at the corners of their mouths,' muttered one party staffer to another as they waited in a crowded room for the announcement, laptops perched on their legs ready to roll out a series of website updates, financial appeals and emails as the winner was announced.

Supposedly a regiment of poker faces, the twitches in the corners of the Huhne team's mouths revealed what a well-sourced Sky journalist had already got running across TV screens: 'BREAKING NEWS: Huhne beats Clegg by 28 votes. 0.07 per cent margin makes him new Lib Dem leader.'

1 April 2008, *Daily Mail*

LIB DEM LOTHARIO: NICK CLEGG REVEALS HE HAS SLEPT WITH 'NO MORE THAN 30' WOMEN IN A TOE-CURLINGLY FRANK INTERVIEW…

The defeated candidate for Liberal Democrat leader, who lost to Chris Huhne by just twenty-eight votes and cultivates an image as a clean-cut family man, has given an extraordinary interview in which he discussed how many women he had slept with…

Conservative MP Ann Widdecombe said Mr Clegg's discussion of the number of his lovers was a 'pretty horrible contribution to a society where morals have just collapsed'…

A backbench Liberal Democrat MP said: 'If only he had got them all to join the party and vote for him, he would our leader now.' A close friend of Mr Huhne's added: 'Chris is far too busy as party leader to get mixed up in anything like this. He barely has time to see his wife Vicky, let alone other women.'

3 September 2009, *The Guardian*

COALITION CHAOS GRIPS THE LIBERAL DEMOCRATS

The frank admission by Liberal Democrat leader Chris Huhne that he would prefer a formal coalition in the event of a hung parliament has caused outrage in Liberal Democrat ranks.

Grassroots activists have long been suspicious of any moves by the party's MPs to secure 'bums on seats' in ministerial cars. Now many are talking of betrayal after Huhne, the activists' favourite in the leadership contest, admitted in a TV interview with Andrew Neil that he would lead his party into a coalition in a hung parliament.

Huhne's apparently unscripted admission came after Neil repeatedly asked him what he would do in a hung parliament in the midst of economic crisis. 'Would you really subject us all to an unstable government facing defeat every night in the voting lobbies, Mr Huhne? Or would you agree a coalition deal?' asked Neil. Eventually Huhne conceded that he was attracted by the stability offered by a formal coalition deal.

'This is madness and electoral suicide. Telling voters we'd enter coalition with another party just says there's no point in voting for us. You might as well vote Labour or Tory as that way you get to pick who you'd prefer in power rather than taking a lucky dip with us,' said one backbench Liberal Democrat MP. 'Doesn't he remember what a disaster it was talking about Cabinet seats in 1992?' added another.

The party's conference organisers now fear a protest during Mr Huhne's keynote speech in three weeks' time. Conference security is being tightened to stop angry activists bringing in car seats to wave in protest during the speech. Organisers fear, however, that members of the Social Liberal Forum will use wheelchairs to smuggle in the protest props. 'How can we say to a wheelchair user, "You look like you've got quite a lot of padding under your bum?",' lamented one conference steward.

23 September 2009, Chris Huhne's speech to Liberal Democrat conference

It is fantastic to see so many party members in the hall today. I know some of you were worried that there would not be enough room for us all and brought your own seats. I salute your resourcefulness.

And I appeal to your honesty. Voters have a right to know what we would do in a hung parliament. If you're out on the doorstep in Milton Keynes, Motherwell or Monmouth and a voter asks, you should give them a straight, honest answer.

You can't one moment be telling them how great the economic crisis is facing Britain, then the next tell them that in a hung parliament we would vote for uncertainty. For risk. For instability.

You can't one moment be telling them how great proportional representation is, then the next tell them that you don't like coalitions.

We must be true to our beliefs. Our belief in PR. Our belief that the swings between political extremes have damaged Britain. Our belief that we need a competent, stable government to steer us back to prosperity.

And our belief that after hard negotiations, if we can do a deal to provide a stable government, we will.

If you are on the doorstep saying that, you won't only be giving an honest answer. You'll also quite possibly be giving the same answer as you've given them for what you have done on your local council.

Talks followed by a joint administration is exactly what hundreds of our councillors have successfully achieved up and down the country.

We know how valuable having people in post is. Because of all those decisions that get made in between council meetings, without needing any vote.

Just as locally, so too in Whitehall we need Liberal Democrats in there every day. Watching every office. Tracking every decision.

Not sitting over the road in Parliament on the sidelines, waiting for a few of those decisions to come to Parliament for a vote…

… And that is why I have asked the party's Chief Executive to conduct a wide-ranging review of the organisational preparations we need to have in place for a viable coalition.

15 February 2010, agenda for 'Coalition preparations committee'

1. Apologies and minutes of last meeting
2. Update on party membership consultation over plans for coalition
3. Policy priorities update
4. Deficit reduction
5. Nuclear deterrent
6. Tuition fees
7. Civil nuclear power
8. Items for debate at spring conference
9. Organisational priorities update
10. Distribution of ministers across departments (see attached note from David Howarth)
11. Short Money funding for coalition partners (see attached note from Whips' Office on required rule changes)
12. Special advisers – numbers/allocations
13. Feedback from Liberal International/sister parties
14. Date of next meeting

15 April 2010, first TV election debate, twenty-three minutes in

David Cameron: You've heard Chris Huhne tonight say he's something different. Yet he also says he wants to form a coalition with either Gordon or myself. Well if it's just a choice between the two of us, look at us both and pick the one you want. What's the point in voting for the Liberal Democrats and not knowing who you'll get as Prime Minister when instead you can make the choice for yourself? Look at Gordon. Look at myself. Pick the one you really want.

Gordon Brown: I agree with David.

The #IAgreeWithDavid hashtag was used seventeen times on Twitter that night, of which eleven were from a Chicago chemical plumbing supplies firm.

1.15 a.m., 6 May 2010, BBC election night programme

David Dimbleby: As the latest rush of results confirm the accuracy of our exit poll, you can see the smiles in the back room where the numbers are being crunched. But, turning back to you, Peter Kellner, there isn't much smiling at Liberal Democrat HQ. They look set to win only forty-six seats – down sixteen on the 2005 result. Tell me, what's gone wrong for their new party leader, Chris Huhne?

Peter Kellner: David, as the exit poll predicted, this is turning out to be a bad night for the Liberal Democrats. Around one in four Liberal Democrat MPs are set to lose their seats. What our exit poll shows is that the party has been badly squeezed by both Labour and the Tories. It looks like that 'I agree with David' moment from the first TV debate – which we've heard endlessly in the last few weeks – had an impact. Voters decided to pick the big party they wanted rather than take a punt on the Liberal Democrats choosing a coalition partner for them. Huhne must now be deeply regretting talking openly about leading his party into coalition. The one saving grace for them is that we look set for a hung parliament, so Huhne may yet still get that coalition with Cameron.

7.03 a.m., 6 May 2010, BBC election night programme

David Dimbleby: Joining me now is the former Liberal Democrat leader David Steel. David, the mathematics of our new parliament are looking pretty clear, aren't they? It's going to have to be a Conservative–Liberal Democrat coalition?

DAVID STEEL: As someone whose heart is on the centre-left, it grieves me to say so but I think you are right. Huhne will have to sit down with Cameron for some serious negotiations.

DIMBLEBY: But wouldn't you prefer a rainbow coalition with Labour, David?

STEEL: It is an option that the Liberal Democrats would be wise to keep open until any talks with the Tories are concluded, but your viewers can do the maths just as well as you or I. With our tragic seat losses overnight, Labour and the Liberal Democrats together don't have enough seats for a centre-left coalition. You'd need what they call a 'rainbow coalition', including all sorts of very uncomfortable nationalist MPs from different parts of the United Kingdom. The maths might work for a single vote, maybe, but any agreement needs to work for the tenth vote, the fiftieth vote and the five-hundredth vote too.

17 May 2010, *Daily Mail*

CUTS FOR YOU, CASH FOR THEM:
TRUE BILL OF LIB DEM HYPOCRISY REVEALED

Sanctimonious Liberal Democrat MPs have been telling voters there is no alternative to big spending cuts. But behind the scenes they have been going on a spending spree on themselves, and many of their close friends are getting the benefit.

TWENTY-SIX new Special Adviser posts (Spads) have been created just for the Liberal Democrats – even though the party previously attacked Labour for increasing the number of Spads.

Despite taxpayers having to pay for the posts, taxpayers don't get a chance to apply for them as they have been rushed through, with friends and colleagues of Liberal Democrat MPs appointed instead.

£1.75 MILLION IN TAXPAYER FUNDING – the cheeky Liberals

have demanded they keep their £1,750,000 taxpayer cash which the party used to receive for being in opposition. Now Lib Dems say the 'Short Money' is still theirs – even though they're in government.

'The Liberal Democrats want money for being in government and money for being in opposition at the same time. Yet they have the cheek to tell us there isn't enough money for our public services,' said Labour MP Tom Watson.

8 June 2010, *The Times*

BRITAIN SET FOR SNAP ELECTORAL
REFORM REFERENDUM IN AUTUMN

The promised referendum on electoral reform could happen as early as September, after a dramatic confrontation between Deputy Prime Minister Chris Huhne and senior civil servants. According to people in the room, the Liberal Democrat leader threatened to 'send you lot to count the paperclips on a Coventry industrial estate'. The outburst came after civil servants claimed that the complexity of the legislation required for the alternative vote referendum meant it could not be held until May 2011 at the earliest.

Chris Huhne's spokesperson denied that the paperclips comment was made. But she confirmed that Mr Huhne had brought to the meeting a complete draft Bill 'written over the weekend' by Cambridge academic and Liberal Democrat MP David Howarth. 'Mr Huhne politely but firmly made the point that if David could write a good Bill in a weekend the civil service should be able to write one in a fortnight,' said the spokesperson.

11 June 2010, Mark Small, Liberal Democrat blogger

Chris Huhne currently seems obsessed with pushing through the AV referendum as quickly as possible. In many ways it is an odd obsession as AV has never been top of the Lib Dem PR love-in hit list. But Huhne is probably right to calculate that the sooner the vote, the higher the chance of victory.

We have already seen a raft of potentially controversial decisions on education, the environment and welfare reform, carefully timed to avoid public decision-making this year, clearing the way for an AV referendum vote before too many of the realities of compromise with the Tories hit.

Better then to rush and hold the vote during the government's honeymoon, however little time that gives the electoral reform campaign to organise.

30 December 2010, Chris Huhne's New Year message to party members

... This most momentous year in our party's history has also been one of the toughest. We can look back on what we have achieved this year with pride. Liberal Democrats back in government. Avoiding the economic disasters of Greece. Our electoral system reformed...

David Laws is leading the way to a more liberal education system, prioritising help for the most disadvantaged at the Department for Education. Nick Clegg is keeping Britain on an internationalist course as the Cabinet member for Europe. Vince Cable is deploying all of his expertise in development economics helping some of the poorest people in the world as the man in charge at DFID...

Next year will be even tougher. There are many debates yet to come and I know that tuition fees are top of the list. Together we made a clear commitment at our special conference in Birmingham when we voted to go into coalition. So if the Conservative Secretary of State for Business Ken Clarke insists on implementing the Browne Review, we will stick to our commitment in the coalition agreement. If a Conservative minister pushes ahead with a Conservative policy rather than abolishing fees, we will honour the coalition programme you voted for and abstain...

9 March 2011, BBC evening news headlines

Now more on our lead story, the government abandoning its tuition fees policy in the face of a backbench rebellion that was threatening to see its legislation defeated.

With both Conservative and Liberal Democrat rebels set to vote against the government, David Cameron decided this evening to pull the legislation to implement the Browne Report after he failed to persuade the Deputy Prime Minister Chris Huhne to back the legislation rather than abstain in the vote.

6 August 2012, *The Sun*

BYE BYE DEMOCRACY

Gloating Labour leader expects to be in 10 Downing Street by the weekend – AND WITHOUT AN ELECTION

Bacon sarnie-loving Labour leader Ed Miliband has been telling friends he will be installed as Prime Minister by the weekend. As Cameron and Huhne come to blows over House of Lords reform, the cheeky Labour leader is hoping that multimillionaire Liberal leader Chris Huhne will sneakily switch sides and make him Prime Minister. 'It's outrageous,' said Tory MP Peter Bone. 'Even my wife knows that the Liberals can't just plant whoever they like in Downing Street.'

7 August 2012, *The Times*

GOVERNMENT ON VERGE OF COLLAPSE OVER LORDS REFORM

Emergency all-night talks between the Conservatives and Liberal Democrats to rescue the government from collapse over House of Lords reform ended without agreement.

The simmering parliamentary row over the timetabling of the House of Lords Reform Bill broke out into a full-scale political crisis earlier this month after Lib Dem leader Chris Huhne warned Cameron that he would use his party conference speech to announce a withdrawal from government unless Cameron whipped his MPs into supporting a parliamentary timetable for Lords reform. With many Tory rebels on record opposing the measure, Cameron has been at pains to point out that he cannot deliver what Huhne wants – and that if Huhne does not back down, the government will fall.

Some Conservatives have been sounding out right-wing Liberal Democrat MPs to see if a coup against Huhne for his high-stakes gamble could be encouraged. 'If the Queen asked Nick Clegg to become her Deputy Prime Minister, would he really say no?' speculated one Downing Street source.

However, Tories fear that Chris Huhne is counting on remaining as Deputy Prime Minister regardless of who is Prime Minister. 'He can remain Deputy Prime Minister regardless of who is in 10 Downing Street,' said one Tory constitutional expert. 'This could be the end for Cameron if he cannot make a deal.'

9 August 2012, *The Guardian*

LORDS REFERENDUM DEAL SAVES COALITION

A dramatic deal between Prime Minister David Cameron and Deputy Prime Minister Chris Huhne has saved the government from collapse.

With the Conservatives and Lib Dems at loggerheads over House of Lords reform, the deal will see the existing Lords Reform Bill mothballed. In return for this concession to Cameron, Huhne has secured agreement for a referendum on the subject on the same day as the next general election.

Although many Conservative backbench MPs are expected to rebel over the referendum, the Liberal Democrats are confident that Labour support will ensure the referendum legislation is passed quickly.

In return, Chris Huhne has agreed to make a public commitment not to oust the Prime Minister before the general election. This is expected to come in a speech to party activists on Saturday, securing David Cameron in 10 Downing Street until 2015.

The legislation for the referendum will be a near carbon copy of the AV referendum Bill, *The Guardian* understands, which was rushed through Parliament in just ninety-six hours in 2010. 'Last time we left nearly all the details to statutory instruments or the Electoral Commission, so there isn't much to change. Pretty much all we need do is delete "the alternative vote" and insert "an elected House of Lords",' said one Lib Dem source close to the talks.

24 May 2014, Mark Small, Liberal Democrat blogger

DIVISION AMONG PLOTTERS SET TO SAVE HUHNE

Brace yourselves. The grim local election results already in make it an odds-on certainty that tomorrow's European election count will see the number of Liberal Democrat MEPs slashed to a tiny handful.

In most parties, most of the time, such a bad result a year out from a general election would trigger a wave of soul-searching about whether to dump the leader and install a fresh face in time for the general election.

There is no shortage of would-be successors circling around Chris Huhne. Friends of Vince Cable (still bitter about the way Huhne blocked Cameron's offer of BIS, switching him into a more peripheral post at DFID), Nick Clegg (still bitter about how Huhne 'stole' the leadership election) and Tim Farron (still bitter about his exclusion from government) have all been falling over themselves to helpfully point out stories which paint their would-be saviour in the best light.

But the very number of the plotters is their weakness. There is too much rivalry between them for unity – and without unity there will be no coup.

They all know the lessons of Michael Heseltine, orchestrating a coup to oust Margaret Thatcher and in so doing also dooming himself to failure in his bid to be her successor.

26 May 2014, Mark Small, Liberal Democrat blogger

ESCHER POLLING WILL SAVE HUHNE'S LEADERSHIP

Leaked Liberal Democrat polls are like London buses of yore. You wait ages for one to come along and then a whole batch come at once, although in the case of the polls they are all trying to take the party in different directions under different drivers.

Or is it that they're like an Escher optical illusion? Because if the leaked polls are to be believed, Cable polls better than Clegg, who polls better than Farron, who polls better than Huhne ... who polls better than Cable.

It is quite fun to read the passive-aggressive warnings from the different polling companies about how they didn't use their normal methodology for each poll (though they took the money to do the polls anyway). But also quite boring once you've read the first few.

All that really matters is to know that with confusing poll numbers all round, there is no momentum for a coup.

7 May 2015, *The Guardian*

HOUSE OF LORDS REFORM SET TO BE VOTED THROUGH

Political reformers are starting to celebrate after the exit poll which got the general election result right also showed House of Lords reform being voted through by 57 per cent to 43 per cent in the referendum held alongside the general election.

Counting of the votes is not due to start until Monday but the clear margin shown in the exit polls means that even the 'No' camp are conceding defeat. Victory for Lords reform would be a consolation for Liberal Democrats as the party faces up to the worst election result in its history.

7 May 2015, *Daily Telegraph*

LIB DEMS LOSE A THIRD OF THEIR SEATS – BUT IT WOULD HAVE BEEN EVEN WORSE WITHOUT AV

Britain's controversial new voting system has saved the Liberal Democrats from disaster. Although Chris Huhne's party lost a third of its seats in the general election, the rump of thirty-one MPs would have been even smaller without the preferential voting system used for the first time.

Among the Liberal Democrat MPs AV saved from defeat is Nick Clegg. Re-elected by a slim margin after the transfers of the Conservative candidate in his Sheffield constituency, his friends say he is already eyeing up a leadership challenge to Huhne.

Leaving his count with his wife, Vicky Pryce, the current Liberal

Democrat leader Mr Huhne – re-elected with a reduced majority – told waiting reporters that he was not rushing to make any decisions about his or his party's future.

One close friend of Clegg said last night, 'Huhne has halved the parliamentary party over two elections. We need a new leader who will double it.'

Chapter 14

What if George Osborne had resigned as shadow Chancellor in 2008?

Alexander Larman

In the version of the story that was leaked to the papers the next day, it was said that it was hard to tell who had been more affected, David Cameron or George Osborne. Gossipy reports circulated that the shadow Chancellor had been near-hysterical, pleading with the Leader of the Opposition to be forgiven for what he called 'a bloody stupid mistake', but it made little difference. Cameron, although in despair at what he had to do, made it clear in an emotional thirty-minute conversation with erstwhile friends and colleagues that there was no other option than to ask for Osborne's resignation from the shadow Cabinet.

Standing by the window in his office in Conservative HQ, Cameron was barely able to look at the distraught man sitting opposite him.

> They'll crucify us otherwise, George. Surely you can see that? This story has all the hallmarks of the bad old days – same old Tories, sucking up to wealth and power, and a bucketload of sleaze as well. And Mandelson, of all people! I'm sorry, but you're going to have to go.

Osborne, blinking back tears, looked at Cameron, who seemed to be shaking slightly at the enormity of what he was saying. 'If you do this … this is the end of everything we've started. The whole modernisation project. Nobody will carry it on without me.'

Cameron had considered this carefully, and had taken soundings from his closest confidants over the previous days, all the while waiting for the scandal to abate. Andy Coulson, his omniscient Communications Director and link to both Fleet Street and the common man, had counselled against the removal of Osborne, arguing that the media storm over what had happened would die down in a matter of days. His advice was tinged with a touch of bias, given that Osborne had been responsible for hiring him in 2007. Steve Hilton, Cameron's shoe-eschewing guru, offered a shrug and the comment, 'If George goes, he goes. Nobody's going to mourn.' And the straight-talking Lynton Crosby, responsible for Boris Johnson's surprise mayoral election earlier in 2008, was blunter altogether: 'He fucked up. Now show that you're a leader in waiting and can him. Nobody's going to give a cat's ass about friendships or loyalty or any of that sentimental bullshit. You're here to win, not to hold reunion meetings of the Bullingdon Club.'

Cameron, instinctively uncomfortable with sackings and major reshuffles, continued to hope that there was another solution. Osborne had telephoned him on the evening before the first big story broke to discuss possible ways of ameliorating the situation.

'Did you do anything illegal?'

'No. Absolutely not.'

'The press are claiming that you tried to solicit a donation.'

'That's untrue. I'm drafting a statement to say that that's anything but the case.'

'It looks bad, George. Taking money from a foreign businessman ... it's the worst sort of compromising position. Opens us up to all sorts of questions about "undue influence" and "cash for access". Blair and Labour were crucified for it, and, Christ, remember Al-Fayed and his brown envelopes? It finished us last time round.'

There had then been an awkward pause. Both men knew what was being left unspoken. It was Osborne who was the first to break it.

'If you think that I should offer my resignation...?'

Cameron spoke to him sharply, as if insulted. 'Did you do anything wrong?'

'Again, absolutely not.'

A sigh down the telephone, whether of satisfaction or exhaustion.

'Good. We'll just have to brazen it out. People don't care about tittle-tattle. There are more important matters at hand, like the recession and Brown's leadership. This will be a 24-hour saga, at best.'

Osborne, by nature a less optimistic man than Cameron, chuckled grimly. 'Well, Dave, I hope you're right.'

A matter of days later, it became all too clear that he had not been. As Osborne prepared to write his resignation letter, he reflected bitterly and with previously unlooked-for self-criticism about how a trip to Corfu had spectacularly derailed not just his political career, but the resurgent fortunes of the entire Conservative Party.

~

Two months before, in August 2008, things had been very different. The strong local election results of May had chimed with a growing sense that after 'the election that never was' of the previous autumn, Cameron and Osborne's message of compassionate Conservatism was finally beginning to connect with a public who had consistently rejected the Tories for over a decade. Boris's victory had been the icing on the cake, of course, but Boris was a maverick, a celebrity politician who could probably have stood for the BNP and had a decent chance of winning the mayoral election. A much greater degree of comfort lay in the 22-point lead in the polls, along with Gordon Brown's disastrous ratings. As Cameron easily bested him at Prime Minister's Questions week after week, it seemed possible, for the first time since 1997, that the two parties would switch places in the House. The recession was horrific, of course, but the sense lingered that the principles of austerity and living within one's means were getting through to voters, whereas Brown's hotchpotch of trying to be all things to all men (save his predecessor) was failing miserably. All seemed to be going about as well as could be expected.

The question that Osborne was asked most in his subsequent interviews was: 'Why did you ever go to Corfu?' His answer, delivered with varying amounts of clarity and candour, was that he went as a private individual to a friend's summer party. That the friend was the billionaire financier Nathaniel Rothschild, scion of the legendary banking industry, meant that there were weightier matters to be enjoyed than a few dips in the pool and copious amounts of cava. The guest list was an impressive one – few were invited who weren't millionaires, leading Osborne privately to joke that he felt like the poor relation – but the figure who the shadow Chancellor was keenest to meet was Peter Mandelson, then semi-exiled to Brussels in the role of European Commissioner.

Mandelson, who had recently engaged in a much-publicised spat with the French President Nicholas Sarkozy about subsidies for European farmers, was a long-standing friend of Rothschild, despite the apparent political differences between the two; his interest in wealth and power, and those who possessed both, normally trumped any ideological concerns he may have had. As Blair's *consigliere* and the spiritual founder of New Labour, he was impressive and persuasive, even as he revelled in his nickname 'the Prince of Darkness'. But it was a different political landscape that had seen him cast out of the inner circles of power, another well-compensated former politician on the EU gravy train.

Over dinner one evening at a nearby restaurant, the Taverna Agni, Mandelson and Osborne sat next to one another. Although the two knew each other by reputation, actual meetings between them had been relatively fleeting, which meant that this was the first chance that both men had had to compare notes on the political situation of the day. Unsurprisingly, the topic of interest that concerned both was Brown. Osborne, who had come to loathe the Prime Minister, listened intently as Mandelson offered a wine-fuelled demolition of Brown's character, ability to govern and general competence; as he later marvelled to his friends, 'I'd known that Mandy hated him, but I'd never quite imagined how much.'

As for 'the Prince', he delighted in the chance to impress the younger man with a worldly show of sophistication and authority. While taking care never to say anything overtly disloyal about the Labour Party, he was unafraid to speak candidly, and vigorously, about the man whom he viewed as his great political nemesis. He believed that Brown would not hold an election before 2010, claiming he was too frightened to go to the country before 'the last possible day that the law allows'. Many of Mandelson's friends had become weary of his set-piece tirades, which had been delivered at the end of the evening in many of London's grandest townhouses, but Osborne, hearing it for the first time, was an enthralled and suitably appreciative listener. The evening ended with handshakes and a general sense of perspectives being shared; Mandelson let it be known that he considered Osborne 'possibly the intellectual equal of anyone in politics today'. From him, that was high praise.

Mandelson was then staying on the yacht of the aluminium magnate, the billionaire oligarch Oleg Deripaska, as Rothschild's house was full; even the super-wealthy had limited bed space. Rothschild invited Osborne onto it the following day, and, in anticipation of the meeting being a worthwhile one, had invited his friend, the Conservatives' fundraiser Andrew Feldman. The opulent setting was one that Feldman and Mandelson seemed more comfortable with than Osborne, who found it surprisingly difficult to converse with Deripaska. In an attempt to bring some levity to the day, he suggested, jocularly, that the Russian might see his way to channelling some money towards the Conservatives' funds. It was meant merely as a joke, but Rothschild and Feldman both overheard the remark.

Later, Rothschild referred back to the conversation with Feldman. 'If you did want Oleg to donate to the party, you'd have to do it through the proper channels. He has British interests, of course, and he'd have to divert any funds through them. What do you say?'

Feldman, a canny and successful man who had never knowingly done anything without care, smiled. 'I'd have to discuss it with Dave, of course. But from my own perspective, I think that it would be a wonderful opportunity for everyone. And I know that George would be thrilled.'

Those words – so fleeting, so poisonous – would represent the basis on which Osborne would be forced from office.

~

No one quite knew how it was that the *Sunday Times* received information linking Mandelson and Deripaska, but a story appeared a week after the party claiming that Mandelson had twice acted to cut European aluminium import duties, and that Deripaska's company Rusal, the world's largest producer of aluminium, was one of the main beneficiaries. He was forced onto Sky News to claim that Deripaska 'has never asked for any favours, I have never given him any favours, and that is what the European Commission in their examination of the issue has very firmly put on record'. As Mandelson was no longer a frontbench politician, the story had little traction and soon faded away, but he was furious, believing that, of all those present, the only people who had had any desire to see him humiliated were Osborne and Feldman. Privately, he joked to friends, 'That's the last time I trust a Tory.' As so often with Mandelson's jokes, there was little humour in them.

The matter would probably have ended there had it not been for Brown's decision to offer Mandelson a position in the Cabinet in late September, as Minister without Portfolio. This was greeted with disbelief and hilarity – as one Tory MP said, 'Oh, to have been a fly on the wall at that meeting!' – but Osborne, ever the tactician, saw an easy way in which he could secure a swift propaganda victory that would discomfit Labour. Thus, he let sympathetic journalists at the *Telegraph* know the substance of the conversation he had had with Mandelson in August, claiming that he 'dripped pure poison into my ear' about the Prime Minister, and publicly followed it with a BBC interview in which he claimed, 'It was very surprising to hear him say that he is joined at the hip with Gordon Brown.'

Osborne's revelations had the desired effect. The 'pure poison' line captured writers' imagination, and headlines accordingly appeared castigating Brown's judgement and what seemed like a desperate and cynical move on his part. Osborne purred with satisfaction at a job well done, even as Mandelson made a statement blustering that what had happened was 'straight out of a dirty tricks department' – *et tu, Mandy*? – and made vague threats about revealing his own side of the conversation, claiming that 'we talked as much about his colleagues and the state of the Tory Party'. But Mandelson knew that Osborne's unflattering remarks about figures on the right of his own party were unlikely to cause him any damage were they to be leaked. Mandelson's humiliation was compounded by some remarks of Cameron's, in which he joked that 'a Mandelson is a period of time between a minister being created and his criticising the Prime Minister', and that 'everyone who knows Peter Mandelson, who's bumped into him recently, knows that he doesn't always have great things to say about the Prime Minister ... it beggars belief that this is going to be a government that isn't dysfunctional and disunified.'

Mandelson was summoned to see Brown for a dressing-down. Observers noted that he left No. 10 'pale and tight-lipped', climbing straight into his ministerial car and not surfacing publicly for the rest of the day. Some speculated that he could be seen weeping. It was, perhaps, no coincidence that the next day he was seen lunching with his erstwhile host Rothschild at Scott's in Mayfair. Both men drank sparkling water and ate lemon sole. An onlooker reported that Mandelson looked, by turns, grim and imploring at the beginning of the meal, 'but a good deal happier at the end'. His revenge was in motion.

~

The letter from Nathaniel Rothschild that appeared in *The Times* on 21 October 2008 was terse. Beginning with a reference to how the paper and the *Sunday Times* 'has made much out of what may or may not have happened at a private gathering of my friends', Rothschild wrote, 'I thought I should make the following observations', focusing on the accusation that Osborne 'found the opportunity of meeting with Mr Deripaska so good that he invited the Conservatives' fundraiser Andrew Feldman, who was staying nearby, to accompany him onto Mr Deripaska's boat to solicit a donation'. He proceeded to sign Osborne's death warrant by noting that 'since Mr Deripaska is not a British citizen, it was suggested by Mr Feldman, in a subsequent conversation at which Mr Deripaska was not present, that the donation was "channelled" through one of Mr Deripaska's British companies. Mr Deripaska declined to make any donation.' Not only did Rothschild appear to suggest that Osborne was corrupt, but he also hinted that he was incompetent as well. When an oligarch is able to take the moral high ground, a problem had presented itself.

Rothschild's loftily stated reason for sending the letter was 'because it turns out that your obsession with Mr Mandelson is trivial in light of Mr Osborne's actions. I also think it ill behoves all political parties to try and make capital at the expense of another in such circumstances.' He sniffily concluded: 'Perhaps in future it would be better if all involved accepted the age-old adage that private parties are just that.' Rothschild did not need to mention Mandelson's involvement, any more than he needed to refer to the business interests that he and Deripaska shared in Montenegro, including a plan that the two men had to turn the unprepossessing location of the crumbling port of Tivat into 'the new Monaco', a haven for the super-wealthy that had a suitably enlightened attitude towards tax affairs. Deripaska, whose multi-billion fortune had suffered in the recent global crash, was especially keen to find an impeccably lucrative source of investment, and Rothschild, if faced between loyalty to friends and to business partners, always chose the latter. Valuing discretion as they did, any unwanted attention that could be directed towards their entirely legal activities needed to be diverted, and quickly. And who better to divert it than the shadow Chancellor?

At first, after Cameron had received Osborne's assurances that there was no truth to the allegations, the Conservatives defended themselves vigorously from any claims of impropriety, describing Rothschild's claims as 'completely untrue', stating that 'the Conservative Party has neither sought nor received any donations from Mr Deripaska nor any of his companies'. Rothschild was fingered as the go-between, and it was stated that 'in a conversation on 18 September, Mr Rothschild suggested to Andrew Feldman that Mr Deripaska wanted to make a donation to the party through one of his British companies. The offer was not taken up.' If the aim behind this was to kill the story and intimidate Rothschild, it failed entirely. The financier, who had once been considered one of the Conservative Party's most skilled fundraisers, hinted that he would go to court to prove that Osborne had wished to explore legal grounds on which he might solicit a donation from Deripaska, and that, while allowing that Osborne had not directly engaged in such a solicitation, he had been an enthusiastic supporter of the idea. He may have been bluffing but, then again, the pockets of his Savile Row suits were famously deep.

Faced with potential ruin, Osborne took refuge in statements that could not be disproved, claiming 'we did not ask for any money, we did not receive any'. This, as most political commentators noted, did not amount to the same thing as denying Rothschild's claims in full. Privately, the shadow Chancellor was mystified by his former friend's behaviour. 'Does he want me to be forced out of my job?' he asked a confidant. It seemed ludicrous that a man whose mother had put money towards Osborne's office for years would now want to see him forced out of the shadow Cabinet, but, as the confidant suggested, 'Perhaps he really is doing all this out of a point of principle – he clearly feels deeply annoyed that his hospitality has been, as he sees it, abused.'

Even in these dark moments, Osborne couldn't resist a moment of dark humour. 'Next time I go to Corfu, I'd better go with Thomas Cook.'

~

The scandal continued into a second, and a third, and a fourth day. Brown described the saga at PMQs as 'very serious indeed', going so far as to say, 'I hope that it is investigated by the authorities.' It soon became known that Osborne had met Deripaska four times over the course of a weekend, rather than the single encounter that he had implied. Even allowing for the small circles that both men moved in, this looked less like coincidence and more like purpose. Hitherto-silent Conservative grandees let it be known that Osborne had been 'ill-advised' to leak Mandelson's comments, and off-the-record briefings suggested that Cameron was considering his friend's position carefully.

Finally, the end arrived on Monday 26 October. An attempt of sorts to broker a truce with Rothschild at the end of the previous week had failed, to Osborne's chagrin; it had initially seemed that he might be persuaded to publish a statement ending the matter, but he demanded in return that Deripaska be allowed to absolve himself from any involvement in the affair. It was felt that this was unacceptable, and that politicians should not be held to ransom by billionaires. It was perhaps no coincidence that the *Telegraph* had run a long story exploring Deripaska's and Rothschild's conjoined business interests that Saturday, nor that the *Sunday Times* had published a signed witness statement from Bill Clinton's former adviser James Goodwin, who had also been present on the yacht, testifying to Osborne soliciting the donation. The knife was twisted by Goodwin's description of his observing behaviour 'which to me seemed unbecoming of one who would wish to take public office'. The *News of the World* ran an interview with Nathalie Rowe, in which she described a series of well-worn stories about her involvement with Osborne nearly two decades before. Nothing revelatory was said, but the cumulative effect was a fatal one. As the *Mirror* screamed on Monday: 'OSBORNE MUST GO'. By 5 p.m. that day, their wish had come true.

~

Originally, Osborne hoped that he might be demoted to another role in the shadow Cabinet, and then returned to the Chancellorship at the next reshuffle. Cameron considered this possibility, but in the end it was Osborne's protégé Coulson who vetoed it. 'It'll be used against us for ever. Now that George is gone, he's gone, at least until we get into office. Then you'll have more leeway.' The reshuffle that took place was prompted by necessity, and so Cameron had little heart to act in any decisive manner. William Hague refused the job, content with his role as shadow Foreign Secretary, and, after rejecting the proposed idea of Theresa May as shadow Chancellor, he appointed Philip Hammond, the former shadow Chief Secretary to the Treasury. Hammond was a safe, if rather colourless, politician who lacked Osborne's flair for gamesmanship and tactics, but, as Cameron reasoned, no period of government could include more than one shadow Chancellor who could become the centre of attention.

For the first couple of months, there was approval that Cameron had acted ruthlessly and in the interests of party over friendship. An editorial in *The Times* noted that 'By sacrificing one of his closest allies in politics, David Cameron has shown that he will stop at nothing to lead the Conservatives to victory', and Hammond's drier, more analytical style of approach saw him aptly suited to shadow Chancellor Alistair Darling, although the apparent lack of dissent between the two about matters economic meant that Hammond was much mocked by sketchwriters for his oft-repeated phrase, 'I agree with Alistair.'

Yet, by the start of 2009, the Tories' apparently impregnable lead in the polls was being cut. From routinely leading Labour by twenty-odd points, they now led by a mere ten or twelve. Brown's personal rating trailed Cameron by a huge factor – there was nothing that could be done about that – but Darling's widely praised economic policies, and the Tories' reluctance to better them, meant that Labour first equalled the Conservatives' record for economic competence again, and then, gradually, took a slender lead. A predicted meltdown at the 2009 local elections did not occur, with Labour taking a respectable second place with 32 per cent of the vote, only a shade behind the Tories on 35 per cent. The Liberal Democrats also had a surprisingly strong showing, mustering 28 per cent; their leader Nick Clegg crowed, 'We are the future now.' Blind optimism, maybe, but savvier commentators noted the echo of Cameron's jibe at Blair in his first ever PMQs that 'you were the future once'; less than four years on, things seemed very different.

The bad luck continued. By-elections that had been written off as easy Conservative victories were either much closer – as in the narrow 271-vote majority that the young Chloe Smith obtained in Norwich North – or lost altogether. Some muttered that Osborne, who had been regarded as a useful by-election strategist, was missed, and doubt was cast about Cameron's wisdom in having sacked him 'over nothing more than tittle-tattle and media innuendo'. Cameron, mourning the death of his eldest son Ivan, seemed in little mood to notice, or care.

The expenses scandal that broke in May 2009 engulfed both parties, and Cameron attracted praise for his sure handling of it with the Conservatives. Yet it was noted that he seemed curiously hesitant at attacking Labour for their involvement in it, missing the opportunity to do real damage to the government. Perhaps it was because he felt that the gentlemanly thing to do was to maintain a dignified silence. This did not stop the media, who tore into every party with gusto, regardless of their normal affiliation. Cameron, many muttered, was losing the urge to fight. What he needed was a number two who really had the killer spirit, who was unafraid to go in for off-the-record briefings and tactical masterstrokes. The 38-year-old backbencher for Tatton certainly had been that man, but now he languished in the wilderness. His name was occasionally mentioned with a mixture of sorrow and regret at the Carlton Club. 'Good man. Savvy.

But really awful judgement ... hanging around with Mandelson and oligarchs like Deripaska ... not what the new Conservatives are all about.'

~

The relationship between the two old friends had suffered as well. When Osborne was received for a weekend stay at Cameron's house in Oxfordshire in early February 2009, a grim, tense affair unlike the convivial get-togethers they had enjoyed the previous year, there had been oblique discussions about the role that Osborne might play in the next election campaign. It was accepted that he could not have a formal position, but could instead become part of a 'brains trust' that would also encompass Coulson, Hilton, Oliver Letwin and various others. Lynton Crosby was approached, but declined on the grounds that he was 'too busy' to take part. Rumours circulated that the fee he was offered was too low. Osborne, with reluctance, accepted, wooed by the belief that, following a victory in 2010, it would be a 'way back'. He felt that the Chancellor brief was unlikely to be his initially, but he privately expressed an interest in the Education position. If nothing else, it was a Cabinet post.

Preparations for the election took place throughout the second half of 2009, with a well-received conference speech by Cameron that sought to strengthen the Conservatives' compassionate credentials, focusing on the theme of the 'big society'. Osborne had always been sceptical of it, preferring a more focused strategy that could easily be explained to voters on the doorstep, but, to his chagrin, he now found that he was merely one voice among many, and a discredited one at that. He offered to work with Hammond on the financial aspects of the manifesto, but was politely snubbed. Finding his non-role frustrating and demeaning, he offered Cameron a choice: give me a proper position, or I'll walk away. Cameron, unable to bring Osborne back into the shadow Cabinet, reluctantly called his bluff, and his erstwhile ally returned to Tatton at the beginning of 2010. Always a diligent constituency MP, he now threw himself into local activities with a grim zeal that prompted some to wonder why, exactly, he was so interested in projects that seemed more fitting to the local council. He couldn't exactly tell them the truth: 'Because I'm bored.'

At last, Brown called the election, which Osborne followed with the enthusiasm of an armchair strategist. His friends despaired that he appeared to be putting on weight, enjoying junk food and not taking the morning runs that he had specialised in while in office. The gap between Labour and the Conservatives had stabilised at around six points in the Tories' favour, which, as Osborne knew, was not enough to give them a majority, especially given the number of seats that they would have to win. If a hung parliament came about, it seemed likely that a Lib Dem party led by Clegg would side with the Tories, but if Chris Huhne or (heaven forbid) Vince Cable were to take the leadership after a disappointing result, it was much more likely that they would support Labour. Osborne occasionally wondered about whether to intercede once again, and then remembered how he had been treated. Lucrative offers of directorships and consultancies reached him almost daily. He privately decided to fight and win his third election, and then stand down by 2015, regardless of what the national result was.

After a series of poorly received leadership debates, in which the challenger Clegg shone, Brown seemed bored and Cameron gave an impression of faint inexperience, the election was held on Thursday 6 May 2010. The Tories eventually took 284 seats, with Labour on 270. The Liberal Democrats did slightly less well than in 2005, retaining fifty-seven out of their sixty-two MPs, and there was the unexpected setback that two of the Orange Bookers, Danny Alexander and David Laws, lost their seats in Inverness and Yeovil respectively. Alexander was defeated by a strong local SNP candidate, Drew Hendry, and Laws, who had recently been outed both as gay and as claiming over £40,000 in second-home expenses, bore the brunt of an expertly vicious Conservative campaign that saw their candidate take Paddy Ashdown's old seat. In his concession speech, Laws, clearly close to tears, announced that 'It was the best of times ... it was the worst of times'. Nonetheless, his party remained a potent ally for whoever wanted to form a government.

Coalition beckoned, but between who? The Conservatives put together a negotiating team including Hammond, Letwin, Hague and Ed Llewellyn. Labour, meanwhile, produced Mandelson, Harriet Harman,

Ed Miliband and Ed Balls. They then waited until Monday 10 May, when Clegg, now devoid of his two closest ideological allies in the party, was joined in coalition talks by Huhne, Andrew Stunell and Paddy Ashdown, all of whom expressed broad sympathy for a Labour–Liberal alliance; Ashdown, in particular, saw this as a chance to right the perceived wrong that had seen Blair reject the chance of a broad coalition in 1997. They met the Conservative team on Monday evening, but, as one unnamed participant in the talks said, 'There didn't really seem to be much interest from the Tories – they seemed to think that it was their right to rule, because they had more seats, and didn't offer anything tangible.' Opening talks with Labour the next day proved a far more amenable exercise. The Lib Dems were offered guaranteed AV, six places in the Cabinet, a veto on any increase in tuition fees and more besides. Ashdown was heard to remark, with something like astonishment, 'It's as if we won the election, and they're doing their best to suck up to us.'

Brown remained an unpopular figure, and Cameron elicited some sympathy for his public argument that the party that had won the largest number of votes should be given a chance to form a minority government. At last, under pressure from Mandelson, a compromise was reached. Brown would pre-announce his resignation no later than 2012 ('after the Olympics, I think'), thereby removing the possibility of his attempting to fight another election. As Prime Minister until then, he would be free to appoint his own Cabinet, bar the six Lib Dem seats, and generally govern with more freedom than he had been allowed since 2007. There was an argument about whether Balls or Cable would serve as his Chancellor – the one moment at which negotiations looked as if they might founder – but eventually a compromise was reached in which Cable became Business Secretary and Balls Chancellor. The situation, as Brown said, could always be reviewed in the future.

When the coalition negotiations came to an end, Cameron, a defeated man, announced his resignation on live TV. His speech was, as with everything that he said publicly, gracious and well judged. Some were surprised that he paid tribute to 'my old friend, George Osborne, without whom I doubt that we would have got nearly as far as we did'. It had become routine for journalists and pundits to blame Osborne for many of the woes and tribulations the Tories had experienced; 'yachtgate' had become sniggering shorthand for the sudden decline in Conservative fortunes from 2008 onwards. But Cameron, wishing to be fair to his old friend, did not engage in recriminations or blame. He took a lesson from his predecessor Michael Howard and remained as leader until the party conference in the autumn, grimly sledging away at PMQs as a relieved Labour barracked him week after week. In response to the question 'Who's your choice of successor?', he prepared the usual slick sound bites, but he knew that the new MP for Orpington – a familiar blond Wodehousian figure whose brother Jo had prized family above career and triggered a by-election in his seat shortly after his victory so that the elder Johnson might return to the Commons – was so widely believed to be the party's real choice that it was all he could do to grin and shrug. Such was his successor's popularity that the little matter that he was already Mayor of London – which would have stymied anyone else's chances – simply seemed to enhance his popularity; as he had said before, 'My policy is pro-cake and pro-eating it.'

Shortly after he was elected leader, easily beating Theresa May into second place, Boris rang Osborne 'for a good pow-wow'. Osborne, by then engaged in a lucrative second career in energy investment, was surprised but not displeased to hear from his Bullingdon Club compadre, not least because a good deal of the conversation revolved around the failings of 'Dave', who was described as being 'the only man alive who couldn't kick a football through an open goal with nobody on the pitch'. Boris, almost as a formality, asked Osborne whether he would be interested in returning to frontbench politics, but he demurred, citing family and other commitments. At the end of a warm but largely token conversation, Boris asked Osborne if he had any regrets about his time in politics. He was met with a sigh, then a weary chuckle.

'Meeting Peter Mandelson.'

~

And what of the Dark Lord? It was rumoured that the price for his machinations was originally to be either Deputy Prime Minister or Home

Secretary, the roles that his grandfather Herbert Morrison had once held. Brown, adopting something of a scorched-earth policy with his appointments, would have made him his deputy – 'After all, he's been doing that job in all but name with Tony and me for years' – but Clegg and, more authoritatively, Cable, vetoed the appointment, arguing that, 'Peter's not a people person, and the coalition has to last.' So another role had to be found for him, both as a reward and as a means of keeping him at arm's length. Something involving a large amount of remuneration, a great deal of travel – on yachts, and otherwise – and with a certain amount of international status to it. Eventually, after a long meeting to discuss the Peter Problem, Brown was seen to smile with what seemed to onlookers like genuine glee.

'I've got it. It's our turn next year to nominate the head of the IMF. He'd be perfect.'

Balls – no great admirer of Mandelson – was the first to raise an eyebrow. 'But he isn't an economist, doesn't have any record in banking and has never served as a finance minister. He's uniquely unqualified for the role.'

Brown's smirk remained undiminished. 'I know. But there'll be people around him who know what to do. And it keeps him out of our hair. And that, frankly, makes it all worth it.'

When a friendly source leaked the news to Mandelson, he was seen to smirk, sip a glass of very expensive Burgundy, and quip, 'So being unpopular has its rewards after all, then.' These rewards – which included an annual salary of around £400,000 a year – more than made up for any fleeting disappointment that he would not, in fact, be emulating his grandfather. And so, as he headed off into the sunset in first-class luxury, he wondered where his first stop for a holiday that year would be. Tivat, he reflected, was supposed to be very nice these days, and it would be good to see his old friend Rothschild. After all, they had a great deal to catch up on.

Chapter 15

What if the Conservatives had won an overall majority in 2010?

Julian Huppert and Tom King

It's the afternoon of 8 May 2015.

The skies are overcast, in contrast to the sunny weather of the previous day.

But even torrential rain can't wipe the smiles beaming from the faces of the two men standing in front of the famous black door of 10 Downing Street.

Each man looks fresh, optimistic and excited, although neither has slept much for two days. The exhaustion of a long general election campaign is visibly forgotten.

As camera shutters click incessantly, one of the men begins to speak.

> Today is the day when Britain turns the page. We have had five years of punitive and unnecessary pain at the hands of a government that never represented the majority of its people.
>
> I am delighted that we have successfully negotiated a programme for government with Ed Miliband and the Labour Party. This is a chance to show once and for all that coalition government can work, and work well, in the interests of the whole country.
>
> Now, for the first time in generations, the British people will have a truly representative government. The two parties we represent account for more than 50 per cent of the popular vote. This is the first time a British government has had an absolute majority since 1931.
>
> From the perspective of the Liberal Democrats, it is an indictment of our outdated voting system that the 29 per cent of the vote that we

secured is in no way reflected in the number of seats we have in the House of Commons.

The need for political reform on an unprecedented scale is surely now obvious to everyone. We are the far smaller parliamentary party despite having won more votes than our coalition partner.

But we are ambitious to change much more than the constitution. Labour and the Liberal Democrats agree on many issues that are fundamental to Britain's interests.

The previous government put its ideological urge to shrink the state before our society's future. But we believe that investing in Britain's future is the right thing to do. So we have agreed an initial programme that will secure and improve our public services, especially our schools and our NHS.

Without creating risky deficits, we can responsibly fund projects that will help us rebalance and reinvigorate our economy. Ed and I both represent seats in the north of England and we are going to make this government the least London-centric in living memory.

Unlike the Conservative Party, which has turned its back on the environment, Ed and I are both convinced that climate change is the biggest threat facing the world today. We will be relentless in our efforts, both in terms of mitigating climate change and in preparing for its impact.

We will govern for the whole of the United Kingdom. We look forward to giving all parts of this great country more power and more freedom. We look forward to a society no longer riven by fear and division. And we look forward to giving each successive generation a better start in life than the one before it.

There will be more details of ministerial appointments announced in the next few days.

Thank you.

With another smile and a nod of the head, Nick Clegg shakes Ed Miliband's hand and the two men turn to enter through that famous door. As they walk up the steps, Clegg puts a reassuring hand on Miliband's shoulder. Britain's first coalition government since the Second World War has officially begun.

~

Five years earlier, another enthusiastic, youngish man in a dark-blue suit had stood on the steps of 10 Downing Street.

As voters went to polling stations around the UK, pundits had been expecting a hung parliament. The exit poll, announced at 10 p.m., seemed to bear this out. Although the Tories had won ground, the story of the campaign had been an apparent breakthrough for the Liberal Democrats.

But as events unfolded, it became clear that Nick Clegg's party had failed to translate the so-called Lib Dem surge into seats. Meanwhile, the Tory election machine had succeeded in using sophisticated new methods of targeting to win key marginals. Analysis showed that the election had been decided by fewer than 20,000 votes across twenty key seats. The most high-profile and surprising casualty of this strategy had been the Secretary of State for Children, Schools and Families, Ed Balls. The boundary changes applied to his seat did him no favours, and he lost narrowly to his Tory opponent, Antony Calvert.

The Conservatives ended up with an official majority of two, with 326 seats in the Commons. However, with Sinn Féin's five MPs continuing not to sit or vote, and allowing for the non-voting Speaker, their effective majority was sixteen.

This slim victory was enough for the new Prime Minister, David Cameron, to claim a vindication of his party's main theme during the campaign: the need to move quickly to deal with Britain's Budget deficit. His first action was to announce, along with his new Chancellor George Osborne, an early date for an emergency Budget, where initial spending cuts would be set out. The Tories' success in painting the financial crisis as a consequence of government over-spending would be sorely tested by the new Chancellor's eagerness to shrink the state.

Cameron's honeymoon was extended by the Labour Party's decision to hold a protracted leadership contest almost immediately after the election. Having lost outright, Gordon Brown had no option but to resign as leader, signalling an opportunity for several hopefuls to throw their hats into the ring.

Initially, it was thought that David Miliband, who had threatened to challenge Brown's leadership several times since he became Prime Minister, would be the most obvious choice for a party that had arguably drifted away from its successful strategy under Tony Blair. But pundits had not counted on the frustration that Labour Party members – and even some MPs – felt. Instead of David, it was his younger brother Ed, until now relatively unheralded, who managed to create enough space, shifting to the left even of Gordon Brown and distancing himself from parts of New Labour's legacy. The trade unions' decision to back the challenger was the deciding factor. Eventually Ed won relatively comfortably as the party retreated into a kind of comfort zone. The Tories used the vacuum that Brown had left to ram home their message that it was Labour that had wrecked the economy.

As the Labour Party vacillated over their leadership election, space was created for the Liberal Democrats to become the voice of opposition to the new government. When the time came for Osborne to deliver his emergency Budget, it was the so-called 'sage of the credit crunch', Vince Cable, who provided the most effective critique. In contrast, the hastily appointed shadow Chancellor, Alan Johnson, seemed uncomfortable in his job, prompting media reports that he lacked the economic expertise to make Osborne's life difficult. David Miliband would have been a more natural choice, but he only reluctantly accepted the less visible role of shadow Foreign Secretary offered to him by his brother, despite his extensive experience with the brief. He, too, cut an increasingly unhappy figure on the front bench.

All of this meant that the Conservatives enjoyed the summer. It looked as if they would reach the end of the year relatively unscathed. But they were soon to find that life with a tiny majority would not always be so easy.

~

12 October 2010. The review of higher education funding and student finance, chaired by Lord Browne, presents its findings.

The review recommends removing the cap on tuition fees completely, allowing universities to charge students at any level they choose.

An increase in the threshold at which graduates must pay back loans is also proposed.

The Business Secretary, David Willetts, immediately welcomes the review and says that many of its recommendations will be implemented in full. However, the Tories go further than the report, saying that maintenance grants – designed to provide extra support to students from poor backgrounds – will be folded into the loans system.

The government's position sparks uproar among students and their parents, and there are a number of major protests, culminating in a rally in London that ends in violence as angry teenagers attempt to storm what they think is Conservative Party HQ.

Ed Miliband had indicated during his rise to the Labour leadership that he wanted to introduce a graduate tax. But before he can confirm his opposition to Browne, Lord Mandelson unleashes chaos in the Labour Party. The former Business Secretary and the man responsible for creating the Browne Review declares that its proposals are sensible and that if Labour had still been in government they would have adopted them in full.

It is an immediate test of Miliband's authority, and one he fails. His decision to reset all Labour policy – famously described as his 'blank sheet of paper' initiative – means that there is no clear line emerging from his shadow Cabinet.

The Liberal Democrats need no second invitation: senior figures, including Nick Clegg, Vince Cable and David Laws, all weigh in to denounce the undermining of one of the UK's greatest exports, its university sector. They slam both the idea of unlimited fees and the Tories' vindictive treatment of poorer students. Clegg's theme of broken promises, which had been a key factor in his popularity during the general election, strikes a chord with voters. The only major party to retain a policy of completely abolishing tuition fees gets a bump in the polls.

~

The Conservatives had felt the first ripples of real opposition. And those ripples would spread. Barely a week after the tuition fees farrago, George Osborne rose in the House of Commons to present the government's spending review. Senior Tory ministers had seemingly been competing to show they were the most committed to aggressive cuts in spending. But Osborne's speech attempted to roll back some of the slash-and-burn rhetoric.

> When this government was elected, Britain stepped back from the brink. In our emergency Budget in the summer, we began the long process of restoring sanity to our public finances and stability to our economy. Today we set out in far greater detail what must be done to make Britain's future secure.
>
> Contrary to what many have said about my party and this government, no one comes into politics to make cuts.
>
> That is why we are protecting our National Health Service and why we want to find extra money for our schools so that we can help our poorest children get a better start in life.
>
> That is why we are also keeping our commitment to increase the international development budget.
>
> But it is most important to be prudent, and we must stop spending money we do not have. The nation's credit card is maxed out. It is time for a sensible, competent approach that helps us to rebuild our economy.
>
> Labour left us to confront the bills from a decade of debt. We are taking our first steps down a hard road, but it will lead to a better future.

In total, Osborne's cuts amounted to more than £100 billion over four years, as the Chancellor attempted to deal with the Budget deficit solely through spending cuts. Welfare and local councils were hit very hard and funding for further education colleges was as good as cancelled. Alan Johnson, speaking for Labour, condemned 'the deepest cuts to public spending in living memory', claiming that the country might tip into what he called a 'double dip' recession.

As Christmas drew nearer, media attention was now firmly on the extent of the savage cuts set out by Osborne. Each week new horror stories emerged of the likely impact, and even in right-leaning publications, such as *The Spectator*, questions were raised over whether it was appropriate to take such a radical approach.

The Mayor of London, Boris Johnson, gradually became one of the more outspoken critics of some of the cuts, claiming that they would harm the capital and act as a brake on its growth. He especially deprecated decisions to reduce support for housing development and transport infrastructure. Even across the Atlantic, mild concern was reportedly expressed in the White House over the depth and pace of the Conservatives' economic retrenchment.

The trend would continue into the new year. But in January there was a welcome distraction for the Tories: the Oldham East and Saddleworth by-election saw the Liberal Democrats gain the seat from Labour after the disgraced Phil Woolas's original 2010 victory was declared void by an election court.

Still, the economy showed little sign of improvement by the time Osborne had to deliver his first full Budget, in March 2011. GDP figures had shown no growth for six months by the time he paraded out of 11 Downing Street with his traditional red box.

Osborne was forced to downgrade growth forecasts significantly, increasing the jitters that had been reported from Cabinet colleagues. But, at the same time, backbench Conservatives were pressing the Chancellor for an even more radical response to the sluggish recovery. His solution was deliberately incendiary. He first adopted the Liberal Democrats' policy of raising the income tax threshold to £10,000, arguing that it was a naturally Conservative move to allow people to keep more of their own money and would help get people back into work. The threshold would be raised gradually over the remainder of the parliament, so that by 2015 citizens would have an extra £700 a year in their pockets.

The Chancellor also cut the top rate of income tax back to 40 per cent. Having commissioned a study from the Treasury showing that the 50p rate raised only a small amount of revenue, he argued that the message it sent was harming wealth creation in the economy.

The cuts would be expensive, but Osborne had a further trick up his sleeve there too. Having originally proposed an increase in VAT to 20 per cent in his emergency Budget, he said that this would now be accompanied by a new bankers' bonus tax – a policy this time stolen from Labour. And he also announced a review of capital gains tax to test whether its many reliefs were being abused by the wealthy, as the Lib Dems had long argued.

The twin tax cut – apparently revenue-neutral, due to the other tax increases – was reported as a masterstroke. Newspapers breathlessly related that the Chancellor had produced not one but two 'rabbits' from his hat, and had managed to position himself in the centre ground again.

Another major effort from Osborne was to demonstrate that the Conservatives were not averse to investment to stimulate growth in the economy. In a move calculated to rile the man now regarded as the king over the water in some quarters – Boris Johnson – it was announced that a third runway at Heathrow would be built, along with a replacement for Trident and the so-called High Speed 2 railway line. This trio of major infrastructure projects was controversial, causing the first Cabinet-level resignation of the Parliament as Justine Greening, the Transport Secretary, resigned after leading a number of campaigns in her own constituency of Putney against the expansion of Heathrow. Tory backbenchers in the shire counties were also deeply upset by HS2 and the impact it would have on what they insisted on referring to as 'our green and pleasant land'.

For the first time, party discipline was becoming a real problem for Cameron and Osborne. Fortunately for them, however, the official opposition was still unable to capitalise on Tory woes. Labour had supported Heathrow's third runway in government and heavyweight shadow Cabinet members still considered it a vital project, even if Ed Miliband seemed disinclined to support it. And HS2 had also been launched under the Labour government.

Once again, then, it was left to the Liberal Democrats to provide a genuine alternative, at least over Heathrow. Zac Goldsmith, the new Conservative MP, was forced to honour his commitment to resign on the issue and force a by-election in his constituency of Richmond Park. His narrow majority of 4,091 was easily overturned by the former MP, Susan Kramer, as voters demonstrated their discontent with the government. Suddenly, the Tories no longer had an official majority.

~

David Cameron's job is becoming more and more difficult. Nos 10 and 11 Downing Street are now dominated by discussions on keeping increasingly vociferous Conservative backbenchers in line.

The main problem is a group of right-wing MPs, led by senior Eurosceptics such as John Redwood. As the sovereign debt crisis in the Eurozone grows, this cabal of troublemakers begins to argue that the UK's membership of the EU is becoming toxic. Their voices are joined by the UK Independence Party, which combines Euroscepticism with anti-immigration rhetoric, emphasising at every opportunity that the government is failing in its target to reduce net migration to the 'tens of thousands'.

Desperately casting around for a prescription that will neutralise this running sore, Cameron and Osborne hit upon what they think is the answer. They will propose a referendum on the UK's membership of the European Union, following a process of renegotiation with other nations, focusing mainly on immigration controls.

Cameron announces the new policy in a major speech at Bloomberg. It is met with dismay by major European and world powers, including Germany, France and the United States, who make clear that while the current crisis creates understandable tensions, it is not the right time for brinkmanship.

Nonetheless, leading Tory backbenchers profess themselves to be delighted with the new policy. They immediately begin to lobby for sympathetic Cabinet ministers to be allowed to campaign for an exit should the renegotiation process fail. It appears that the immediate crisis has been averted for the time being. Cameron and Osborne can permit themselves a cautious sigh of relief. But the attrition of a small majority is already taking its toll, only a year and a half into the parliament.

Meanwhile, north of the border, another political force has arisen. A strange kind of mirroring is occurring; just as nationalistic identity politics are reasserting themselves through UKIP in England, the Scottish National Party has triumphed in the Holyrood elections, winning a majority that many thought would be impossible under the PR system used to elect the Scottish Parliament. The SNP uses its new platform to demand an independence referendum for Scotland. A new wrinkle in the UK's rapidly ageing constitutional framework is set to appear.

~

With so much media attention on the flatlining economy and on European issues, it was almost forgotten at times that the government still had a legislative agenda. Yet the impact that this was having on public services was, at times, remarkable.

Michael Gove, the Education Secretary, was busily overseeing an explosion in the number of academy conversions in England's schools, and introducing new qualifications and tests almost on a daily basis.

Theresa May, the Home Secretary, was also busy, introducing so-called Sheriffs to replace police authorities, and scrapping the identity cards introduced by the Labour government but keeping the underlying database, to be combined with broad legislation collecting communications data on the entire population of the country.

But the most controversial reform to be put forward by a Cabinet minister was rapidly becoming another thorn in the side of the government. In early 2011, the Health Secretary Andrew Lansley had revealed the result of his several years' experience shadowing the brief: an ambitious reorganisation of the entire apparatus of the National Health Service.

But the Health and Social Care Bill was mired in difficulty. Lansley's plan to abolish primary care trusts and strategic health authorities was meeting with vehement opposition from within the NHS, as well as from opposition parties. The introduction of so-called clinical commissioning consortia, to be run partly by GPs, was also considered a somewhat 'courageous' move in Whitehall.

The Bill also encouraged NHS trusts to pursue non-NHS income by removing the previous cap on private earnings. It was a clear sign that the Tories wanted to move the service towards a more commercial footing and away from its publicly provided status. Private healthcare executives were informed by an adviser to David Cameron that the NHS would in future be a state insurance provider, not a state deliverer. Criticism of Lansley's reforms for failing to provide sufficient safeguards against private companies exploiting the NHS steadily mounted.

Initially, the opposition parties latched onto the cost of the scheme.

It was projected that the funding for the reorganisation might need to run to as much as £3 billion, an extremely large sum given the spending cuts being undertaken in other areas.

But once the nurses and doctors united in their outrage, it was only a matter of time before the reform train hit the buffers. The final nail in the coffin was the intervention of Sarah Wollaston, the Tory MP for Totnes. The former GP had already rejected a ministerial post on the basis it would prevent her from speaking freely on issues that concerned her. Now she used her independence at a decisive time, warning the Prime Minister that the NHS would go 'belly up' if the NHS reforms were pushed through.

Cameron had to act. He put the Bill out of its misery, and Lansley would be quietly reshuffled out of government at the next available opportunity. He would be replaced not by Wollaston – who had burnt her bridges and was rumoured to be considering resigning the Conservative whip – but by an old stager with a safe pair of hands.

Stephen Dorrell had been Health Secretary before and his experience in the post stood him in good stead. He quickly began to rebuild relations with the NHS community, arguing for a minimalist change in the law rather than a total redrawing of management structures. His focus on improving healthcare at the front line – mainly by reducing the number of people going to hospitals – received a positive hearing and saw the beginnings of a common agenda on the integration of health and social care.

The Tories had been saved from themselves this time. The process of democratic scrutiny – and the independence of backbench MPs – had resulted in better policy.

~

This battle over one of the key issues in domestic policy only temporarily distracted the politicians and the press from wider concerns.

The Prime Minister, now fighting off rebellions from backbenchers over Europe, immigration and the economy on an almost weekly basis, was seeing support in the country ebb away as more and more voters responded to the perception of chaos within Conservative ranks. The attrition of parliamentary management was also taking its toll on the Whips' Office, with pairing of MPs suspended and every vote now susceptible to tactical chicanery, whether from opposition parties or from Tory MPs eager to trumpet their independence.

And now a new foreign policy problem was rearing its head. Syrian President Bashar al-Assad was wreaking havoc in his own country, 'gassing hundreds of innocents in Damascus' according to the media. Cameron and his Defence Secretary Philip Hammond introduced a motion that would have condemned Assad's behaviour and given Parliament's assent for a limited bombing campaign.

But the machinery of government was now malfunctioning. Labour and the Liberal Democrats united in opposing military action, arguing that Cameron would be setting up conditions for regime change and that Britain had intervened foolishly in the Middle East too often before.

Cameron could have salvaged the vote with a display of unity from his own party, but instead he presided over the biggest rebellion of his prime ministership to date. More than thirty Tory MPs voted against him, and it was clear from the debate that many more were reluctant in their support.

The ship of government seemed increasingly to have been holed beneath the waterline. Political commentators wracked their brains attempting to find the last occasion on which Parliament had successfully prevented a government from pursuing its preferred foreign policy. Cameron's authority appeared to have been critically undermined. The process of European renegotiation, already strained, took another hit, with Britain's place in the world increasingly diminished.

It was becoming increasingly apparent that the two referendums on the horizon could well coincide. The SNP began to brief the media that the Westminster government was going to scupper Scotland's chance to have a historic choice by confusing the issue and holding the two votes on the same day.

Sure enough, the date originally planned for the Scottish referendum – the same day as the local elections in May 2014 – was pre-empted by an announcement from Downing Street. The EU referendum would also be held on 22 May 2014, as the SNP had warned, in order to coincide with the European parliamentary elections.

The Scots were left little choice but to postpone their own referendum until later in the year. Senior SNP figures such as Alex Salmond and Nicola Sturgeon pulled no punches in their furious response, and there was an immediate increase in their popular support, although opinion polls also showed that the public favoured further devolution over full independence.

~

19 March 2014. George Osborne is delivering his fifth Budget of the parliament, and perhaps his most important. With just two months until the European elections, and the accompanying referendum on UK membership of the EU, the government is in full propaganda mode.

Thankfully for Osborne, the economy has finally begun to show signs of picking up. There was a return to slow growth in 2013, and now he can forecast the same for 2014. It's enough to ease the pressure slightly.

But then Osborne mentions the importance of the European Union to the UK, and preaches the vital need to increase the country's exports to its close neighbours. The same backbenchers who had previously been waving their order papers in glee now sit stony-faced.

A couple of weeks after the Budget, the UK Independence Party calls a press conference. The event is shrouded in secrecy, with the location only revealed to a select band of lobby journalists. Initially it is party leader Nigel Farage who appears before the cameras. Wreathed in smiles, he lays into the government for failing to represent Britain's interests in Europe, and for what he calls an 'undignified stitch-up' to ensure that the referendum goes their way.

He then invites not one, but two Conservative MPs to join him on the stage. Douglas Carswell and Mark Reckless are the two in question, and it rapidly becomes apparent that the Prime Minister's and Chancellor's clear support for EU membership has convinced them to defect.

Carswell claims that the Tory leadership is 'not serious about real change in Europe' and is 'more comfortable being a small clique and sitting in Downing Street'. His frustration over the conservatism of the Conservatives is welcomed by Farage and echoed by Reckless.

The Tories attempt to shrug off the damage, but they are now officially a minority government. With two UKIP MPs on the benches of the House of Commons, there is now even more risk of backbench Tories kicking up a stink and rebelling on key votes.

~

In the week before the European referendum, tensions are running high. Only UKIP are officially against remaining in the EU, and Nigel Farage is a divisive figure, but there are concerns among leading Conservatives as well as Labour and the Liberal Democrats that the economic recovery is not yet strong enough to have convinced voters that Britain's future is secure within Europe.

On the eve of the vote, pollsters are unwilling to make a call, with many saying it is still on a knife-edge. What is clear is that UKIP's support for the European Parliament elections appears to be at an all-time high, and they look likely to win more seats than any of the three major parties.

At 10 p.m. on the day of the referendum, an exit poll is released. UKIP have indeed come first in the European elections, but the public has voted fifty-five to forty-five in favour of remaining in the EU. It seems a classic case of voters having their cake and eating it too – registering a protest over Conservative weakness, but not at the cost of throwing everything up in the air.

Cameron seizes on the referendum victory as a lifeline, claiming it as a vindication of his strategy. But it fails to convince his more sceptical MPs, and there are renewed rumours of further defections by characters such as Peter Bone and Bill Cash.

A few months later, the Scottish referendum takes place. The three major Westminster parties are able to join forces to create sufficient doubt among voters' minds over leaving the union, using their victory in the EU referendum as evidence that the UK is better together than apart. Without the threat of an exit from the EU, the SNP finds it difficult to whip up anti-English feeling, although the independence campaign still gains more than 40 per cent of the vote.

It is clear that neither referendum has completely ended the story. Nationalism is here to stay – but as the Prime Minister broods over the inevitable general election, now only months away, it seems more likely that traditional concerns will sway swing voters.

~

7 May 2015, 9.55 p.m. David Dimbleby begins his usual marathon broadcast, for the first time from Broadcasting House.

It's been the most exciting, unpredictable election for a generation. And what an extraordinary race it's been. It began as a two-horse race; it ended with three starters at the line. And in four minutes' time, when we have our exit poll, we'll have our first clear indication of who is the winner – if indeed there is a clear winner.

Whether Ed Miliband can overcome the surge of the SNP in Scotland, whether David Cameron can overcome all the problems he has faced and return triumphant to No. 10, or whether Nick Clegg can use this second chance to take his party into government in a coalition ... all will become clear over the course of the next few hours.

As Big Ben strikes ten, we'll be able to give the result of our exit poll.

And it's 10 o'clock. And this is what we're saying: it's going to be a hung parliament. No party has won a majority.

But just look at those figures. It's extremely complicated. The Conservatives have lost a considerable amount of support, down to 30 per cent. That leaves them on a predicted 250 seats – still the largest party in the House of Commons, but well short of a majority.

But as you can see, the next largest vote share is not for Labour, but for the Liberal Democrats. Nick Clegg's party has come second in the popular vote on 29 per cent. That means they may have gained up to fifty seats – we have them on ninety-nine, their highest since the party formed in the late 1980s.

And here are Labour – down to just 27 per cent, lower even than in 2010. They look like winning around 232 seats – and that's so low partly because of the extremely strong performance of the SNP up in Scotland. They look like they've won more than forty-five seats, with most of those coming from Labour.

All of this means that it will be the Liberal Democrats, and Nick Clegg, who are the kingmakers. They can do a deal with either the

Conservatives or Labour to form a coalition, and either way the two parties would have a working majority. It is surely the dream scenario for them to have a chance of power after so many years, and the frustration of narrowly missing out in 2010.

There's still a long way to go and exit polls aren't certain. But it looks as though the shape of British politics may have been changed decisively tonight. Stay with us to find out how things unfold.

Chapter 16

What if David Miliband had beaten Ed Miliband in 2010?

Stuart Thomson[1]

Amid the balloons and flashing lights of Labour's 2015 election victory, David Miliband delivered one of his most impassioned speeches:

> This election win is a victory for all the people of our country. Our Labour government will stand up for a fairer society. It will not divide to conquer. It will give chances to everyone – the young, the old, the poor. It will give chances to those that feel that they have little to look forward to. This is a Labour government that will transform our country. That is the promise I make today.

That Miliband was able to deliver a victory speech at the 2015 general election did not come as a total surprise. It was, however, the sight of the Miliband brothers, David and Ed, embracing at the victory party that was one that few ever thought they would witness. In a sibling rivalry that had threatened to derail the party, supporters of the two men had traded blows ever since the leadership election of 2010.

The leadership battle itself had been tense and, at times, highly personal. Despite protests of friendships and brotherly love, few believed this by the end of the contest. The fact that the younger brother, Ed, had run his older sibling, David, so close in the first place created a tension which was to beset the party in the following years and was used constantly by their political opponents.

The 2010 contest showed that Labour still had to overcome the divisions that had been created by the rivalry between Tony Blair and Gordon Brown. The media portrayed David as the heir to Blair and Ed as the heir to Brown. But while Ed did all he could to revive a new form of left-wing populism, David was determined to build on the achievements of the Blair era.

The talk among activists and supporters at the general election victory party – as reported by the media – was focused less on the win and more on whether the bitterness of the Blair–Brown era could be avoided this time around. As party-goers were reported saying:

'Labour has regained the trust of the people, but David needs to maintain the trust of his party. You ask me whether that means ensuring unity and I would say yes. Action would need to be taken against whoever is causing disunity, whoever they are. He has done it once, he may need to do it again.'

'David needs to listen to those who want less accommodation with the failing market – like his brother. Labour can shift power in this country if David has the appetite for the fight.'

'David needs to act in government exactly as he has in opposition. He needs to show the same determination and steel.'

The leadership contest

The election of David Miliband as Labour Party leader on 26 September 2010 surprised few, despite how close the contest seemed to look in the closing weeks. David had been the front runner from the outset and the odds-on favourite. While Ed Balls, Diane Abbott and Andy Burnham had all fought their corners, the contest was all about whether Ed could overtake his older brother. David, for his part, needed to overcome his early shock just of being challenged by Ed.

In the early weeks of the contest, everything appeared to go according to script. David and Ed each spoke glowingly of the strengths of the other and of their respective efforts to reunite the party. The nature of Labour's defeat in 2010 under Gordon Brown had led some in the party to conclude that it needed to rediscover its soul – the Ed version. Others pointed to the narrowing of the party's electoral appeal to its core heartlands and the need to talk again to the country as a whole – the David version. David also argued that 2010 was 'a change election and we were not the party of change'.[2]

It soon became clear that a purely Blairite New Labour approach was not going to win David the leadership. His early talk of 'Next Labour' shifted towards warnings of the dangers of simply recreating New Labour – although he could never fully escape Blair's legacy. One of the most enduring images of the contest was created by *The Times*'s Peter Brookes, who drew a stern-looking Miliband holding a banana with his shadow in the shape of Tony Blair. One legacy in particular was difficult to overcome – the Iraq War. Ed and the other candidates were quick to put as much distance as possible between themselves and the decision to invade Iraq. David could not do this, and anyway did not want to; but he did stop defending all aspects of the conflict.

The role of government in the economy developed as an issue late in the campaign, but David did much to reassure the trade unions, who had initially appeared to be being won over by Ed's more leftist approach. While David did not bow to pressure to rule out any further privatisation, as some unions had called for, he did enough to demonstrate that a Labour Party led by him would adopt a more muscular approach to the role of government, not giving the market a completely free rein. He also countered strongly any idea that he was advocating a break in the link between the party and the unions. And while the other candidates talked about the battles of the past, David focused on challenging the Conservative–Lib Dem coalition's austerity programme, helping to cultivate an image as the only one who stood a realistic chance of winning the next general election.

But David did not concentrate only on the economy; he shamelessly borrowed some of his brother's talk of bringing younger people into the party to campaign on new issues such as climate change, successfully marrying this approach with more traditional Labour themes of equality and the need to deal with the challenges facing the NHS and the welfare state for the next generation.

Recognising that he was often perceived as lacking the common touch, David made sure he was seen out and about in the country, alongside his fellow MPs – who he made a special effort not to treat as his intellectual inferiors – talking to meetings of party members and groups of trade unionists. He fed back into the campaign what people had been telling him, and used his family carefully in media opportunities. Where his brother was, in the end, unable to overcome his image as a geek and as the candidate of the trade union left, David brought with him the gravitas of having held one of the highest offices of state, and a respected record in government – and he worked hard to show that he was capable of being the candidate of change as well.

In the end, David topped the count on first-preference votes and picked up enough transfers from the third, fourth and fifth placed candidates to take him over the finishing line just ahead of his brother. But it was not a decisive win, and it did not put to rest the Blair–Brown battles of old.

The David Miliband-led opposition

Aiming to heal the divisions revealed by the leadership contest, David's first move was to encourage his brother to stand for election to the shadow Cabinet. Ed agreed and did well; he still commanded considerable support among the Parliamentary Labour Party. David gave him not only his old position of Energy and Climate Change, but a new role responsible for increasing the level of activism and participation in the party – building on the 'Movement for Change' David had established during the leadership campaign. He hoped that community organisation and activism would help the Labour Party to plug into real local concerns. Despite Ed's obvious commitment to his new role, however, his supporters, especially in the trade union movement, saw it as a snub, not just to Ed but also to the unions themselves; they thought he should have been given one of the major offices.

In the event, Ed enjoyed spending much of his time abroad, trying to draw together coalitions in support of measures to combat climate change; he had more photo opportunities with foreign dignitaries than the shadow Foreign Secretary. This role had initially been given to John Healey, following his good polling in the shadow Cabinet election, but Ed overshadowed him on the international stage and William Hague, the Foreign

Secretary, bettered him in Parliament. Healey went quietly and with little fuss, being replaced by Douglas Alexander.

David understood that his most important relationship would be with his shadow Chancellor. He viewed Ed Balls as too dangerous an appointment, fearing that he would use his position, just as Gordon Brown had done, to build an alternative power base. The two men also disagreed over Labour's policy on the deficit: Miliband stuck to the 2010 general election pledge to halve the deficit by 2014, whereas Balls opposed it. Miliband accordingly gave the post to Yvette Cooper, Ed Balls's wife. Although she brought obvious strengths to the role, the Tories, and the media, enjoyed the opportunities this created to suggest an opposition riven with family rivalries. Ed Balls was instead made shadow Secretary of State for Health. These appointments helped to show that David was his own man; his Labour Party would not be a pale imitation of either Brown's or Blair's.

Shadow Home Secretary went to Alan Johnson, a popular appointment, helping to counter the perception of Miliband as too aloof and intellectual. Johnson not only brought plain speaking to the shadow Cabinet, he also proved more than capable of getting the better of Home Secretary Theresa May, especially when the coalition continued to fail to meet its own immigration targets. Miliband was also quick to promote some of the 2010 intake into junior positions, including Chuka Umunna, Rachel Reeves, Stella Creasy and Michael Dugher; and Dan Jarvis was given a swift elevation on his election to Parliament in a by-election in 2011.

Both media and government made it their mission to try to discover fault lines between the two Miliband brothers. Sometimes, they did not have to try very hard. It was clear that Ed was not deliberately trying to destabilise his brother, but equally he did little to close down his own supporters' briefings or counter-briefings. Any announcement from David would often generate a response from an 'insider' critical of the approach. In turn, David's supporters suggested that Ed was not strong enough to control his own followers. Constant low-level internal sniping left Labour looking divided and the leader as if he lacked control over his own party. Unless David took action, he was in danger of losing the 2015 election before it got anywhere near.

The two brothers – or, at least, their supporters – clashed over a range of issues. Ed's camp criticised what they saw as David's failure to challenge the position of business, especially big business, to argue for higher business taxes, to take climate change seriously, or to support reform of the House of Lords or devolution to England's cities. Ed's supporters saw David as repeating the failings of the Blair era. As a result, the media could always rely on Labour conferences for a string of stories about splits, with former ministers only too willing to share their opinions. This culminated in Ed's speech to the 2013 conference, which came over almost as an alternative leader's speech. He spoke about the need to challenge the powers of capitalism, to protect the environment from 'predatory' businesses and for the need for Labour to break the status quo; a very different story than the one David was telling. The electorate heard, loud and clear, a divided party that seemed to have learned nothing from the fight between Blair and Brown. Labour was not at ease with itself.

In the end, David was left with no choice but to remove Ed from his shadow Cabinet. While the move shocked some of the Westminster commentators, it demonstrated to the electorate the strength of his leadership; it showed that he was prepared to make tough decisions. Where Blair had bottled removing Brown, Miliband proved that he was not about to make the same mistake. The sacking also had the effect of dampening the sniping at a critical time. The unions, and others in the party, could see that David meant business. With a general election starting to loom, David began to look like a potential Prime Minister.

The policy agenda

In his acceptance speech as leader, David Miliband had made every effort to show that an active government could bring economic, social and environmental benefits. He had already targeted 'immoral' City excesses during the campaign, arguing that 'a new era of shared prosperity' could only be created if the high pay and bonuses of the City were challenged. One of his recurring criticisms of the coalition was its failure to regulate the banks effectively; he committed Labour to doubling the bank levy and investing the proceeds in skills development for the young. The proposals proved popular and Miliband began to make ground against the parties of the coalition.

One of Miliband's main policy proposals was the introduction of a mansion tax of 1 per cent on the value of property worth over £2 million; the revenue would be invested in house building. This was not simply a tax on the rich, he maintained, but part of an effort to transform the lives of the poorest, especially young people. However much pressure he came under from the media and the Tories on the policy, Miliband did not budge. He felt passionately that a fundamental change was needed if there was to be any prospect of improving the life chances of the young. By giving himself several years to advocate the policy, he demonstrated a dogged determination that people came to admire. He also proposed the creation of a British Investment Bank out of the nationalised banks, turning the BBC into a cooperative to give licence-fee payers a voice and ending the subsidy of private school places.

As had Tony Blair, Miliband believed in the need to set targets to spur government action. This included a house-building target of 240,000 homes a year – echoing a pledge made by Labour in 2007 that had never been met – and a steadily rising target to take children out of poverty. He adopted one of Ed Balls's policies from the leadership campaign – a graduate tax – as a way of helping students hit by the coalition's decision to raise tuition fees. Particularly given the Lib Dems' U-turn on the policy, young people featured heavily in Labour campaign materials and party election broadcasts; Miliband attacked the coalition's approach of favouring older people over younger ones in the policies being pursued to reduce the deficit. This theme of the 'lost generation' peppered his speeches and many policy ideas were hooked onto it. He drew comparisons between the damage inflicted by communities across the country under Thatcher with the approach of the coalition: to him, they were 'extremists, and ideologically driven'.

These messages found resonance with an electorate that seemed prepared to listen to an alternative to the coalition's absolute commitment to austerity. Miliband recognised and talked about the needs for spending cuts but always in the context of protecting those left most vulnerable. He compared this publicly to the coalition's ideological belief in cuts and a smaller state as ends in themselves (whether this was true or not).

Foreign policy, though, remained an Achilles heel. Miliband possessed a strong internationalist outlook and believed firmly in the value of intervention, but struggled to keep his party united behind this agenda. British action on Iraq (which Miliband had supported in 2003) and Afghanistan had put people off international adventures; there was little appetite, either in the country or the Labour Party, to get involved in disputes overseas.

Throughout his policy programme, Miliband tried to stick to the analysis of why Labour lost in 2010 that he had delivered in the leadership election:

> We were not the party of fairness any more, and unless we can recapture that we will not win the next election… Too few people had a sense of what we wanted to do in the future – we ended up with a campaign based on the fear of electing the Tories. We weren't proud enough of our record, we weren't humble enough about our mistakes.[3]

David's search for new policies for what Labour 'wanted to do in the future' drew on a plethora of ideas from think tanks at home and abroad. This helped Labour to seem fresh, while the coalition was compared to a 'one-trick pony, only capable of talking about cuts'.

He had learned from Blair that Labour only wins when it can be trusted on the economy. He appreciated that he needed to tackle the crash, its causes and its consequences in a forthright manner. He did this by claiming that Labour had no choice but to bail out the banks; along with Cooper, he constantly challenged Osborne by asking what he would have done under the same circumstances. He also pointed to the return of growth under Brown and Chancellor Alistair Darling, which, in his words, was 'more than the coalition had ever achieved'. This helped to counter the coalition's attempts to place blame for the crash solely on Labour, though it did not remove it completely.

This approach was accompanied by a refusal to hide from the need to make some cuts in spending. Miliband and Cooper put forward clear ideas about where they should fall, including, in particular, corporate tax reliefs, and aimed to strike a balance between raising taxes and lowering spending.

This clear economic narrative was combined with some popular and eye-catching initiatives; not least, Miliband championed action against 'tax-dodging' multinationals, and even put forward a draft international agreement to show that he understood what was really needed. Combined with the mansion tax proposal and action against the banks, he was able to claim that Labour was 'the party of a truly united kingdom, working together'.

Miliband *v.* Cameron

While the Prime Minister was good at engaging with the country, communicating well and being emotionally in touch with its concerns, Miliband did not always make a similar connection. Miliband's defence of the achievements of the Blair–Brown era also meant that Cameron continued to try to tar Miliband with Labour's failings in office. And the Tories pointed to the lack of trust between the two brothers; if Ed didn't trust his own brother to run the Labour Party, why should anyone else trust him to run the country? Though Cameron appeared to continue to rely on personal attacks even when the polls said people wanted a positive vision of the future.

And the coalition grew steadily less popular as the cuts imposed by the Chancellor, George Osborne, caused growing unhappiness. Miliband and Cooper both targeted Osborne as the government's weakest link. They also did their best to drive home the obvious differences between the two parties of the coalition. The fact that Labour appeared to have a realistic alternative vision helped them gain traction. In simple terms, Labour's talk of fairness was contrasted with a lack of fairness delivered by the cuts.

The Liberal Democrats ended up absorbing much of the blame for the spending cuts, even though in fact they had acted as a brake on the more zealous and divisive of the Tories' proposals. Many Lib Dem activists and supporters would rather have done a deal with a Labour Party led by David Miliband – had that been on offer during the coalition negotiations – than with the Conservatives, and throughout the parliament there was a steady stream of defections of councillors and party members to Labour. Shirley Williams spoke for many Lib Dems when she welcomed Miliband's approach to economics and banking regulation, and his internationalist approach and support for the United Nations in trying to resolve the conflicts in Afghanistan and Libya.

According to the polls, Miliband was gaining momentum. Labour looked on course to do well in 2015.

The Tory earthquake

It was soon clear, however, that David Miliband was never going to enjoy a particular rapport with the Scottish electorate. The rise of the Scottish National Party had started before Miliband took over but he at least attempted to tackle it head-on. After the SNP swept to power in the Scottish Parliament elections of 2011, Miliband took Scotland seriously and recognised that spending time and effort there was much needed. He also fully understood the historical importance of Scotland to the Labour movement.

Cameron, meanwhile, took the opportunity to try to kill off Labour in Scotland. His announcement of a referendum on independence was greeted with huge enthusiasm in Scotland. There was never any chance that Labour would campaign for anything other than the union, but Miliband was careful not to associate his party too closely with the Conservatives. In a carefully orchestrated and well-resourced campaign, Labour did its best to set out a positive vision for a socially inclusive union. While the eventual outcome was only a narrow victory for the 'no' side, Labour was seen to have had a good campaign. Miliband's efforts turned out to be a wise investment come 2015.

Immigration was always a difficult policy area. Miliband knew that he had to appear tough on immigration controls, but this conflicted with his internationalist beliefs when the refugee crisis started to emerge in the wake of the conflicts in Libya and Syria. The question of intervention in Syria was another problem for Labour; Miliband supported the government in its vote on military strikes in August 2013, despite unhappiness among his MPs. In the end, however, the backbench rebellion was limited, and the government's motion passed easily with Labour support. No. 10 welcomed Miliband's clear line and praised him for being 'serious' about the matter. To the public, this simply reinforced Miliband's growing reputation.

On Europe, David Miliband's problems were more limited. The party was, for the vast part, pro-European and was quite happy to let David Cameron struggle to control his own MPs. Miliband welcomed the Prime Minister's announcement of a referendum on EU membership, while attacking Cameron for thinking mainly of attempting to save Conservative seats from the threat of UKIP.

The Prime Minister, meanwhile, was facing a huge challenge in terms of the polls; the economy was stubbornly failing to recover and support for the Conservatives was gradually eroding. Pressure was growing within the Liberal Democrats for an end to the coalition, though the majority believed that it was better to stay and hope that an improving economy – when it came – would save them.

In the end, it was George Osborne who paid the price.

Osborne was never popular within his own party; he was often considered to be occupying his position solely because of his close relationship with Cameron. In opposition it was only Cameron's firm support that had saved him when it was revealed that, along with Labour Cabinet minister Lord Mandelson and Russian oligarch Oleg Deripaska, he had attended a party hosted on a yacht by the financier Nat Rothschild. The experience of being booed at the Paralympics in 2012 showed that he had few supporters among the public too. The tentative economic recovery of 2011 had seemed to stall in 2012, the Budget deficit was still growing despite the cuts, and the 'omnishambles' Budget of 2012 showed a lack of political nous. Osborne consistently trailed Yvette Cooper in the polls as the most capable Chancellor. In October 2013, therefore, Osborne and William Hague swapped jobs, Cameron's loyalty to his old friend preventing him from sacking Osborne entirely. Some less sympathetic commentators accused him of sentimentality but Cameron knew he had to do something to stop Miliband's rise becoming unstoppable.

The 2015 election

As the 2015 election approached, a slight recovery in the economy helped the government's position. Miliband's economic policies had generally proved popular, but weaknesses remained. He seemed unable to say exactly where most of the cuts that he agreed to reduce the deficit would come from. The widespread perception that Labour was open to immigration – constantly stressed by Lynton Crosby, the Tories' campaign manager – also cost them support. The Conservative campaign was dominated by the dangers of voting Labour, and the potential role of the SNP, which was clearly making inroads against Labour; the Tories warned that SNP leader Nicola Sturgeon would be the real PM under a Labour government.

The Conservatives also warned of Labour's internal conflicts, although this had less resonance since David had got rid of Ed, and the internal sniping had gone largely quiet. Their main lines of attack were to try to tarnish Miliband with the failings of Blair and Brown, but this was only partially effective. David Miliband was not Gordon Brown; he was not a frightening prospect as Prime Minister; he had had a good record in office, he had experience of government and he appeared to be able to take tough decisions. His commitment to greater equality and social mobility appealed to an electorate sick of austerity; the Tories' attacks on the mansion tax as the politics of envy backfired, as Miliband was able to accuse them of standing for privilege and wealth, and not caring about the life chances of the young people the proceeds of the mansion tax were designed to help. Miliband's efforts to woo business helped too; he never looked like the kind of enemy of capitalism his brother and his supporters sometimes had, and he was obviously not in the pocket of the trade unions. In the end Labour looked like a potential party of government and Miliband looked like a potential Prime Minister.

Miliband's robust showings in the television debates put paid to the Tory line that he would be subservient to Sturgeon and the SNP. However, with opinion polls predicting a close result, the choice of potential coalition partners remained a live question for all the parties. Miliband was clear in stating that whatever the outcome, Labour would govern alone. A vicious attack by the *Daily Mail* on Miliband, his record in government and his family (not least his father), coupled with printing pictures of his children, brought collective outrage – and the dignified way in which he responded delivered a wave of public sympathy and support.

David also made good use of the campaigning base that he had initially charged his brother with building. This on-the-ground support, which was particularly strong in key marginals, was combined with the latest online campaigning techniques. Unlike most other Labour politicians, Miliband knew that without Facebook, Twitter and other social media, Labour risked being left behind. A student of US politics, he learnt from the best in this field; mixing old and new campaigning to good effect.

For all Miliband's positive campaigning, he was not averse to putting the Tories under pressure over their potential coalition partners; UKIP's leader, Nigel Farage, was portrayed as Cameron's Sturgeon. Cameron's promise of an EU referendum had failed to quell the rising tide of UKIP support, and they looked capable of unseating Tory MPs in at least nine seats – enough to be a worry for Cameron if the outcome proved to be close.

The outcome was just enough for Labour. On 7 May 2015, Labour secured 275 seats to the Conservatives' 273. Liberal Democrat voters proved more resilient and less frightened of a Labour victory than had been predicted, and the party managed to hang on to thirty-three of its seats (enough for Nick Clegg to remain as leader, at least in the short term). The SNP made a major breakthrough, winning forty-two seats at the expense of Labour and the Liberal Democrats, but Miliband's investment in Scotland during the referendum campaign, coupled with his robust attacks on the coalition's Thatcherite approach, had at least protected some Labour seats north of the border. UKIP managed to win six seats.

It was another hung parliament. It was not a storming victory but, in comparison with the 2010 result, it was a good Labour performance. The outgoing coalition parties lacked enough MPs to form a government, and in any case there was little appetite among the Lib Dems for repeating an experiment that had seen them lose a third of their seats. The SNP refused point-blank to discuss any form of arrangement with the Tories. David Miliband thus took his place as the new Prime Minister at the head of a minority government, as he had promised during the campaign – even though this meant he was heavily reliant on the good will of others.

Assessment

Battles between two politicians within the same party are nothing new in politics: think of Blair and Brown, Thatcher and Lawson or Wilson and

Brown. What made the David and Ed contest different was the family relationship.

It has been argued by some that the brotherly fight in 2010, and Ed's sacking in 2013, hobbled the party and made the crucial difference when it came to failing to win a majority in the 2015 election. Others point to David Miliband's failure to fully address the deficiencies of New Labour. But he did succeed, at least to an extent, in shifting the Labour Party back towards the centre ground of British politics. He appreciated, too, that voters who had supported the Liberal Democrats in 2010 but disliked the coalition could not simply be assumed to transfer their support to Labour; he didn't take anyone for granted. He delivered a consistent message over the parliament and did his best to address Labour's weaknesses (mainly on the economy) and make the most of its strengths (on the NHS and education). In this way, he took lessons directly from the Tony Blair political playbook. His policies chimed with public sentiment and set out a clear narrative. His style was clear and decisive and when he needed to take action, he did.

Perhaps Miliband's greatest achievement in opposition was to rebuild Labour's image as a credible alternative government. For all their attempts to destabilise him, Cameron and Osborne genuinely feared him – and with reason. Cameron would never have moved Osborne from the Treasury if he had not been worried he would lose the next election.

A Labour minority government dependent on Liberal Democrat or SNP support may not be everyone's favourite form of government, but just as the country learned to live with a coalition, it can learn to live with a minority government too. The question now is whether David Miliband has the approachability and the skills needed to work with others. Any sign of weakness, and the fear is that he will be challenged from within. Divisions remain beneath the surface. We have a David Miliband-led Labour government – but for how long is unclear.

Notes

1. With thanks to Jessica Asato and others for taking the time to discuss this chapter with me and for the very valuable comments from Duncan Brack and his fellow reviewer; they were undoubtedly right!

2. Andrew Rawnsley and Toby Helm, 'David Miliband warns that re-creating New Labour is not the way back', *The Observer*, 16 May 2010.
3. John Baron, 'David Miliband in Leeds: Rebuild Labour as a Movement for Change', *The Guardian*, 18 June 2015.

Chapter 17

What if Ed Balls had won the Labour leadership in 2010?

Tony McNulty

As dawn approached on 8 May 2015, Ed Balls got ready to go to the count in his Morley and Outwood constituency, confident that he had seen off a strong challenge from his Conservative opponent. TV election coverage showed that the country was going Labour's way. Barring accidents or another 2010-style opinion poll debacle, the country was returning a Labour government after just one term of coalition – and he was going to be the new Prime Minister.

~

On his way to London after his victory speech, Balls's thoughts turned to that awful night in 2010 when Labour lost so badly. Having suffered such a disastrous defeat, the party should have stepped out of the limelight immediately. Instead, it had created chaos and confusion by trying to stay relevant, play a part in the post-election talks and maintain some sort of role in government. It had been painful to watch the slow demise of his mentor, Gordon Brown. The Liberal Democrat leader, Nick Clegg, had made Brown's leadership itself an issue in the discussions with Labour over coalition – and had done so in an offensively personal manner. Brown first accepted that he would leave by October, and then sought to backtrack before he eventually agreed that a new leader would be in place by September. For Balls, this had been a sad end to an illustrious career; Gordon had deserved a more dignified departure.

During the weekend after the election, those who had favoured a deal with the Lib Dems, especially Peter Mandelson and Andrew Adonis, had held the upper hand, but by the Monday, more and more party voices were coming out against. Opposition to coalition grew – as 'the ghost of Ramsay McDonald hangs heavy over the Labour Party, and no leader wants to find themselves seen as a Judas, clinging on to power by selling out'.[1] One former Home Secretary, John Reid, objected to any attempt to include the Scottish National Party in any arrangement for fear of the electoral consequences for Labour in Scotland.[2] For others, there was a real aversion to any deal at all that included the Liberal Democrats; another former Home Secretary, David Blunkett, accused them of behaving like 'every harlot in history', and warned that the important thing was 'not what a small group of people in each of the major parties feel in what increasingly looks like a bunker, but what do people out in the country feel...'[3] Others felt, as Glasgow MP Tom Harris put it, that his party needed to be careful about being seen to be 'scrabbling around in a very ungracious way' to hold on to power.[4] In the end, even Adonis accepted that the 'party was exhausted, demoralised, almost leaderless, with many ministers and MPs anxious to escape into opposition and stay there for a good while recuperating ... the will to power was not there'.[5]

Balls had regarded these discussions about potential coalition as a complete distraction. Labour had been rejected by the electorate after being in power for thirteen years; and in any case a Liberal Democrat–Labour coalition would not have commanded a parliamentary majority. Time was needed, he had felt, for reflection, for healing and for rebuilding; but speed was also crucial – a new Labour leader, elected as soon as possible, would be able to take the party through this process with confidence. He understood, too, that the entire political class suffers from emotional fatigue at the end of any election campaign, and while the victors have adrenalin, novelty and excitement to see them through, the vanquished have nothing except fatigue and it gets right into the bones – metaphorically and physically – if you let it. Balls knew Labour could not afford to let it.

The constitution, the electoral arithmetic, Brown's resignation, Cameron's 'big and comprehensive offer' to the Liberal Democrats, the promise of a referendum on electoral reform, the economic crisis, the novelty of a new government – it all pointed to Labour needing a strong voice. Balls knew that if the party waited too long it would come to be seen as irrelevant. Furthermore, it would give the Tories the freedom to define Labour in the most negative fashion possible, framing all the country's problems as the fault of the outgoing government. If Labour allowed itself to sink into an introspective black hole, by the time it emerged it would find it hard to get heard at all, let alone on its own terms.

So, during that post-election weekend in May 2010, Balls was clear that the first thing to do was to ensure that a new leader was elected as soon as possible. He exerted all his influence to ensure that the overwhelming wish of the Parliamentary Labour Party – for a short, sharp campaign – prevailed.

The party's National Executive Committee met to discuss the options at the same time as Clegg and Cameron held a sunny – and somewhat bizarre – press conference in the garden of 10 Downing Street. Happily for Balls and his allies, the NEC opted for the short campaign, albeit by the narrowest of margins. Nominations for the position would open on 24 May and close on 27 May; complaints about this short time frame, notably from Ed Miliband, John McDonnell and Diane Abbott, were dismissed as delaying tactics. The vote was to be concluded by 7 July. Labour would have a new leader in place before the summer and before the coalition was able, Balls thought, to hoodwink the public by blaming the country's problems on Labour and Labour alone.

Balls knew that the timing of the campaign was everything. He already had his team in place, he had the money and support he needed, and he had been thinking through the arguments, policies and plans for moving forward for a long time now. Once he had secured the thirty-three MPs he needed for the nomination, he told his team to stop – the bare minimum was enough. He had always thought there had been something undignified about how he and others in Gordon Brown's team had run round trying to secure as many nominations as possible in 2007.

David Miliband announced that he was running on 12 May and Ed Miliband on the 14th and a media frenzy erupted; it soon became clear that there would be untrammelled media psychobabble about the two brothers fighting each other until the contest was over. They both soon had their thirty-three nominations and more – as did Andy Burnham, when he joined the race. There was some surprise that Ed Miliband had stood; in comparison with the others, he was the least experienced in terms of high-profile and front-rank political jobs, and he tended to be seen not just as Gordon Brown's junior adviser but as junior to Balls too. Burnham's strategy was to present himself as transcending the continuation of the Brown/Blair proxy war that Balls's and David Miliband's candidatures seemed to offer, but the addition of Ed Miliband to the race confused this line; in the end Burnham's supporters argued that he was far more experienced than Ed Miliband and certainly equal in experience and skill to the other two.

As the nominations were closing, there was the usual failed attempt by the hard left to secure a candidate: John McDonnell tried, as did Diane Abbott. Despite McDonnell's withdrawal just before nominations closed, Abbott could still not muster the thirty-three MPs necessary. Calls from the hard left for colleagues to lend supporting nominations to ensure as wide a range of options as possible on the ballot paper went unheeded; David Miliband briefly supported this view but was so ridiculed by the other candidates that he quickly changed his mind – which did nothing to counter his image of vacillation and procrastination. Most Labour MPs believed that if a candidate could not muster the requisite thirty-three names, there would little chance of them winning the election. The party was about power, about radicalism, about changing people's lives; it wasn't a debating club full of comrades clutching Mao's *Little Red Book*.

When nominations closed on 27 May, there was no female candidate. Some pressure was put on Harriet Harman to stand but she made it clear that she was happy to stay as deputy leader for the foreseeable future. So the contest would be between four men – all of them Oxbridge, all of them former special advisers. Some less than loyal party members joked that they thought Labour's version of diversity should mean more than simply including one Cambridge graduate.

For the media, the only issue was the family soap opera, a modern-day Cain and Abel. The press were mesmerised by the duel between the two brothers, and it helped neither of their campaigns. Whenever either of them announced a new policy or initiative, the first question they were asked was 'What does your brother think about it?' Newspapers ran stories about how the contest was affecting members of their family, articles on the views of their late father Ralph, as well as their mother, and endless stories about everything except what either brother had to offer the Labour Party and the country.

Eventually, the discussion moved on to other areas, but the negative coverage against both Milibands continued. The press and the TV recalled how indecisive David had been when he had failed to take the opportunity to stand against Gordon Brown for the leadership back in 2007. It was reported that he lacked the 'killer instinct', that he had no 'judgement' or would only move if he could guarantee the outcome. Most stories about David came complete with 'that picture' – the one from the party conference in Manchester where he was waving a banana and looking slightly less than prime ministerial. The nastiness grew and it was increasingly rumoured that much of it came from his brother. This was untrue but it added to the melodrama and made for another round of psychobabble-fuelled speculation.

Stories also started to emerge about Ed Miliband's inexperience and indecisiveness. It was said that he had turned prevarication into an art form. Apparently he had been in favour of a third runway at Heathrow when Gordon Brown was in the room and against it as soon as Brown left. He was derided as a nice man, and a clever man too, but someone who belonged in a seminar room or a lecture theatre, not in the Cabinet room. It was also claimed that he dismissed the record of the outgoing Labour government far too easily, to a point approaching disloyalty. It was whispered, too, that he had been one of the most enthusiastic for a deal with the Liberal Democrats; Ed 'Ramsay' Miliband, as he was unkindly referred to, was said to be determined to heal the split between Labour and the Liberal Democrats that had endured since the 1920s. This was completely untrue, but the story stuck, and did damage.[6]

Between the negative briefing over policy and substance and the ongoing coverage of the soap opera of the family feud, both of the Miliband campaigns were stalling. And neither was Andy Burnham cutting through to the public or party members, despite conducting a serious and thoughtful campaign. This left Ed Balls.

Balls knew if he was to secure the leadership, he had to come up with a plan for the party's recovery and success. The future couldn't simply be business as usual, but neither, he thought, could it be a facile run to the comfort of the left, which is where Labour often ends up when it loses. If the contest ended up as New Labour versus Old Labour, then nobody won. If it was a Blair versus Brown rerun, then nobody won. If it was some sort of seminar rooted in solutions that had not changed for fifty years and were still rooted in the old Clause 4 of the party, then nobody won.

Balls also knew that he would have to shake off the perception that he was Gordon's boy, that he was a bully and that he was not always at his best at the Commons Dispatch Box. During May and June, he went out of his way to lighten his tone, to sharpen his focus and to take a breath at the box. He explained to audiences how, in part, he rushed sentences for fear of his old stammer recurring. A softer, more attractive Balls was beginning to emerge. The press ran stories on the number of marathons he had run – including the London Marathon – to raise money for charities that worked in the area of speech difficulties; this added a more human dimension to Balls's persona and lessened the bullying image. He encouraged stories about his lighter side – he always cried watching *The Sound of Music*, he cooked for constituency volunteers, he baked his family birthday cakes and he was learning how to play the piano.

And he continued to get under Cameron's skin. Even in government, Balls had seemed to irritate Cameron on the opposition benches. In those summer months of 2010, he continued to play off Cameron's irritation, succeeding in coming over, more often than not, as the more experienced and intelligent statesman, above the fray, while 'Flashman' got 'redder and redder, posher and posher', as the tabloids had it. Labour's back benches loved it.

The new Chancellor, George Osborne, announced that there would be an emergency Budget on 7 June, setting out the coalition's plans for tackling the economic crisis. Alistair Darling, not Balls, was the shadow Chancellor, but as the most knowledgeable leadership candidate on financial matters, he made sure not to miss the opportunity. He arranged a set-piece speech for the day after the Budget – and just a few days before the leadership ballot papers were sent out to Labour members.

Speaking at Bloomberg Business on 8 June, Ed Balls aimed to appeal to both Labour's hearts and its minds. He stressed repeatedly that Labour was a party of government; when Harold Wilson had described it as 'a moral crusade or it was nothing', he did not mean a 'morally pure perpetual opposition or nothing'.[7] Balls wanted the party to 'open up, reflect, reinvent itself and move beyond New Labour' – not because New Labour was bad but because the times had changed.

Labour had saved the economy when it had bailed out the banks in 2008. But this was only the first step to recovery, a recovery which Osborne's emergency Budget risked undermining. He argued that the Budget was based on four untruths: first, that the economic crisis was all Labour's fault; second, that the markets demanded deep cuts to avoid a 'Greek-style' crisis – they didn't, and anyway the UK was nowhere near the Greek position; third, that Osborne's policies, including the Budget, would result in economic growth – they wouldn't, they were in danger of choking off demand at the very point it was beginning to recover, thanks to the Labour government's response to the crisis; and fourth, that Osborne's notion that anyone who wanted a 'less steep plan for reducing the deficit' was a 'deficit denier' who would 'wreck the economy' – but when the independent Office for Budget Responsibility produced its first report in the summer of 2010, it showed that, thanks to the Labour government, borrowing was falling and growth was returning.[8] Osborne's Budget, and the entire thrust of his economic and fiscal policy, was 'wrong in its analysis of the past, reckless in its diagnosis of the present; and downright dangerous in its prescription for the future'.[9] Balls hammered home each and every point in what was regarded as his finest speech since becoming an MP.

Balls offered a credible alternative to the coalition's stark austerity. Labour would never be the party of cuts – especially as this would fail to get the economy going again – so he stressed that the deficit would be dealt with as the recovery grew. 'There are no deficit deniers here – but austerity is not the way to go forward.' Balls reminded his audience that Clement

Attlee had created the welfare state and the National Health Service and rebuilt the country with an economy in a much worse position than the current one. He questioned whether the Chancellor was really that bereft of ideas, that ignorant about the cruelty he was unleashing. Deliberately echoing John Smith's words on the night before he died, in May 1994,[10] Balls concluded that he wanted to be a Labour leader to finish the job started by Attlee and carried out with such courage and devotion by all Labour's leaders since:

> 'The opportunity to serve our country – that is all we ask.' We owe a debt of inspiration to John Smith, and a debt of honour to Neil Kinnock. We will always owe a debt and our gratitude to Tony Blair and Gordon Brown – but we move on. We move on to respond to our time the way all our leaders responded to theirs.

He continued, saying:

> We need to offer people today the answer, the vision, the dreams that all these leaders offered in the past. We have to move on and we have to move beyond the sterile factionalism of recent days. Let us take the fight to the Tories and this squalid coalition. All I ask is the same chance to serve.

The speech was received politely by the business audience in the room, but it was the reaction of party and union members, and the press, that mattered. Finally, a leadership contender had got up off his knees and articulated the start of a fresh message.

The speech triggered a steady flow of support away from the Miliband brothers and towards Balls and became the key event of the leadership contest. When the votes were counted, Andy Burnham was in last place, Ed Miliband and his brother David were almost at level-pegging in second and Ed Balls was well ahead. He remained well ahead as Burnham was eliminated and as David nudged his brother out of second place.

It was commonly agreed that had the leadership campaign been longer and the vote held in September, as many had argued for, then the Miliband brothers could have succeeded in getting out from under their initial negative media coverage; each could have had the time and space to establish their own unique selling points. But time was the one thing they didn't have, and they remained stuck in their initial images, a reincarnation of the Blair/Brown fights of old. An online cartoon portraying David as 'Mr Prevarication' and Ed as 'Mr WhatshouldIdo', with two unnamed shadowy figures lurking behind them, went viral and their support slipped further and further away.

~

Balls moved quickly. He immediately announced an emergency six-point plan for the party. He scrapped the election of the shadow Cabinet – arguing that he needed to be free to pick his own team and be held accountable for his choices. He insisted that the Parliamentary Labour Party let him appoint his own Chief Whip; there had been talk of elections for the post, but he believed it was time for the PLP to be as disciplined as the party's membership wanted it to be. He initiated a review of party disciplinary procedures and promised that action would be taken if needed.[11] He announced a policy development review, stressing that his eye was on the future and finding the answers for the next ten, twenty and fifty years, not what the last Labour government did or did not do. He was not afraid to acknowledge mistakes or apologise for failures, but he wanted the party to move forward. He wanted a 'big, open' team to carry out this ambitious programme and he launched a national recovery tour to listen to the people and explain the direction Labour was going in.

Central to the first weeks of his leadership was success in making sure that the coalition's rhetoric about the economic crisis did not take hold. Balls reflected that had the party given in to those who wanted a longer timeframe for the leadership campaign, Osborne would have been free to frame the economic debate himself and few would have listened to Labour. In reality, the financial crisis was an international one and Labour had led the recovery, which by 2010 was beginning to bear fruit; the coalition had therefore backed austerity as a matter of choice, not necessity.

The coalition's attempts to deride Labour by using terms of derision such as 'not fixing the roof while the sun was shining', or 'giving the car keys back to the people who crashed the car', were so ridiculed that they had to give up using them. And the government gave the new leader plenty of ammunition. Why, Balls argued, were the Tories cutting back on infrastructure spending when, if anything, more was needed, not less? He knew that the voters had not yet forgiven Labour, but they were at least prepared to listen to Labour's new leader, and his fresh and vigorous vision; the coalition's assertions and policies did not go unchallenged.

If he was to be seen as a Prime Minister-in-waiting, Balls knew that he had to become more of a team player. His charm offensive during the leadership campaign had helped, but he knew that he had to do more, to work with people he had disagreed with in the past and to recognise more fully when someone had something to offer. A keen student of US history and politics, he had learned from Doris Kearns Goodwin's classic book on President Lincoln, *Team of Rivals*.[12] He offered David Miliband the role of shadow Chancellor and asked Andy Burnham to stay on at Health. He appointed Harriet Harman shadow Foreign Secretary and Yvette Cooper shadow Education Secretary. He kept Alan Johnson on as shadow Home Secretary and Ed Miliband on as shadow Energy and Climate Change, while Vernon Coaker became his new Chief Whip. He made clear that he wanted to be much more collegiate than either of his two immediate predecessors and that – crucially – he would work closely with David Miliband to ensure that the country benefited from both of them. The Blair/Brown 'TB/GBs' were not to be repeated.[13]

There were also senior roles for two other key supporters. John Healey was to head up the policy development programme, which Balls stressed would build on the best of Labour's history as well as being forward-looking and innovative, to understand its past failings but to develop a programme for the future. Tom Watson was appointed to work with Coaker in developing the interface between the party in the country and the party in Parliament. Balls was clear that the relationships between each of the component parts of the party – PLP, membership, unions, other affiliates – together with the process of electing the leader, the state of the party in Wales,

Scotland and the English regions, the role of the membership, and discipline within the party needed to be reviewed after thirteen years in government.

These initiatives were to take on more importance over the following year. The 2011 Scottish Parliament elections were disastrous for Labour – the party lost seven seats overall, but was eclipsed by the SNP in twenty of the constituency seats as the nationalists took votes from Conservatives and Liberal Democrats as well as Labour, enough to form a majority government. Balls could see the longer-term damage this might do to Labour, whose Scottish base was vulnerable to the attractions of nationalism and independence, particularly with a Tory-led government in London, and asked a triumvirate of Scottish Labour veterans – Alistair Darling, Douglas Alexander and Jim Murphy – to undertake an in-depth review of every aspect of the party in Scotland. The team was given carte blanche and told that no stone should be left unturned in scrutinising the strengths and weaknesses of the Scottish party and all alternatives and solutions should be looked at in depth.

Balls had never worked in the Whips' Office, but he did not understand why a core of perpetual rebel MPs who seemed to delight in opposing the Labour line in the Commons – in or out of power – were never dealt with. Some had, over the years, voted against the party line on as many as 500 occasions. While some of the rebels – such as Dennis Skinner, a regular fixture on Labour's fundraising circuit – did all they could to support the party and the leadership when they agreed with it, others seemed to be Labour only as a matter of electoral convenience and demonstrated no allegiance or loyalty to the party at all. Balls did not want to be a control freak; he understood that the backbenchers needed more space to debate issues than had been the case when Labour had been in government, but this had a limit. Watson and Coaker were asked to look at parliamentary discipline and report to the leader before the next election.[14]

The public standing of Labour's position on the economy ebbed and flowed, but the coalition's line that everything wrong was Labour's fault never quite took hold. Once he got over his disappointment at the leadership result, David Miliband responded well to Balls's vigorous approach and took to his new role with relish. He was able to argue convincingly that cutting the deficit too swiftly had stalled the recovery; Osborne had sucked the life out of the economy and his misguided austerity had stifled demand. On top of that, in the 2012 Budget he cut the top rate of income tax from 50 per cent to 45 per cent – which served no purpose other than to line the pockets of the rich.

Miliband's response to Osborne's 2012 Budget was perhaps his finest hour. Dismissing the Budget as an 'omnishambles', he was able to tackle Osborne with the weapon that all politicians fear most – ridicule. As he pointed out, the Budget was 'marked by a series of low-level cock-ups and retreats – from the pasty tax to the granny tax, the charity tax to the churches tax and even a caravan tax'. The impression emerging was of a Chancellor who was out of his depth and had no idea what he was doing. Miliband went further – he accused Osborne of being in the grip of his officials, for between them, he, his brother and Ed Balls had recognised a dozen schemes and hare-brained wheezes that officials had tried to get past new Chancellors before. 'You'd wonder if the Chancellor had even read the Budget before Budget day,' he concluded.[15]

When Osborne appeared on the platform of the London Paralympic Games in September 2012, he was met with a chorus of boos. As an observer said at the time, 'Commenting on rumours that Osborne would be moved, a senior adviser to Miliband said in July 2012 that "we hope he stays as Chancellor until the end".'[16]

Under pressure from Balls and Miliband, Osborne slowly shifted his policy to a new Plan B, just the direction Labour had been arguing for. The two made a strong team. Every time Osborne missed a deadline, had to apologise that growth had not achieved its forecast, or had to shift direction in response to the economy's failure, the Labour team would pounce. At the same time, they added more shape and structure to Labour's economic policy, rooted in the vision outlined by Balls's Bloomberg Business speech in June 2010. There was a new confidence on the Labour side, which only grew as growth stalled, jobs were not created and many regions did not experience any recovery at all. Labour maintained a small then growing lead in the polls on all measures of economic competence The 'omnishambles' Budget and the failure of the austerity programme damaged the government's reputation for economic competence and led to growing disputes between the coalition partners across a wider and wider range of issues. The more the coalition parties squabbled, the more Labour looked like an alternative government. The more the *raison d'être* for the coalition – fixing the economic crisis – faded, the more the reasons for supporting it disappeared.

~

As Balls drove to London after his victory speech at his count on 8 May 2015, he knew that he would soon be making another speech as leader of the largest party and the next Prime Minister. He reflected that there were three reasons behind his success – the early leadership election; the Bloomberg anti-austerity speech; and his ability to develop a working and constructive relationship with his rivals, especially David Miliband. The contest timetable had meant that the Tories never had the opportunity to embed a 'blame Labour' narrative in the public consciousness. The speech had set out an inspiring and unifying vision for economic recovery without austerity. The powerful partnership between Balls and Miliband had contrasted sharply with the increasingly bitter divisions that had emerged between the coalition partners.

He smiled as he thought how long it had taken him to understand that working with your rivals was so much more effective than fighting them. Funny old game, politics.

Notes

1. Jonathan Powell, *The New Machiavelli: How to Wield Power in the Modern World* (Bodley Head, 2010), p. 35.
2. Denis Kavanagh and Philip Cowley, *The British General Election of 2010* (Palgrave Macmillan, 2010), p. 217.
3. Andrew Adonis, *Five Days in May: The Coalition and Beyond* (Biteback, 2013), p. 109.
4. Kavanagh and Cowley, *The British General Election of 2010*, p. 217.
5. Adonis, *Five Days in May*, p. 141.
6. The 'Ramsay' epithet harked back to the party's mythology around the previous leader, Ramsay McDonald, who had split the Labour Party in 1931 by forming the national government – see also Powell at n1.

7. He was invoking the spirit of Harold Wilson, who coined the phrase at the 1962 Labour Party conference.
8. 'The "medicine" we had administered in 2008 was working. In the face of huge scepticism, I had often said that growth would return at the end of 2009. It did.' Alistair Darling, *Beyond the Brink* (Atlantic Books, 2011), p. 309.
9. Many of these phrases are lifted, with some paraphrasing, from the speech Ed Balls actually gave: 'There is an alternative'; Ed Balls's speech at Bloomberg, 27 August 2010; http://www.edballs.co.uk/blog/?p=907.
10. BBC, 'Labour Leader John Smith dies at 55', 12 May 1994; http://news.bbc.co.uk/onthisday/hi/dates/stories/may/12/newsid_2550000/2550803.stm
11. The result of the 'review into the discipline of the Parliamentary Labour Party' was a series of recommendations about how to deal with discipline. Balls wanted there to be more scope for discussion and debate, but the quid pro quo was strong discipline. Labour MPs' voting records were to be examined and Balls promised that there would be expulsions if necessary.
12. Dorothy Kearns Goodwin, *Team of Rivals: The Political Genius of Abraham Lincoln* (Simon & Schuster, 2005). Lincoln offered his most bitter party rivals – Seward, Chase and Bates – important roles in his administration.
13. The 'TB/GBs' was John Prescott's pejorative term for the unrest between Blair and Brown – based, one assumes, on the 'heebie-jeebies'.
14. In the end, the NEC barred six MPs from standing again for Labour.
15. See Denis Kavanagh and Philip Cowley, *The British General Election of 2015* (Palgrave Macmillan, 2016), pp. 6–9 for a detailed discussion of the 'omnishambles' Budget.
16. Ibid. p. 7

Chapter 18

What if Scotland had voted 'Yes' in 2014?

Stephen Daisley

7 June 2018, Cambridge, Massachusetts

Martha Minow gazed out at the black and crimson hordes and felt an involuntary gulp in the back of her throat. Her disquiet was only faintly connected to the ill-tempered clouds looming above her little square of Cambridge, though they had not been expected and were not helping matters. Minow's equally sudden and unforeseen elevation to the president's office was now two weeks past but she was still trying to catch up in a job that seemed to have a gas pedal and no brake. *Gulp.* The law school had hardly been a kick-back-feet-up post but the scale was slightly less daunting. Her eyes, as if to underscore the point, drew back to the rows upon rows of eager, fresh-faced students.

A shard of steel to the gut brought her to her feet. *This is silly. You've done this a thousand times. Get on with it.* Another gulp and then she was ready. 'Ladies and gentlemen, graduates and faculty, parents, guests, and other friends of Harvard, welcome to graduation 2018.'

The figure seated to her left could not have been a sharper contrast to the newly appointed president of Harvard University. He was self-assurance personified, feigning a look of interest in Minow's introductory remarks but in fact rehearsing jokes in his mind, occasionally struggling to stifle a chuckle.

Outside his hearing, Minow's words softly reverberated through the audio system.

> Our speaker joins a distinguished roll call of Scots who have delivered our commencement address. Thomas Carlyle spoke before the graduating class of 1875; Alexander Fleming, the class of 1945. John Buchan graced us in 1938 in the final years of his life. Most recently, in 2008, thousands crammed into Tercentenary Theatre to hear another of your fellow Scots, J. K. Rowling.

The guest speaker snapped out of his self-admiring reverie. His smile cut in half; his teeth began to grind under a grimace.

'Perhaps appropriately, maybe even presciently, her talk was entitled, "The Fringe Benefits of Failure".'

Molar juddered against molar, but President Minow continued, oblivious. 'Please join me in welcoming the former First Minister of Scotland and, for six weeks, the Prime Minister of an independent Scotland – the Right Honourable Alex Salmond.'

~

19 September 2014, Glasgow

'History has been made, and unmade. After 300 years of union with England, Scotland will become once again an independent country.'

The news anchor had prepared two versions, both crafted to capture the import of the moment and perfected after hours of practice in the dressing-room mirror.

The numbers were more prosaic than the lofty rhetoric. 'Yes' had scraped through in the Scottish referendum with 50.3 per cent, on a turnout of 92 per cent. In the end, only 20,000 ballots separated the two campaigns but the knife-edge result had been hinted at in the first declaration Clackmannanshire, considered a bellwether area, had returned a victory for 'Yes' by just seventeen votes.

Four hundred miles south in Downing Street, David Cameron glugged a very large dram of Bruichladdich and cast aside the typed pages he had only minutes ago been annotating.

'Boris it is then,' he mumbled almost silently, still too shocked to summon up vitriol.

A considerate tap on the door. Cameron's principal private secretary slid in, almost apologetically.

'Is this what I think it is, Chris?'

'Yes, Prime Minister. It's the palace.'

Cameron downed another swig of his single malt and dropped the crystal tumbler onto the sheaf of papers. Through the amber remnants in the bottom of the glass, Cameron's scrawl was barely legible at the top of the document: 'Win – EVEL'. The Prime Minister's study was still now, save for the piercing white flashes that accompanied Alex Salmond's beaming face on Sky News.

By morning, the removal vans had arrived at No. 10 and George Osborne was at the Westminster home of Graham Brady, chairman of the 1922 Committee. It was already too late. A backbencher had agreed to take Chiltern and make way for Boris, a selfless act for party and country. The peerage, ministerial sinecure at the Foreign Office and clutch of handsome directorships down the line were but polite adornments, you understand.

It had to be Boris. Brady knew; his members knew; Boris certainly knew; and, deep down, Osborne knew too. They had lost Scotland and if they mishandled the negotiations to break up the United Kingdom – the idea, the very words that expressed it, threatened to induce nausea – they could lose the rest of the country too. Osborne had a hunch how the next few months would play out; the precision of his predictions was scarcely satisfying.

In Brady's study, too, Sky News held court. Presenter Niall Paterson, squinting through sleep-deprived eyes, teed-up for the viewers as the feed cut to Bute House, the Edinburgh residence of Scotland's First Minister.

'... Alex Salmond, who has achieved something his predecessors as leader of the SNP could only dream of – here is Alex Salmond.'

~

19 September 2014, Edinburgh

Salmond drank in the applause and adulation of staffers, both political aides and the civil servants finally liberated from pretended neutrality. Conflicting emotions tore at him: the exhausted joy of victory, the pang for those not here to share it, and a fierce determination to get to work – he caught his breath and finished the thought – building a new country, an independent nation.

The first task was national unity.

> There are no nationalists and Unionists anymore, no Yes and No – only Scots working together to create a strong country and a fair society. 'Work as if you live in the early days of a better nation,' because, fellow Scots, after years of longing and decades of dreaming, finally we do.
>
> And to our friends south of the border, we are not leaving you. We are merely finding our own way in the world. England will always be our closest ally and her people our dearest neighbours. We will still share a currency and a central bank and trade as member states of the European Union. And of course Her Majesty will still be our head of state, as the Queen of Scots. The Scottish government stands ready to work constructively to secure a dissolution of the Union that is fair and equitable to both sides.

It was a speech of 'uncommon magnanimity for a political bruiser like Salmond', the *Glasgow Herald* commented in a leader the following day. 'Statesmanlike' was *The Guardian*'s appraisal. Even the *Daily Telegraph*'s Alan Cochrane praised the 'dignity' shown by his arch-enemy, though he wondered how long it would be before Scotland's major towns and cities saw 'skirmishes in the streets'. The cybernats, the SNP's online army of vitriol-flingers and patriotism-impugners, harrumphed at the last part but were too giddy with triumph to make much of a fuss. Neither Cochrane nor they could have foreseen how mantic his words would prove to be.

~

3 October 2014, Nuneaton, Warwickshire

The moment the billboards went up, Osborne knew they were in trouble A gaudy poster showed Alex Salmond carrying a tartan swag bag with a giant cartoon £ sign jutting out. 'DON'T LET HIM GET AWAY SCOT

FREE.' UKIP. Smack-bang in the Midlands. The general election just got infinitely more difficult, the Chancellor sighed to himself.

This is why they needed Boris. The former Mayor of London had been elected to replace David Cameron as Conservative leader, but not before an unexpected groundswell of support had gathered around backbencher Peter Bone. Boris seemed on his way to victory by acclamation, George Osborne and Theresa May having recused themselves and thrown their support behind the 'blond bombshell'. Bone was initially written off as a crank obsessed with the manifold iniquities of the European Union. 'The Conservatives would sooner elect a teapot to lead them into the general election,' Matthew Parris assured readers of *The Times*.

Within twenty-four hours, the Twitter and Facebook pages of Conservative supporters were adorned with Union Jack teapot logos in support of the Wellingborough MP. His campaign attracted hundreds of earnest young right-wing activists and his public meetings brought out Tory members and non-members alike, even in the bitter November chill. Bone offered himself as a 'common-sense Conservative' who could cut through the 'north London, hug-a-hoodie liberalism' of the Cameroons and speak to the country at large, including working-class Labour and UKIP voters.

A Bone-led Conservative Party would campaign to hold a referendum on Britain's withdrawal from the EU, pull out of the European Convention on Human Rights, impose a ten-year moratorium on immigration and legislate to reinstate the death penalty, corporal punishment and grammar schools. The BBC would be privatised, the Department for International Development abolished, and the smoking ban repealed. 'Oh,' he would add theatrically when he was done rhyming off his to-do list at yet another village hall event, 'and I will proclaim 20 September – the anniversary of the Bruges speech – Margaret Thatcher Day.' Rapturous applause was guaranteed every time.

The Labour Party could not believe its luck. It was usually the left that lost its mind and threw electability to the winds. Now the Tories had their own militant tendency to contend with: the 'Continuity WI', as *The Independent*'s John Rentoul dubbed them, or 'blue-rinse Bennites' in the jottings of *The Observer*'s Andrew Rawnsley. Over strategy suppers at Boris Johnson's townhouse, they were more commonly referred to as 'the bastards'. Simple, crisp and with a familiar ring to it.

For a time, the Blairite rump in the Labour Party had mulled a putsch against Ed Miliband, aiming to boost the party's appeal to centrist voters affronted by the Bone insurgency. But they could never quite get it off the ground. Not only were they divided over whether the ticket should be Tristram and Liz or Liz and Tristram, but Labour's sentimental attachment to its leader, however weak and feckless, remained strong. Miliband would stay put until the general election, which he might even win. If the possibility filled moderate Conservatives with foreboding, it was nothing compared to the horror such an outcome inspired in the Blairites.

Eventually Bone's campaign ran out of steam as party grandees, most with bitten tongues, closed ranks around Boris. But the piper had to be paid. Johnson shifted right and promised the next Tory government – with luck, shorn of meddlesome Liberal Democrats – would crack down on immigration and crime and legislate for a referendum on BBC privatisation. Fixed-term parliaments – a long-running bugbear for the backbenchers – would go, and the international aid budget would be cut and reallocated to the Foreign Office. Margaret Thatcher Day would become a reality but would fall sometime in July (when everyone was on holiday or too harassed by children to notice, Boris did not add). In exchange for dropping out of the race altogether, thus allowing a smooth transition to No. 10, his rival demanded an undertaking that Cabinet ministers would be allowed to campaign for an 'Out' vote in a referendum on EU membership. *The Sun* billed it the 'Bone Ultimatum' and, with a few provisos, Boris agreed. After years of plotting and planning, he was finally Prime Minister.

Now George Osborne, tasked by the incoming PM with winning a majority in May, had to parry a populist UKIP campaign against what Nigel Farage called the 'ingrate Scots'. Public sentiment had turned hostile after the 'Yes' vote in September and private polling showed strong majorities in England and Wales in favour of blocking Scotland from using the pound and gaining accession to the EU. 'England expects revenge,' one Tory pollster told the Prime Minister and Chancellor. The former was cynical enough to give them it, the latter noted with growing unease.

~

5 January 2015, The Scotland Office, Whitehall

There was trouble in the air; Alex Salmond could sniff it. The location was the first hint. This was the inaugural meeting of Scottish and UK government principals to reach an agreement on the timetable for formal independence and to determine an equitable division of the assets. The First Minister and his advisers had always assumed that these discussions would take place in Downing Street. Instead, they had been relegated to Dover House – 'Colonial House' per Salmond – as though Johnson wanted to play down the significance. 'Good luck with that,' remarked one of Salmond's aides drily.

As they waited for the Prime Minister to arrive, Salmond and his *consiglieri* made a final run-through of tactics. *Calm but firm. Accommodating but strong. Don't try to bluff but don't give away the farm either.*

'It's very important that we get agreement on the Queen of Scots stuff,' Salmond announced to the room. His deputy, Nicola Sturgeon, seated a cool distance away, bulged her eyes and caught herself on the brink of a despondent headshake.

A spin doctor cleared his throat. 'I think we should focus on currency at this session. We'll have plenty of time to work on the constitution.'

'Should I use Geoff's line about the UK's economic security?' Salmond ventured, uncharacteristically anxious.

'Doubt it'll fly,' a special adviser replied. 'They get Brent crude alerts on their phones just like the rest of us.'

Brent crude had tumbled to $50 a barrel since the referendum, but in the upheaval and the excitement only experts and economists were talking about oil prices; Salmond had no need to rid himself of any troublesome priests since the Scottish public seemed joyously oblivious to the looming catastrophe. Support for the SNP was sky-high and some predicted that the party could take as many as thirty seats in the general election, the last UK poll Scotland would take part in. The nationalists' campaign slogan – 'The Best Deal for Scotland' – pitched them as the party that would make sure Scots weren't short-changed in the negotiations. (One SNP candidate was forced to stand down when he rephrased the mantra as 'We'll Finish the Bastards Off'.)

Whenever opposition politicians brought up the value of oil revenues, Salmond would smile beatifically and insist that the market would correct itself soon enough. As a former oil economist, he knew the Rebecca-of-Sunnybrook-Farm routine would only work for so long before the voters started to get cold feet and began questioning the affordability of independence. 'Look on the bright side,' he had quipped in Cabinet just the other day. 'Maybe there are secret oil fields after all.'

Everyone laughed but Sturgeon.

Half an hour after the scheduled start time, the doors opened and George Osborne strode into the room, flanked on either side by twice as many aides as Salmond had come armed with. The Prime Minister had been detained on a national security matter, the Chancellor essayed; would they mind terribly if we made a start and maybe he'll manage to join us later?

Every ounce of instinct told Salmond to kick up a fuss, stand up and walk out. Johnson had pulled the rug out from under him. Embarrassed him by sending his No. 2 to lead the negotiations. What kind of good faith could they have now? Instead, he clamped his lips, then forced a shallow smile. Like it or not, they were holding all the cards.

An hour later, he would be in a Park Lane hotel suite turning the air blue and burning with ire that he had not gone with his intuition and walked out.

Osborne had been blunt-polite, that curious mixture of good manners and ruthlessness particular to the English petit-aristocracy. The UK government had been willing to reach a monetary arrangement – so much for 'walk away from the UK and you walk away from the pound', Salmond huffed silently – but within a strict fiscal framework requiring a mixture of significant reductions in public spending and revenue hikes, as well as abandonment of proposals to cut corporation tax rates and air passenger duty.

'No, I'm not prepared to agree to…' Salmond began, sincerely indignant.

'It doesn't matter.' Osborne tossed his hand a touch more imperiously than he had intended. 'Currency union's off the table now. It's politically impossible. YouGov has 61 per cent opposed to any currency deal with Scotland. Our internals have it closer to 70 per cent. The breakdown for the Midlands is eye-watering.'

'Well, the Midlands will find it even more eye-watering when they have to do without our balance of pay—'

'Alex, it's a non-starter. It'll kill us with our own voters, undecideds hate it, and UKIP is gearing up to cane us over it. Keep the balance of payments; we'd rather keep Downing Street.'

Salmond was, perhaps for the first time in his political career, if not his life, speechless.

The Chancellor continued: 'We're also going to have a problem with sharing DWP infrastructure until you get your own set-up…'

Across the room, a deep sickness gripped Sturgeon's stomach and for a moment she feared she might vomit right there and then. Osborne wasn't bluffing.

Then Salmond piped up: 'Do we get to keep the Queen?'

~

8 May 2015, 10 Downing Street

Boris Johnson's hair was perfectly manicured this morning; manicured to be neat, not its usual sculpted tufts of straw. The desired image was calm, in charge, don't frighten the horses. As he opened his mouth to speak, the Downing Street photographers attacked all at once with their flashes.

> I have attended Her Majesty at Buckingham Palace, where she has commissioned me to serve as Prime Minister of a coalition government. Mr Farage will serve as Deputy Prime Minister and Foreign Secretary. The full details of the ministry will be provided to the gentlemen and gentleladies of the press in good time.

The Tories had fallen twenty-seven seats shy of a majority, a slip-back on their 2010 result. UKIP took thirty-nine seats, most of them from Labour heartlands in the north, where immigration and fear of a Labour/SNP coalition had been central. In Scotland, Labour leader Jim Murphy had retained his seat along with sixteen MPs from the party's Glasgow and Lanarkshire redoubts. The SNP had captured thirty, more than double its best-ever haul, but its inflated talk of holding the balance of power in the new parliament proved to be just that.

Tory moderates were aghast at Boris's deal with UKIP. Three Cabinet ministers resigned while others let it be known they would not work with a junior UKIP minister in their department. It was a modest rebellion but, in years to come, historians would agree that it marked the point at which a Conservative split became inevitable.

In the battle to replace Ed Miliband, neither the Blairites nor the left got their way. Alan Johnson surprised everyone with a last-minute entry, handily tossing aside Chuka Umunna and Andy Burnham. (There had been an effort to get Jeremy Corbyn on the ballot but even sympathetic MPs grasped the danger of entryism under the £3 supporters scheme and refused to sign his nomination papers.) The prospect of a Johnson *v.* Johnson match-up at Prime Minister's Questions delighted the sketchwriters, but nothing could have prepared them for the first joust. Alan cheerfully flayed Boris with nicey-bloke charm, joking about their starkly differing backgrounds and life experiences. Even the Tory back benches chortled along as their leader was forced to grind out a smile. Their laughter was quickly curtailed when Good Cop sat down and his rougher colleagues began machine-gunning the Prime Minister about his controversial past statements and those of his new deputy, Mr Farage. Three questions were given over to the term 'piccaninnies' alone. By the half-hour's conclusion, Boris looked worn out and frustrated. It would prove to be one of his better performances.

~

3 August 2015, 11 Downing Street

Veronica Lawson had been a secretary in the Chancellor's office for almost thirty years. She had brought tea to Nigel Lawson and something stronger to Norman Lamont on Black Wednesday. Ken Clarke had been her favourite – and her least favourite? Well, she couldn't possibly say, but during the first ten years of New Labour, she would often drown the cacophony of bellowed profanities and airborne mobile phones in Shostakovich's second piano concerto.

The close proximity to power made her privy to the comings and goings of the most important men and women in the land. She overheard secrets and picked up snippets of landmark policies before anyone else. And yet she was the soul of discretion, a rare employee of Downing Street uninterested in gossip. Today she was planning the Chancellor's diary three months in advance and— coffee! She'd forgotten the coffee.

A light tap on the door and she let herself in with the steaming china cup.

'I'm well aware of what we said during the—'

The Chancellor sounded angry and ... something else...

'They're our biggest trading part—'

She placed the coffee on his desk but he continued his conversation and did not acknowledge her. That was un— The milk!

'Can't we at least string this out a bit?' she heard as she rushed out of the office.

On her way back in she heard the fury rising in the Chancellor's voice and ... still, she couldn't put her finger on it.

'It's the f–ing European Commission. Procrastination and bureaucracy are the only things they're any f–ing good at.'

Veronica placed the miniature milk jug next to the untouched coffee and turned to walk out.

'We had an agree—'

That was it, the elusive emotion. It was desperation.

Osborne hung up the phone and turned ashen as he ran the conversation through his mind. As his secretary left the room, she heard him pick up the receiver and begin to dial.

'Hello, Alex? It's George. There's a problem. No, it's not about the Queen.'

What Veronica did not know, but what Osborne was about to recount to Salmond, was the other end of his conversation. As he mouthed the words, it felt like he was listening to someone else say them. Scotland's application to join the European Union as an independent country had been rejected out of hand. Spain had confirmed that it would veto any such expansion and it was not the only member state to give notice. Since the 'Yes' campaign's narrow victory in the Scottish referendum, there had been a surge in nationalist and separatist movements across the EU. The capitals of Europe had watched in horror as secessionist parties swept local and provincial elections and demanded plebiscites of their own as a condition of cooperating with national government. The only way to stop the surge was to supply a dramatic example of the consequences of breaking away. Scotland was to be shut out of the EU *pour discourager les autres*.

When the news broke, high-street retailers flocked to the exit, followed by supermarkets, service sector firms, much of Silicon Glen, and any major interest that didn't have 'Scotland' in its title. Even among those, there were deserters – Newcastle-bottled Irn-Bru was an innovation, to say the least – and each day the tally of departing jobs exploded again. In an exquisite act of corporate trolling, Tunnock's announced it would stay.

Europe always does for you in the end, Osborne mused, remembering the recent history of the Conservative Party. The government was banking on an early EU referendum so that the Scots could take part and, they calculated, secure a majority for 'In'. It was why negotiations for Scotland's departure were being spun out. Without Scotland, it was impossible to say which way the vote would go. 'We can't have Brexit *and* Jockxit,' quipped one Treasury Spad, too clever by half. In the spirit of democracy, for which the Tories have always been famed, the Chancellor convinced the Prime Minister privately to rat on the promised plebiscite. It was now a matter of stringing along Farage until the polls picked up and the government could seek a fresh mandate. Osborne was not optimistic, but it was all they had.

~

2 November 2015, Bute House, Edinburgh

The moment George Robertson walked into the room, he knew Salmond was itching to make a deal. Baron Robertson of Port Ellen, as the one-time student radical was now known, had been dispatched by the Prime Minister to handle the latest headache in breaking up the UK. Salmond had made much during the referendum campaign of ridding Scotland of the moral obscenity of the Trident nuclear deterrent. NATO did not take too kindly to one of its key members losing her nuclear capabilities, even temporarily. Salmond was told in no uncertain terms: if the subs and the warheads left the Clyde before the UK government had found a suitable replacement site, Scotland would be barred from NATO.

Robertson cleared his throat. 'The Prime Minister is prepared to—'

Salmond's head shot up from the papers on his desk. He looked tired, haunted almost. 'A fifty-year lease on Faslane and Coulport during which they are de facto UK territory.'

Robertson sputtered. 'What?'

Salmond pressed on. 'You heard me. The UK will have effective sovereignty and will control all points of entry and egress. The base will operate as at present but it wouldn't be on Scottish soil, at least not for fifty years.'

'In exchange for what?' Robertson tried but failed to conceal the cynicism in his voice.

When Salmond named his price, Robertson winced, but he knew Downing Street would stump up. This was the sort of nationalist they could work with. He also knew something else: the books weren't looking good. If they were asking for this much, they weren't looking good at all.

They chatted for another twenty minutes – some detail, mostly politics – before Robertson got up to leave and Salmond to walk him out.

Robertson stopped at the door and turned, presenting his best sympathetic face.

'Was it worth it?' he half-asked, half-wondered, aloud.

Salmond rocked on his heels. 'Honestly, George. I don't know.'

~

15 December 2015, Edinburgh

It would come to be known as 'Swinney's folly', but in truth Alex Salmond was the driver of the SNP's last-ever Budget. Brent crude had dipped below \$40 a barrel and despite a well-received bid to join EFTA, Scotland's impending isolation from EU markets had already crippled the food and drink industry. What loomed larger in Finance Minister John Swinney's mind, though, was the deficit. The nationalists had poured scorn on the Institute for Fiscal Studies when it had forecast a Scottish fiscal gap of £7.6 billion, and they had been right to. The actual figure was almost double that. Scotland was deep in the red and bleeding pints by the second.

Swinney had approached the IMF while Salmond, unbeknownst to his Cabinet colleagues, had tapped up the Russians, the Iranians and the Chinese. Moscow and Tehran offered diplomatic sympathy but little else; Beijing didn't even respond. The IMF was persuadable but contingent on a programme of severe – they preferred 'ambitious' – public expenditure cuts. The Finance Minister relayed the terms to his boss, advising against such measures. Swinney was a fiscal conservative, not a state-slashing libertarian; this was, he warned Salmond, 'Thatcherism with turbo boosters'.

With alternative options scarce on the ground, Salmond decreed that their only choice was their only choice. The financial solvency of an independent Scotland, the very country itself, was at stake. Swinney kept these words in mind. They sustained him as he oversaw the drafting of a Budget and gave him some confidence when he presented it to Cabinet.

There would be dramatic cuts to public spending and sharp tax hikes in all income brackets. Free personal care, tuition, childcare and prescriptions would go. Co-payments would be introduced for primary healthcare and outpatient hospital appointments, while public sector pay would be reduced and a quarter of the workforce laid off. Corporation tax would be abolished to incentivise investment, and foreign companies would be encouraged to buy and develop as much land as possible.

We are not privy to the discussion that ensued. Perhaps we will find out under the thirty-year rule, perhaps never. What we know of what happened next is this: Nicola Sturgeon walked out, accompanied by half the Cabinet. One week later, she announced the formation of the Scottish Progressives. In all, a quarter of nationalist MSPs crossed over to the new party, which pledged opposition to 'SNP austerity'. The split deprived Salmond of his majority and he was forced to rely on Conservative and

Liberal Democrat votes to push through the Budget. To make matters worse, a typo inadvertently tripled funding for Gaelic, a gaffe spotted by the political editor of the *Daily Record* and carried the next morning under the headline 'EPIC GAEL'.

The SNP's poll ratings fell faster than the oil price and the streets swelled with protestors – 100,000 in Edinburgh, 250,000 on the Scottish Trades Union Congress demo in Glasgow. Other marches turned violent and every night viewers would tune into the STV *News at Six* to scenes of placards flung at police and water cannons set on students. The most infamous was the 23 January protest on Glasgow Green, or 'Bloody Saturday' as it came to be known. A larger than expected crowd made policing impossible without kettling, but this only produced a crush in which eight people were trampled to death and hundreds injured. A mob rounded on two officers who had become separated from their colleagues and pursued them along Templeton Street. PC Christopher Kerr, cornered, watched as Sergeant Stephen Mahoney was beaten and stamped to death, before the twenty-strong throng turned its attention to him. In a blind panic, Kerr unholstered his Glock 17 9mm and fired at his assailants, killing three – four when Iris Kinney was counted, for she had been in her garden across the street tending her roses when the stray bullet struck her chest and collapsed her lung.

~

1 February 2016

Public appetite for a second referendum now sat at 69 per cent; if one were held, the Unionist side would win comfortably. Jim Murphy wasn't willing to take the risk and campaigned instead for a mandate to negotiate a new treaty of union, announced at the launch of Scottish Labour's election campaign in Glasgow. This transformed the 5 May Holyrood election into a referendum on returning to the UK. Murphy, for reasons passing understanding, insisted on referring to it as 'Scotland's transfer deadline day'. He resurrected his autumn 2014 tour and addressed thousands in town squares up and down the country atop his Irn-Bru crate.

It was a thoroughly dishonest campaign in the best of Scottish Labour traditions. Murphy promised reunification on roughly the same terms as the old devolution settlement: higher public spending per head, a powerful Scottish Parliament, and an alternative to the hard-right governing agenda at Westminster. In different times, popular cynicism would have greeted such dubious assurances, but the voters, surveying the chaos unfolding around them, were in no mood for details.

~

24 March 2016, Calton Hill, Edinburgh

Invoking his largely unchecked powers under the interim constitution, Salmond retitled himself 'Prime Minister of Scotland'. It was under this nomenclature that he officiated at the independence day celebrations in Edinburgh. Given the public mood, he was advised to downplay the event, but Salmond was not going to miss his day in the history books.

In the event, there was little in the way of glory. The clear skies predicted by the weatherman were supplanted by dark, pregnant clouds that burst open and never seemed to stop for the rest of the day. Sean Connery, billed to return to Scotland, missed his flight at JFK, while the car bringing Winnie Ewing to open the proceedings got caught in traffic for an hour. As they waited, the few hundred drenched souls who had turned up to watch the festivities were treated to the very best the Scottish folk scene had to offer. When the wind-battered dais collapsed midway through Eddi Reader's rendition of 'Scots Wha Hae', uncharitable sorts took it as a blessing. The gales bore a more ominous verdict from on high during the closing prayer, when the Moderator of the General Assembly of the Church of Scotland beseeched the Almighty's wisdom and guidance and was summarily struck by a flying traffic cone and briefly knocked unconscious.

The slapstick scenes brought the evening news its highest ratings in decades and made cracking copy for the papers. They also dramatised the sense among many Scots that independence was a rolling disaster, one that was making them and their nation a laughing stock around the world. For those still minded to give independence a chance, it would be tragedy, not comedy, that changed their minds.

~

3 April 2016, Rutherglen, Lanarkshire

No one ever established when *Mic na h-Alba* (Sons of Scotland) was founded. It had no constitution and no public meetings; it was not the kind of organisation that kept minutes. As far as anyone could tell, it began as a violent fantasy for hardline cybernats but was soon brought to life in a loose network of ultras and militants who believed in 'direct action' to rid Scotland of 'the enemy within'. At first, it was hate mail, but those missives lost their potency after one agitator posted his ten-page 'Treason Indictment' to the Bank of Scotland and his mortgage application to Ruth Davidson. The *Miccers* moved on to letter bombs, most of which proved to be duds; their most fearsome strike involved blowing an ear off a Labour MSP's dog.

'Sgùr' was what changed *Mic na h-Alba* from punchline to grisly byword for nationalist extremism. 'Sgùr' spray-painted at the entrance to the *Scotsman* newspaper building; 'Sgùr' daubed in deep red on the steps outside BBC Scotland. 'Sgùr', the sign-off on a *Mic na h-Alba* blog execrating the English-born population of Scotland. And when the flames were finally doused and the bodies removed, the police found a word carved into the front door of the Wright family home, just two months after they had moved from Nuneaton to Rutherglen: 'Sgùr' – 'Cleanse'.

Salmond condemned each outrage angrily and promised every resource to hunt down the Wrights' killers. He visited the fire-gutted semi on a quintessentially Scottish suburban street to lay flowers and, to his surprise, found himself mouthing the Lord's Prayer as his eyes moistly traced the sickly black cavities of burnt-out windows. 'A pall of darkness has fallen over Scotland,' he told the waiting cameras.

> This is not what our country is about. This is not why we struggled for independence. Anyone who comes to raise their family, advance their career, or enjoy a better way of life is welcome. No matter where they come from, they belong here. Racism and terrorism do not belong here. They do not represent the aspirations of the people of our nation,

> a tolerant and decent people. A pall of darkness has fallen over Scotland but together we will drive it back with the light of love.

It was Salmond's finest speech – but if it brought solace to others it did nothing to console him. It was getting away from him and he knew it. His benediction was not just for the Wrights.

~

6 May 2016, Bute House, Edinburgh

That the SNP was finished was well known, but confirmation came around 2 a.m., when the results flooded in from Scotland's first and last election under independence. Labour swept all before it, taking eighty-two of Holyrood's 129 seats. Jim Murphy, whom many had doubted and only the most perceptive had kept faith with, was Prime Minister of Scotland. The SNP and the Scottish Progressives were annihilated. Nicola Sturgeon – gone; John Swinney – gone. Alex Salmond clung on by a handful of votes, but resigned from Parliament several months later. The Scottish Tories, as much to their own surprise as anyone else's, became the official opposition.

Salmond sat with his back to his desk, studying a framed copy of the *Scottish Sun*'s front page from 19 September 2014: 'YES WE CAN'. Behind him, Jim Murphy was on television promising Scotland's return to the United Kingdom before the year was out. The crowd hollered in lusty assent. The people of Scotland have spoken, thought Salmond, and decided they do not wish to speak for themselves. He drained the last drops of Glenmorangie from his glass and headed upstairs. The dream was dead.

~

1 December 2016

The 2016 Treaty of Union, facilitated by the Acts of Union passed at Holyrood and Westminster, returned Scotland to the fold. The Tories took the opportunity to crowbar in some wish-list items. The name 'United

Kingdom' would be discontinued in favour of 'Great Britain', an entity into which Northern Ireland was also incorporated. Under the Act, Great Britain would be indissoluble except by Britain-wide referendum. The devolved administrations would be standardised, the Scottish Parliament enjoying the same powers as the Welsh Assembly and the remainder being retrenched to Westminster. All administrations were to be known as executives, not 'governments', the Scottish Cabinet was to become the 'ministerial council' and the Cabinet Secretary title reserved for British Cabinet ministers.

A few other nasties were snuck in by Conservative ministers. There would be no return to English taxpayers subsidising more generous public expenditure north of the border; a new formula would ensure funding was equalised across Britain. The Scottish Parliament would lose its powers over planning permission – a sop to the shale gas industry – and MSPs would be banned from debating reserved matters.

It was a lamentable deal for Scotland, as the public would come to see in time, but in the early years most were just relieved to be back in Britain. When Jim Murphy and Boris Johnson emerged from Bute House, holding aloft their copies of the Treaty of Union, a throng of thousands welcomed them with ecstatic applause. Union Jacks were draped from windows and flown from car aerials. When the announcement flashed on the news screen at Glasgow Central Station, commuters broke into a spontaneous chorus of 'God Save the Queen'. Eight months of independence had been more than enough for Scotland; now the country yearned to get back to normal – to security, to certainty.

If the decision to secede from the UK had been made rashly by many, inflamed by grievance and sentiment, the acquiescence to the terms of the new union was no less ill-judged. But it was what Scotland wanted, what Scotland got, and, some would say, what Scotland deserved.

~

7 June 2018, Cambridge, Massachusetts

'So in the end, Labour governed an independent Scotland for longer than the SNP?' Martha Minow enquired bloodlessly. The former SNP leader's speech had concluded with polite applause from the rain-soaked graduates and now he was doing a Q&A with the university president.

'To my mind we were only independent during my six weeks,' Salmond maintained. 'Everything after that was just one long tug on the forelock.'

And did he feel any animus towards Jim Murphy for taking Scotland back into Britain, or Nicola Sturgeon for splitting the nationalist movement?

'No, I'm not a bitter man. I see myself as a latter-day Fletcher of Saltoun, fighting in Scotland's interest. But, like him, I found there's aye a parcel of rogues in a nation.'

Minow began to wrap up. 'I'd like to thank our guest Alex Salmond for a provocative and illuminating address and I'm sure everyone here will want to join me in...'

The academic paused and turned to Salmond. 'Did you ever find out about the Queen? Would you have got to keep her?'

Salmond drilled back into his teeth, then managed a smile.

'Yes,' he lied.

Chapter 19

What if Lynton Crosby had changed sides in 2015?

Adrian Moss

8 May 2015

The clock in the hall struck eleven, and silence swiftly fell on the crowd behind him. He took the deepest of breaths and brushed imaginary dust from his suit jacket.

He smiled, pre-empting the question…

'Ready, Prime Minister?'

… and then nodded.

The door opened and he walked out into a blast wave of cheers and the dazzling blitz of camera flashes.

It was only ten yards to the microphones but it seemed to stretch for ten miles. He eventually made it and clutched the podium with relief. Smiled a winning smile. Let the applause continue. Listened to the cheers and wild whoops of joy. And then held up a hand.

Gradually, little by little, the noise dissipated.

He smiled again.

'Earlier this morning, I had the honour of visiting Her Majesty the Queen, and she has asked me to form a government. I have accepted. It's been quite a night for Britain and there are many people to thank. First of all, I'd like to thank the electorate for their trust they have put in me, and in the Labour Party that I am so proud to lead…'

The applause began again, and the cheering echoed around the street and up and down Whitehall.

This time though, he let it carry on.

January 2015

By the time the long campaign began in earnest it was obvious that Ed Miliband had three big electoral problems. The first was Scotland. Decades of monster majorities had led to a blithe acceptance within the Labour Party that they could secure fifty-odd Scottish seats without even having to print a leaflet. Now, unbelievably, there was serious opposition. His second problem was the incoherence of the Labour Party's offer; fine sentiments do not a message make. The semantic awkwardness of their policy 'visions' plainly mystified the voters. His third problem was that the polls all pointed to a hung parliament, and that meant that sooner or later he would have to make his mind up about who he was going to go to bed with.

The Labour Party also had three problems, the first, second and third of which were Ed Miliband himself. Ed was well-meaning but goofy, with the exasperating air of an obstinate nerd. He was a regular victim of the press photographer's art and whatever his team tried to do, he just could not connect with the voters. Born into socialist royalty, with a Fairtrade spoon in his mouth, his only experience of the real world was limited to whatever he saw on TV, glimpsed through a car window or extrapolated from the pages of *The Guardian*.

He was, in essence, unelectable.

Despite this, the polls were in stalemate and had been for weeks. The electorate seemed to want rid of the Tory-led coalition but needed to find positive reasons to vote Labour. Time and time again, having waded through swampy acres of soggy platitudes, they found themselves hopelessly lost, and so returned, empty-handed.

The issue was that although Ed believed he was surrounded by people with keen minds, political cunning and years of frontline experience, no one could come up with an idea remotely good enough to make a difference. Although he did quite like the 'promises set in stone' concept.

Five weeks to go – Saturday

Saturday saw Ed, drained from the rigours of the phony war, walking up on the heath and grabbing a little time to himself. He loved the views and anonymity of the green open spaces, and the fact that no one ever came up to talk to him.

His work mobile was safely locked away in his study, so when his personal phone rang he assumed it was Justine asking what time he'd be back. He answered it without looking at the screen.

An unmistakably Antipodean voice said, 'Ed? It's Lynton Crosby here. How would you like it if I made you Prime Minister?'

Ed assumed it was a joke call, probably Liam Byrne arsing around again, and his initial reaction was to prepare to become a bit cross.

'Liam?'

'Ed? Come on, mate. How about it?'

Gasping through a colossal wave of ice-cold comprehension, Ed realised that it was actually Crosby.

'But why?'

That's all he could come up with at the time. Years of higher education, of fine-tuning his not-insubstantial intellect, of debating the finest minds in the political world – and this was his pathetic response.

'But why?'

He could have kicked himself.

'Because I've had enough of these toffee-nosed wankers, Ed. I've had my fill of being the funny colonial in the corner office and maybe, maybe, I just fancy upsetting the apple cart.'

Ed tried harder this time.

'But seriously. Why?'

'If you really want to know the truth, I've just had the mother of all fall-outs with clever-dick Gideon and I told Cameron it was him or me. So he gave me some vintage public school charm bollocks and then the old-boy network closed ranks. So here I am. Footloose and fancy-free and from what I've seen of the shambles you've got going on there, I reckon you need me.'

Ed said nothing. With the phone clasped to his ear, he looked blankly across the London skyline. The cool spring wind pulled at his cagoule hood.

'You still there, wonder boy?'

'Yes. Look, Lynton, I have two questions.'

'Go for it.'

'How much is this going to cost?'

'Nothing. I'll be doing it for love. Well, the laughs anyway. What's your other question?'

'How did you get this number?'

There was a pause. And then:

'Don't be such a silly prick, Ed. I have everybody's number.'

Ed gulped but pressed on.

'What makes you think you can help us, Mr Crosby?'

'Three things. One. Who? Who's going to win you the election? Your gang of idiots have no idea. Two. How? How are you going to get the key people to vote for you? Platitudes and waffle won't cut it and that's all you've got at the moment. And three. You. Christ on a very fast motorbike, are we going to have to get to work on you.'

'That's a bit rude, if you don't mind me saying so.'

'It's a nasty old game, politics. When can you be back home?'

'In about fifteen minutes.'

'Good. Justine's just said she's putting the kettle on.'

Four and a half weeks to go – Monday – Brewer's Green

Crosby strode into the room where the election team and senior MPs had gathered, and Ed followed. The room stared, some with open mouths. Incredulous, astonished.

Ed began.

'OK, everyone. This is Lynton Crosby and I'm pleased, in fact I'm thrilled, to announce that he will be working as our election guru from now on. He's going to win us the election.'

Only those who have experienced a night in the deepest reaches of the Sahara would have known the purity of the silence that followed this statement.

'I have discussed the terms of our agreement with Lynton and have received assurances that he has severed all ties with the Conservative Party.

In fact, the contract we have both just signed has a binding clause to that effect.'

Douglas Alexander was the first to break.

Icily.

'Why were we not informed of this decision?'

'Because I couldn't risk any leak to the press before we came to an agreement. I'm sure you understand, Douglas.'

Lucy Powell was next.

'This is outrageous. I thought we were supposed to be a democratic party? What about the NEC? What about the idea of collective decision-making?'

Ed nodded sympathetically.

'Sometimes, Lucy, we have to do what's in the interest of the country. The country needs a Labour government. We need to win. Lynton will win us the election. I'm afraid it's as simple as that.'

He continued.

'I know that you will have some very forceful views on this and I will talk to you all, both collectively and individually, later today. In the meantime, I would like you to listen to this presentation and to what Lynton has to say. I think much of it will change your minds.'

An intern crept forward and offered Crosby the remote control for the projector. Crosby put the remote on the desk and took his jacket off. He looked at the front row.

Ed looked focused. Balls looked lightly amused. Dougie Alexander looked like he was going to explode with fury.

'Good morning, team. First things first. Who's in charge of this campaign?'

Four hands were raised; those of the General Election Co-ordinator, the General Election Campaign Director, the Party Executive's Executive Director for Elections and the Director of Policy. In a typical Miliband moment, Ed raised his hand too.

Crosby let this tableau stand for a moment.

'And there, my friends, you have it. You can't have four – sorry, five – people steering the ship at the same time. It's a disaster waiting to happen.'

The hands went down.

'Ed just introduced me as your election guru. That's not going to fly. From this moment I am assuming complete command of the Labour Party election campaign. The strategy starts with me, the buck stops with me. You listen to me, you answer to me and that's that. Unpalatable, I know, but either you want to win or you don't.'

It has always been a battle getting to the top table in the Labour Party, and those that make it can normally start a fight with a cotton bud, or at the very least provoke an argument in an empty lift. Accordingly, an announcement of this stripe would normally have resulted in a riot of condemnation, shouting and insults. On this occasion, though, the sheer shock seemed to nullify it all.

They just sat and stared.

Crosby nodded.

'OK. To work. It's a favourite phrase of mine that you can't fatten a pig on market day, which leaves us in an extremely difficult position. Ideally I would have liked to have begun twelve months ago, but we are where we are, so we're just going to have to force-feed Mr Porky and see how he fares at auction.'

The mention of force-feeding and the allusion to the meat industry went down very poorly.

'Right. This session is down for an hour but we won't be needing that. In fact, this is going to be pretty quick. Every minute that goes past is another minute nearer the count, and the one thing we can't afford to do is sit around talking bollocks when there are votes to go out and get.'

He stopped and looked at the audience. No one stirred or demurred.

'Good. So any campaign needs rules and these are the rules. Meetings start on time and the first meeting of the day will be at 5.45 a.m.'

Ed looked alarmed.

'I'm not really a morning person...'

'Well you are now. 5.45 a.m. My office. Review of the day meeting at 11 p.m. Long hours. But you know, it's only about the next five years of being in charge of 65 million people. If you really want it I'm sure you'll all be able to do without too much sleep.'

He let that one settle.

'Second rule: if anyone believes we're aiming for a coalition then they can leave now. Anyone? Anyone at all? No? Good. From now on anyone mentioning the C-word in terms of a positive outcome will be physically thrown from the building with the imprint of my size ten throbbing on their arse cheeks.'

There was a murmur and Crosby stopped pacing and raised an eyebrow. The murmuring stopped.

'Third rule: stick to the script.'

He picked up the remote and started his presentation. There were just three slides. Normally there were upwards of fifty. That sort of stupidity was going to stop.

'Right. This may shock you. First of all, your research up until now has been crap. And I don't just mean unclear or subject to deviation. It's. Been. Crap. Here's the news for those of you still living in 1997. You have lost Scotland. It's gone. You have been wiped off the face of the Caledonian world. Forget it and move on. Every minute you spend on the doorstep north of the border is a minute you've flushed away. You've got to let Scotland go.'

Douglas Alexander shook his head, Jim Murphy looked crestfallen. Alistair Darling, down for the day, looked enigmatic. Or something. It was always so hard to tell.

'You've lost Scotland, you don't stand a chance in the south-east and you'll never win in the Shires, which leaves three areas. The first is the Labour heartlands – those areas where you've got more than a 10,000 majority. They're safe. We don't bother with those.'

There was a loud expression of disapproval. Crosby looked round the room until the noise died down.

'You don't invade territory you already own. Defend it but concentrate your best forces and your best resources on capturing the ground which leads to victory. It's not bloody rocket science.'

'So where? Where do we campaign?' spluttered Angela Eagle.

Crosby flicked a button on the remote and his second slide came up.

'Here.'

There was another murmur around the room.

'But we're already campaigning there. They're our 100 target seats,' said Chuka Umunna.

'Clever boy. If somewhat innumerate. What you are looking at here is the 120 seats where you will be campaigning. Eighty targets and your forty softest marginals. Eighty to win and forty to keep. And notice, my friends, you will NOT be campaigning for the seat of Twitter bloody North. It doesn't exist.'

There was a noticeable frisson from the members of the Digital Taskforce.

'Yes, you, you bloody heroes, sitting in the warm, playing silly buggers preaching to the converted. Here's the news: invest in some rainwear and a pair of strong boots, you're going to be knocking on doors with the rest of them until further notice. We're going to be using social media later on to target voters, not to bore the poor sods to death. Oh, and that reminds me, call off your troops from the south-west. I don't want to hear a peep from the Labour Party from Cheltenham to Land's End'.

Ben Bradshaw raised his hand.

'I'm sorry? Could you clarify that?

Crosby smiled.

'Of course. The Tories are currently flying under the radar. They are committing everything they've got to smashing the Lib Dems into tiny little pieces. If they succeed, then you'll all be warming your cheeks on the opposition benches until 2020. We cannot, must not, will not, detract a single vote from the Lib Dems in the south-west. If it wasn't too late I'd recommend you withdraw every candidate you've got down there, right now.'

'Preposterous.' Wee Dougie Alexander had been holding it in but couldn't contain himself any longer. 'What about UKIP?'

Crosby fixed him with a stare over the top of his glasses.

'Piss in the wind. They'll steal thousands of votes from you where you can afford to lose them. Other than that they'll simply soften the ground for your message.'

Mystified looks passed around the room.

'And' – here he looked directly at Lucy Powell – 'forget the youth vote. They don't.'

Powell glowered and Crosby smiled sweetly.

'Right. That's it. That's the "Where". This afternoon we look at the "How".'

Muttering broke out and Crosby held up a hand.

'Oh yes, one more thing.'

The chat stopped again. What now?

'Four million conversations? Bollocks. Keep it to 100,000 and make sure you listen to the answers. And, I am only going to say this once, stop telling the world you're having 4 million conversations. Do you think the RAF sent out a press release every time they bombed Berlin? Never, ever, tell the world what you're doing or how you're doing it. It's the height of stupidity. You people have brainwashed yourselves into an admiration of openness that is frankly laughable. Have some bloody secrets. Now go, go and reflect, make phone calls, just go and do something. Everyone back here for two. I'm going to tell you what to converse about.'

Crosby beckoned Ed and they left the room together as the uproar began. Texts were sent and within minutes the editors of all the national newspapers and the news broadcasters were screaming down telephones. Political journalists and commentators whipped themselves up into a frothy mess of speculation. Twitter approached meltdown.

~

'That went better than I expected,' said Ed, after they'd found an empty office. There was a pause before Crosby leant forward.

'OK, Ed. Much of what I'm going to say now is going to be painful, but you're an intelligent man. You know this is for the best.'

Ed shifted in his seat and smiled a smile he didn't feel.

'Right. First, we need to make you look human and, at the same time, prime ministerial. Not an easy task. Second, we need to make you look like a decisive decision-maker; a guy who doesn't take any shit. Third, you're going to have to be the future: the man who can lead the country to better times.'

'OK.'

'You're a nice guy, Ed. People who know you, like you. The problem comes when you put on a suit and pretend to be a politician. So, from now on, two days a week, you're going to be that gentle, nice Ed. Jeans, jumper, comfy shoes.'

'Jeans!'

'Yep. And you're going to be volunteering. Charities, hospitals, drop-in centres. No whistle-stop tours. A full day's work in each. Bedpans and broomsticks.'

Ed stared.

'The rest of the week you'll be suited and booted and travelling by helicopter. Visiting industries, chambers of commerce, business parks and attending conferences.'

'I don't like helicopters.'

'Learn to love them. Politicians travel by train and battle-bus. Statesmen travel by helicopter.'

'What conferences?'

'Any we can find. IT, telecoms, holidays, medical, retail. Anywhere they'll let us in. So, that then brings us to the new decisive Miliband. You're going to have to take on the unions.'

'That's not going to happen. They'd never stand for it.'

'They won't have to. It'll be stage-managed. You'll make a statement, they'll protest, you'll come down hard and they'll publicly roll over. It's in their interest to play along.'

'What makes you so sure they will?'

'I happen to know what the Tories are planning with their Trade Union Bill. Your militant brothers have no option but to help you and I'm going to tell them how they can. Just a little bit of theatre. No biggie.'

Ed couldn't help but laugh. Sometimes events become so surreal that hysteria becomes the only escape.

'And then there's the Scottish question. You're going to be addressing that tonight.'

'I am?'

'The press conference is already booked. We've let it be known that this is a game-changing statement.'

'But what...'

'Later. The third element we need to pin down is how you're going to get people to believe that you're their future leader. I'll be honest with you, Ed, that's one I have yet to crack, but if you get the first two right, the third should follow naturally. Your new slogan will help.'

'My new slogan?'

'One Nation. A Better Nation.'

~

Five minutes past six and the room was packed. Every paper was represented, every broadcaster had the cameras rolling, every political journalist was there. There were twenty-eight from the BBC alone.

Ed clasped the rostrum and came to the end of his statement.

'So, I promise you, the British public and Ms Sturgeon and Mr Salmond in particular, that a coalition with the SNP is not going to be an option I will ever consider. Ever. The Labour Party is the One Nation party. We stand in this election as the only party who cares for every citizen in that nation. The SNP does not believe in the concept of one nation; in fact its primary reason for being is to break up that nation. This, my friends, will not stand. The SNP openly detests the Westminster government and yet hopes to become part of it. That will not stand either. I say this one more time and it is a firm and binding promise: there will be no Labour–SNP coalition. A vote for Labour is simply that. A vote for one nation; a better nation.

Now, I understand that all of you have been working very long hours, as have I. For that reason, I won't be taking any questions. It's going to be a long campaign so, tonight, I urge you to go and see your families and loved ones instead.'

He left the stage and walked off as the predictable din erupted. Crosby, waiting in the wings, smiled and gave him a thumbs up.

'Congratulations, Ed. You've just shot your first fox.'

Three weeks to go

'Mr Miliband, do you accept that when Labour was last in power it overspent?'

The nation shifted in its seat and leant in a little closer to the TV screen. In press offices across London, fingers hovered over keyboards.

Ed smiled. It was the dream question, phrased exactly how Crosby had said it would be.

'Yes. Yes, I do and I'd like to say three things about that. First, we have to hold our hands up, apologise and admit that in our desire to boost public services and civic amenities we spent more than we should have. We didn't see the recession coming – but then, to be fair, no other country did either. Second, I'd ask you to remember what a dreadful state our hospitals, schools and social services were in when we came to power in 1997. The Tories had decimated them; they always do. I'm proud we spent the money we did in building and renewing our great public services. Without that investment we wouldn't have the new schools and hospitals we do now. Third, I'd say that we've learnt. Just like every family does when it invests in an extension, or a new car or that attic conversion and when the payments begin to get difficult you wonder if you've done the right thing. But if you've ever been in that position you know that the benefits of that investment are for the long term. Next time, though, as a family, you'll budget much more accurately. And so will we.'

It wasn't a perfect answer but then it didn't have to be. In those 120 seats that mattered, the few thousand voters to whom it was directed heard it, and got it.

Fox number 2. Dispatched.

Two weeks to go

The South Bank. A warmish Saturday morning. The smell of bacon rises and wafts towards the river. A huge, warm-hearted crowd clutch paper plates and chatter and laugh. There are a lot of servicemen present and they're smiling and laughing too. Volunteers stand over innumerable hotplates and barbecues and their colleagues slice bread and make sandwiches.

Celebrities hand out free bacon sandwiches and cups of tea. Where needed, vegetarian bacon sandwiches are distributed. The press are loving it.

A thunderous cheer goes up as casual Ed, in jeans and a sensible jumper, sits down, holds up a bacon sandwich and waves it at the cameras. Focus lenses are pulled, a thousand cameras flash. He smiles, he jokes and he reminds the crowd that unless the target of £50,000 is reached he won't be eating anything.

The *Daily Mirror* has organised this, and paid for it. There's not a Labour placard or poster anywhere to be seen and Help for Heroes is having a field day. That's a lot of money and exposure for one Saturday morning.

The following day, *The Sun*, its own fox shot, covers the event and Labour's unexpected three-point rise in the polls with the front-page headline: 'Streaky!'

One week to go

Monday evening in London. Russell Brand sits alone and reads a booky wooky.

In a mason's yard in drizzly Kent, a large slab of limestone sits, unused and unmarked.

Monday evening in Gloucester. Jenny Keaton sits with tears streaming down her face. She's just watched a two-minute film about rough sleepers, which had been sent to her on Facebook. The lad who'd been speaking to Ed in the video reminded her so much of her eldest...

Tuesday evening in Nuneaton. Clare Stone clutches her mouth as she watches a two-minute film on Facebook about a family dependent on food banks. Wasn't that the very food bank that Ed had helped out with the week before? So sad. Something should be done. It's a disgrace.

Wednesday; Worcester. Alison Watts is on Facebook catching up with friends. She notices a post that has been sent directly to her. It's a video. About the NHS. Alison's mother has only just come out of hospital. It's something very close to her heart at the moment. She clicks play.

'In politics, where reason and emotion collide, emotion invariably wins,' Crosby would later say after the election.

In May 2015, economic security was the choice of reason, but hope is a very powerful emotion.

Election night

Michael Gove is in trouble. His blithe dismissal of the astonishing exit poll looks like he'll be eating his headwear before the night is over.

As predicted, Labour are being wiped out in Scotland but Rugby, ninety-sixth on their target list, sees a 6,000 Conservative majority turned into an 850 Labour majority.

Bristol North West, eighty-eighth on the list, returns a 2,000 majority for Labour. Nuneaton, Gloucester, Worcester all turn red.

The Lib Dems hold Wells, Cheltenham and Bath.

Lynton Crosby phones Ed, who's sitting on a sofa in a drab cottage sitting room in Doncaster, and says, simply, 'It's going to be tight, but I think we've sold the pig.'

Friday 8 May 2015

Eventually the cheering died down.

'I'd like to thank David Cameron and Nick Clegg...'

A few good-hearted boos. He raised his hand.

'... for their good wishes as I begin the process of forming a government. I will be in discussions later today bringing together the best minds within the party to deliver our key policies and to bring hope to our country.'

He paused.

'The road we have travelled has been a difficult one and no one knows better than me the need for consensus as we face the troubled times ahead. We have been given the opportunity to rebuild broken Britain and I give my solemn vow here, today, that we will strain every sinew to do just that. My team will include those from all standpoints in the party, both those with experience and those without; those from the so-called left and those from the so-called right. We will repay the confidence given to us, we will deliver our promises and our work starts now.

'Thank you.'

May 2015–16

It took just seven days before the first serious Cabinet arguments began; ten days before the internecine briefings started and a mere fortnight to get to the first resignation.

The long-promised utilities cap was brought into law that autumn. Within weeks the shareholders of the companies watched in glee as global oil and gas prices started to plummet. Millions of UK customers were now locked into capped contracts, suffering yet again from Labour's particular and idiosyncratic brand of economic husbandry.

The pre-election deal with the unions fell apart and Londoners got used to walking and cycling to work as crippling public transport strikes brought the capital to its feet.

The first Budget set out the initial tranche of public sector cuts, which included an end to all privatisation initiatives and an immediate freeze on NHS budgets. Over 100,000 operations were cancelled during the strikes that followed, and three Cabinet members voluntarily took the short return trip to the back benches.

The steel industry faltered, fell and collapsed completely, swamped by a global glut of steel and bled dry by Ed's previous 'green' taxes. The voters of Port Talbot and Scunthorpe promised a terrible revenge.

The beleaguered government tried to nullify the PFI contracts Blair and Brown had organised in their previous administrations, but found itself embarrassingly and expensively beaten in court.

By the time Ed had reached 100 days of his premiership, the mood in the country had turned spectacularly sour. The newspapers mocked the government for its 'emperor's new clothes' style of policy-making and its incompetent economic naivety.

Two quick deaths and a defection and Ed found himself reliant on the SNP to pass legislation. With his press office denying that it was anything like a coalition, Ed found all his time taken up with hard bargaining before reluctantly giving up ground.

So Ed did what all leaders do in times of crisis. He announced a reshuffle.

Acknowledging that pragmatism wasn't working, Ed went back to the principles he had first picked up as a child hiding under the dinner table in Primrose Hill, when he'd listened to the adults hold forth over the vegetable lasagne and non-fascist sauvignon. Out went anyone who had served in the Blair Cabinets and in came the battalions from the left.

It was time for a radical new vision for Britain, whether Britain wanted it or not.

2017

A year later, two men take a post-lunch Sunday walk on a frosty footpath. A gentle stroll in wellies. They come to a five-bar gate, lean on it and look over the frozen Surrey heathland.

'I told you it would be a long game. Bet big, win big.'

'Well, you've got plenty of time to fatten the pig this time around.'

'Christ on a very fast motorbike, Michael; by 2020 you'll be the only bloody pig within a hundred miles of the market. The Tories will be in power for generations.'

A pause lingers as that sinks in and then, smiling, they turn back to the frozen footpath and walk on.

Chapter 20

What if Andy Burnham had won the Labour leadership election in 2015?

Asa Bennett

Andy Burnham was under no illusions now. He had been in charge for nearly a year, but was Labour leader in name only. He dreamt on taking office of being a peacemaker, promising to be the man who would unite a troubled party after its two general election defeats, yet now he found himself under attack from all sides, with few friends left in the shadow Cabinet. The fact that the Labour Party had gathered for its second annual conference under his leadership gave him little to celebrate, as the mood among delegates in Liverpool was morose. Barely anyone had confidence in Burnham's leadership, with most keener to discuss only one question – who would replace him?

The leadership chatter deeply troubled Burnham, who had been cooped up in his hotel room all evening working on the keynote speech he would give the following day. Aides had tried to shield him from the rumours when they first started doing the rounds, but after a while it became pointless, as he could see for himself how things had changed. Shadow Cabinet meetings had become increasingly ill-tempered, with members either directly challenging their leader or sitting quietly and working on what cutting one-liners they would use when briefing the press afterwards. Burnham asked his aides to find out which of them were complaining about him to reporters so that he could sack them, but thought again after he was informed who was being indiscreet. 'You'd be the only shadow Cabinet member left,' his spin doctor Kevin Maguire warned him.

Most Labourites had a reason to dislike their party leader. Moderates thought he was a sell-out, while those on the hard left thought he was little more than a 'red Tory'. Despite the party being a broad church, one man's name never went away as a leadership challenger – Jeremy Corbyn, the stalwart socialist whom Burnham had pipped to the post in the leadership race. His followers saw him as the king over the water, the man whose time would come after having victory denied to him in the leadership race, while centrists just wanted Burnham gone. The media hadn't helped calm things down in the party by talking up the prospect of a Corbyn-led challenge – dubbing it 'Coupbyn'.

Andy Burnham had given his life to the party, spending years on the campaign trail, getting to know the key players, hobnobbing with union bosses and schmoozing MPs in the Commons tea room and out on the football pitch. He risked derision with his love for the Labour Party, proudly promising during the leadership campaign to 'put the party first'. 'Country first!' one of his rivals, Liz Kendall, shot back in a bid to score points off him. Burnham didn't care as he felt he was just speaking the truth. But after many months fighting to stop Labour splitting into what pundits increasingly saw as two parties within a party, his mantra was being sorely tested. He increasingly wondered how he could put the party first, when it seemed to want the man who came second instead. How had it come to this?

~

The race to succeed Ed Miliband had started out nicely enough for Burnham, who swiftly became the front runner. His name recognition put him ahead of Yvette Cooper and Liz Kendall, while he had been receiving positive noises from Unite union leader Len McCluskey. The unions had helped Ed Miliband beat his brother David to the top job in 2010, so every endorsement for Burnham's candidacy would be crucial. Burnham decided it was best to publicly champion the unions, rather than be embarrassed about them, so he brushed away questions about their influence by describing their help as the 'cleanest money in politics'. Some of his aides wanted him to rule out taking any money from them for his campaign bid, but Burnham pointedly refused to do so, telling one reporter, 'I won't let those Bullingdon boys dictate how we involve working people in this election.'

There was a fierce debate in the Burnham camp about how he should position himself in the race, with Yvette Cooper gaining attention for criticising the party's 'anti-business, anti-growth and ultimately anti-worker' agenda under Miliband. Some of his aides wanted him to trump Cooper's rhetoric by delivering an even more pro-business speech as a way to differentiate himself from the Miliband era. Plans had already been drawn up for this, with a speech drafted to deliver in the City, in which he would praise businesspeople as 'heroes', admit that his party 'got it wrong on business', and urge members to 'celebrate the spirit of enterprise'. 'We mustn't forget about Nuneaton Man,' one adviser reminded Burnham, referring to the seat lost by Labour in 2010 and held by the Tories five years later, which showed that they were on track to victory.

Others were sceptical about this approach, arguing that it would hamper Burnham's efforts to appeal to Labour's left-wing members, and allow him to be lumped in together with Cooper and Kendall. He needed his party's backing before he could speak to the wider electorate, they insisted. 'You can't start wooing back Nuneaton Man until CLP Man has elected you,' one remarked. Burnham was shown the latest private polling, which indicated that Kendall was floundering, despite offering 'harsh truths' to the party on issues such as its need to back increased defence spending. She wasn't offering harsh truths, Burnham concluded, she was just being harsh. The polling also showed that activists felt markedly warm towards Jeremy Corbyn, a candidate who had only scraped onto the ballot paper at the last minute and was now just a few points behind him in the race. If Corbyn's popularity was a sign of how the party was feeling, Burnham decided, he had to respond to this rather than deliver pro-business speeches and offer more of the same.

Corbyn's struggle to make it onto the ballot paper was tense, and alarmed the Burnham camp as the drama of his prospective candidacy captured the media's attention. Corbyn needed thirty-five MPs to back him in order to be a candidate. No more than twenty genuinely supported him, so his supporters had been touring the parliamentary estate trying to buttonhole those who hadn't made up their mind. 'Even if you don't support Jeremy, the party needs to widen the debate,' MPs were being told.

Burnham knew he had to appear open to the idea of Corbyn being seriously considered for the leadership, despite privately thinking that he would be a disaster. The Labour Party at times was like a brotherhood, which liked to stick by its leaders, no matter how ineffective they might be – as with Gordon Brown and Ed Miliband. In this spirit, Burnham let it be known that he welcomed any move to 'widen the debate' by including Corbyn on the ballot paper. Senior Labour MPs responded well to this, with Frank Field remarking, 'It won't harm Andy's campaign, but it could help to widen the choice for the whole party.'

Corbyn's nomination process was chaotic, with the final MP he needed coming in just seconds before the deadline. Burnham's team hoped that the sight of Corbyn limping onto the ballot paper would dent his momentum, showing that there was barely any appetite in the party for what he had to offer. But if anything the drama saw Corbyn's popularity start to snowball, as more and more activists took an interest in this 'outsider' candidate. Pro-Corbyn activists started to make themselves heard under the '#JezWeCan' banner, while papers devoted coverage to 'Stormin' Corbyn'. 'Judging by the media, you'd think Jeremy was the only person running,' Burnham fumed to his aides; 'We need to get back in there!'

The opportunity came a few weeks later, in July, when MPs had to vote on George Osborne's welfare changes. The Chancellor suggested that 'progressive' MPs on the Labour benches should be prepared to back his reforms. Labour's interim leader Harriet Harman's initial response split the shadow Cabinet, as she urged the party to back the benefits cap and not oppose cuts to tax credits. She argued that Labour's election defeat in May had meant that the party had to change its tune on welfare, but three of those fighting to succeed her disagreed. Cooper, with her campaigning hat on, argued against it in shadow Cabinet, while Corbyn happily tore into the idea of Labour waving through welfare cuts – helped by the fact that he had the freedom to do so from the back benches. Burnham, as shadow Health Secretary, did his best to argue against it, but felt constrained by collective responsibility from expressing his views publicly.

Cooper and Burnham both offered impassioned critiques when the shadow Cabinet gathered to consider Labour's position. 'I believe tax credits are one of the biggest and best things we did, because they support people in work and get people into work,' Burnham declared; 'We can't stand by and let Boy George hack away at them.' But both of them were swiftly silenced by Harman. 'You seem to have forgotten that I'm the leader,' she told them. 'I know you are focused on your campaigns, but remember that we need to be taken seriously if we ever want to get back into government.'

Burnham, torn between his lifelong loyalty to the party and his personal ambition, did not know what to do. His leader wanted him to stand aside and let the Chancellor slash billions off welfare. Corbyn was able to condemn it as loudly as he liked, which would give his campaign a further boost just when Burnham was fighting to stay relevant in the race. He knew that resigning would devastate the shadow Cabinet and antagonise his colleagues, but would it spell the end of his leadership campaign? Times had changed since the last leadership election in 2010, with MPs having just one vote in the leadership contest; activists now had just as much power over who the next leader would be. Corbyn had managed to whip up grassroots support and electrify the leadership race, despite having paid little attention to the party line in his time. If members were warming to an anti-cuts fighter like Jeremy, Burnham thought to himself, why couldn't he muscle in on the act?

The shadow Health Secretary weighed up his options as MPs debated the welfare cuts. Either choice would be messy. Abstaining would allow him to argue against them while remaining in the shadow Cabinet, but he knew that he would be repeatedly asked why he hadn't stuck to his principles by resigning to vote against them. The subtleties of Cabinet collective responsibility would mean little to the average voter, he thought to himself, especially one who had just had hundreds of pounds taken away as part of the Chancellor's latest benefits squeeze. 'Do I really want to be the next Nick Clegg?' he pondered, recalling the tuition fee protests caused by the former Liberal Democrat leader's controversial U-turn in 2010.

His mind became clear as the welfare debate drew to a close. He would use this vote to make a stand. He started drafting a statement on his phone, explaining his reasons for leaving the shadow Cabinet. Walking along the corridor to the voting lobbies, one Conservative MP asked him if he would be joining 'the progressives' in backing these cuts. Burnham winced and shuffled towards the queue to vote 'no', finishing off his text as he went. His statement read:

> I have always put the party first, but tonight I have to think of the nation. I fully respect my colleagues and want nothing but the best for the party, but I cannot in good conscience stand by and let these unfair cuts happen. I will do everything I can to fight the Tories every step of the way, even if it means doing so from the back benches – my constituents will expect no less.

The following morning's papers were unanimous over the big story of that vote – the shadow Health Secretary's resignation. Burnham's aides had been busy talking up his 'principled exit' to reporters, while the man himself put on a sombre face for the cameras. However, he allowed himself a momentary smile on reading the broadly sympathetic coverage. Most papers gave readers an overview of Burnham's career, underlining the significance of his decision to leave his shadow Cabinet post on an issue of principle. Corbyn's vote against the welfare cuts, on the other hand, received barely a mention, except for the front page of the *Morning Star*, which accused Burnham of 'ripping off' his position.

Burnham's campaign was delighted with the press coverage, as it advertised to voters his opposition to an issue – welfare cuts – with which few would disagree with him. It also drained his rivals' campaigns of attention, killing the hype around Corbyn's rise and leaving Kendall and Cooper looking like establishment figures. Both women had remained in the shadow Cabinet, but that was little consolation for how much their campaigns were floundering. Their failure and Burnham's media domination infuriated moderates, who vented their frustrations by giving vicious briefings to the papers. 'Andy is such a flip-flopper, ask him what the time is and he'll give you five different answers,' one shadow minister quipped.

The resignation may have made Burnham enemies among the moderates, but it did wonders for his anti-austerity credentials. Unite had been on the point of telling its members to give Corbyn their first preference, but Len McCluskey announced that his union was proud to back Burnham, saying he was 'unafraid to fight for what he believed in'. Other unions followed suit, while many MPs jumped onto the Burnham bandwagon to endorse him. Burnham sought to contrast himself with Corbyn by ramming home his experience, telling activists in the final televised debate on Channel 4, 'I know how to get things done and how to stand up for what I believe in. Other politicians put themselves first, but I'm putting you – the party – first.'

While Burnham soared, Cooper and Kendall flagged; their attempts to chide him for quitting the shadow Cabinet backfired by depicting them as 'continuity' candidates. Corbyn fought his corner in this encounter, but put some wavering voters off by shouting at moderator Krishnan Guru-Murthy when he brought up his relationship with extremist groups like Hamas. Burnham, by contrast, came across as the calm, principled and experienced candidate.

The result of the leadership election was close; Burnham beat Corbyn in the eventual run-off by 51 per cent to 49 per cent. Burnham was genuinely delighted, though he had to speak through boos from his rivals' supporters as he rose to give his victory speech. 'This party has been through a lot over the last few months. Now you've placed your trust in me and together we will rebuild,' he declared. His triumph was awkwardly undercut on TV, with the cameras picking up on activists trickling out of the room during his address. Corbyn was nowhere to be seen, though he popped up shortly after in a packed Red Lion pub in Westminster, where he led supporters in a rendition of 'The Red Flag'. The main news that day was Burnham's victory, but everyone knew that the war was far from over.

Burnham moved quickly to assert his leadership by assembling his shadow Cabinet, swiftly promoted his loyalists. Michael Dugher was appointed shadow Home Secretary in recognition of his work as Burnham's campaign manager, while former paratrooper Dan Jarvis received the shadow Defence brief. Keir Starmer, the former Director of Public Prosecutions who had only become a Labour MP that May, became shadow Justice Secretary, while Heidi Alexander became shadow Foreign

Secretary. Burnham extended an olive branch to the moderates by bringing in Yvette Cooper as shadow Chancellor, and new MP Wes Streeting, the former NUS president who had backed Liz Kendall, as shadow Education Secretary. Burnham persuaded Cooper by appealing to her sense of party loyalty, but Kendall refused a post as she could not bear the thought of working with her former rival. Burnham was particularly pleased to persuade Tessa Jowell to act as shadow Communities Secretary, a gamble that paid off massively when she became the party's London mayoral candidate and took back City Hall from the Conservatives the following May. Her success was one of the few crumbs of comfort for Burnham in the May 2016 elections, which saw the SNP sweep the board in Holyrood and the Conservatives hold Labour off in many English councils.

Burnham tried to placate Corbyn and his allies by making him shadow Health Secretary. This, Burnham's team told reporters, was a major vote of confidence in Corbyn, as the leader was entrusting him with an important brief that he had previously held himself. Burnham had been quietly pleased that Corbyn had accepted the job, as he judged that he would repeat Burnham's old approach under Ed Miliband, railing at Tory austerity while sticking up for 'Labour's NHS'. The pair took part in a joint photo-op at the Royal Sussex County Hospital soon after the leadership election. 'As leader of the party that created the National Health Service, I'm proud to have a fighter like Jeremy speaking up for it,' he told reporters. The smiles were genuine, but tensions would start to build once they got down to working together.

The Labour leader survived his first conference, in Brighton, without trouble; activists were still getting used to the new regime. Corbyn spent the conference touring anti-austerity rallies, delighting crowds of supporters by reprising his anti-austerity campaign speeches. Burnham popped into one and was cheered to the rafters when he reminded them of his stand against Osborne's welfare cuts. Journalists who had flocked to the seaside expecting to witness open warfare in the Labour Party were left disappointed by how things seemed to tick along without a hitch. Some blamed the good weather, joking that few MPs could get mad when they were at the beach and enjoying the sun.

What mattered for Burnham was that his party felt united under his leadership. His keynote address went down well in the conference hall: they laughed at his jokes, they clapped at all the right points. 'Let me be straight with you, Conference,' he told delegates, 'it was a tough campaign.' He recalled a late campaign meeting in a church in Sheffield, when an audience member had pointed out that he had been speaking for twenty minutes under a sign saying 'Repent: JC is coming'. 'Well, I'm delighted to say that JC is here, in my team, helping Labour rebuild, renew and revive!' he added. Activists in the conference hall lapped it up, with some breaking into a good-humoured 'Jez We Can!' chant in response.

The rest of the conference went as planned, with exhibition stands for groups like CND existing peacefully in the same building as those for big banks. Corbyn supporters tried to table a motion to debate Labour's position on Trident, but failed to get enough support – though Burnham was warned by one of his aides that he may have been saved by the fact that delegates to the conference had been chosen before the leadership election, so probably did not reflect the new membership of the party. 'This will change next year,' he sighed.

~

One year later, Burnham had never been under so much pressure. The leadership contest may have ended months before, but the Labour leader felt as if Jeremy Corbyn and his allies had never stopped campaigning. Burnham's aides were all too aware of the conference chatter in Liverpool, with rumours going around that pro-Corbyn campaigners had nearly gathered the forty-six MPs needed in order to trigger a leadership election and nominate him as a candidate. They had also heard that Corbyn was preparing to resign 'on principle' from Burnham's shadow Cabinet, with shadow Treasury Minister John McDonnell and shadow International Development Minister Diane Abbott following suit.

The moderates were just as annoyed with Burnham, and did not hide their contempt for his style of operating. The papers were full of critics – 'Andy is just a Scouse Ed Miliband,' one Kendall ally was quoted as telling the *Telegraph*. One friend of Cooper's – many thought the shadow

Chancellor herself – explained why Burnham was so disliked to *The Times*: 'We're being just as loyal to him as he was to us during the election.' A few MPs broke cover to criticise the Labour leader. 'If we could change our leader as easily as Andy changes his mind, we'd be on our way back into government,' Simon Danczuk wrote in his *Mail on Sunday* column. Burnham couldn't help laughing at this, remarking to his aides, 'Has there ever been a leader Simon liked?'

Despite the flak, Burnham wasn't worried about any attempted putsch by the moderates, as his team knew that they had yet to coalesce around an obvious challenger. The two names that kept coming up were Chuka Umunna, who had gone to chair a Small Business Commission for George Osborne, and David Miliband. Some rankled at the idea of letting another Miliband run Labour, but others were in awe of his experience. 'David is respected on the world stage,' one supportive MP told friends, claiming that both US presidential contenders, Donald Trump and Hillary Clinton, rang him for advice every week. Cynics in the party pointed out his liking for the high life, with one scoffing, 'Would he give up dinner with the Clooneys for this?' Dan Jarvis was viewed as too loyal to his commanding officer, as befitting a former soldier, while many of the new class, like Jim McMahon and Jess Phillips, preferred not to rock the boat.

Many Corbyn supporters felt that their man had been robbed of what was rightfully his, with some of them taking to the streets outside the conference venue to demand another leadership election. They had taken to calling themselves 'True Labour', in a subtle jab at Burnham's time serving in Tony Blair and Gordon Brown's New Labour governments. Only a few of the protesters were Labour members, however, while others had declined to join while Burnham was leader. Police looked on as protesters waved signs and chanted a range of slogans, with some choice terms of abuse including 'Red Tory' and 'Burn-sham'.

Corbyn made clear his disapproval of the protesters, telling the media, 'I believe in a kinder politics.' However, the shadow Health Secretary's attempt to stay above the fray infuriated Burnham aides, who felt that he was tacitly encouraging the plotting by displaying a marked lack of enthusiasm for defending his leader in the media. When the BBC doorstepped him as he left his hotel and asked if he felt Burnham should stand aside for another leadership contest, Corbyn responded gnomically, 'Our party is at its best when it is democratic and inclusive ... I believe in doing things by persuasive, democratic means. If members want to have a mature debate about our party's future, then that is what should happen.' One of Burnham's aides texted his opposite number in Corbyn's team to try to get his boss to toe the line, but received the curt response: 'Welcome to the new politics.'

The Labour leader had tried his best to keep Corbyn happy in his shadow Cabinet by giving him a free vote on issues of principle on which he disagreed. The shadow Health Secretary had done so on many occasions, forcing a compromise out of Burnham on the party's position on bombing so-called Islamic State in Syria, so that he gave the closing speech against action, just hours after Burnham had opened the debate by giving the case in favour. But their collegiate way of working had cooled over the following months. The Labour leader's commitment to the NHS had divided opinion among the grassroots. Supporters trusted him when he promised to stop the Tories 'dismantling our NHS', but others, especially the more left-wing activists who had joined to support Corbyn, recalled Burnham's record as Health Secretary in Gordon Brown's government; they would mutter under their breath about the privatisation of Hinchingbrooke Hospital, which had happened under Burnham's watch. Burnham's tortuous defence of his record as Health Secretary during the leadership election – and particularly one *Newsnight* interview in which he failed to explain how much privatisation was acceptable – bolstered his critics. The Tories, too, never shied away from mocking Burnham whenever health came up as an issue in the Commons; David Cameron enjoyed reminding MPs that the Labour leader was 'the only man to have ever privatised an NHS hospital'. Burnham's own view was that some degree of market intervention in the NHS was acceptable; but he felt that he could not say this without alienating half of his party. By giving Corbyn the Health brief, Burnham had sought to reassure his doubters, but many activists believed that this simply highlighted how out of step he was with the membership.

Corbyn went on to exploit this vulnerability just days before Burnham's second party conference with a particularly passionate speech on health. The shadow Health Secretary had been invited to address a pro-NHS rally by anti-cuts activists in Tredegar, birthplace of Aneurin Bevan, the Labour politician celebrated for creating the health service. However, the tone of Corbyn's speech was much more personal than normal, with several passages viewed as thinly veiled swipes at his own leader's record in government.

Corbyn started out innocently enough with a tribute to Bevan, 'the man who gave us the vision of the National Health Service'. Warming to his theme, he spoke of his desire for a society 'where all are equal in worth and value, and where that value is not purely a monetary one', and for a 'supportive, inclusive and compassionate' society. 'There are plenty of people these days who believe in grabbing as much as they can for themselves, and letting the markets loose on our health service,' he declared. 'I am not, and will never be, one of them!' Corbyn's Tredegar Speech, as it came to be known, spread like wildfire, with Labour members rushing to watch his rhetoric online. 'If only Labour had a leader like this fighting for the NHS!' the *Morning Star* declared the following day.

Corbyn and Burnham found themselves at odds not only over the NHS but over Europe too. The Labour leader was an unabashed Europhile, who wanted Labour to fight to stay in the European Union at any cost. Corbyn, who had voted to leave the EEC in 1975, held the opposite view, his Euroscepticism resting on his fears for workers' rights in a capitalist Europe. He never hesitated to remind voters of his beliefs whenever he spoke in public. One of his favourite topics was the proposed Transatlantic Trade and Investment Partnership, a controversial deal being negotiated between the EU and the US that the unions argued would undermine employment rights. As Corbyn put it, TTIP showed 'how corporatists in Brussels want to ride roughshod over the rights we hold so dear'. Burnham strongly disagreed, at one point mocking Corbyn's views as 'Red UKIP' during a shadow Cabinet meeting. The Tories were not the only party to be at war over Europe.

The gathering talk of a leadership challenge at conference was particularly galling for Burnham, as he had hoped to use his leader's speech to needle the Prime Minister over his delayed referendum. Originally pencilled in for June 2016, diplomatic deadlock over Cameron's renegotiation had meant that the referendum on Britain's membership looked likely to be in 2017 at earliest. 'It's David Cameron's Neverendum story!' Burnham's one-liner for the TV bulletins was going to be; but he knew that Labour's leadership woes would be all the media would be focusing on.

The Labour leader understood the risks of ignoring the critics, remembering all too well how his party had suffered under Brown and Miliband's leadership, yet had done nothing but limp on to election defeat. He had to seize the initiative and issue a 'put up or shut up' challenge to Corbyn and any presumptive challengers. Nigel Farage had just managed it in UKIP, seeing off a challenge by his only MP Douglas Carswell, and in the process consolidating his authority. Why couldn't it work for him?

Burnham had been humiliated by the relentless arguments with his colleagues and the constant stream of briefing against him in the press. He felt he had only one way to save his party from a slow death, killed by infighting. He began working on a new part of his conference speech, which he was sure would dominate the news bulletins.

'I know the party comes first, so you can trust me to do the right thing,' he would tell members. 'This is why we will hold a leadership election now. We can have the wide debate over the direction of the party we need, and come together again in time for the 2020 election.' He knew another election was risky, but he believed it was necessary in order to save the party he loved from itself. The party needed time to work out why it had lost two elections in a row, and to develop the top talent that could help it achieve great things in government.

Andy Burnham knew that his decision could stop him from ever becoming Prime Minister, but he needed to confront his critics once and for all. Chuka Umunna would not be able to back out of the race this time, while Jeremy Corbyn's supporters would not be able to complain about the leadership ignoring them.

New Labour had delivered a lot in government, and Burnham knew that without power the party could do nothing to improve people's lives. If Labour wanted a leadership contest, he would give it to them, and finally hope to prove that he could put his party first.

Chapter 21

What if Boris Johnson had become Prime Minister after the European referendum?

Andy Mayer

Prologue

Following the defeat of David Cameron's Remain campaign, the Prime Minister's resignation was inevitable. His pre-election statement, 'Brits don't quit', was amended to '… for at least a couple of hours.' And might have included the punchline: '… you ungrateful bastards, see if I care.'

The leadership election that followed was a contest between Theresa May and Boris Johnson. George Osborne had expected to run, but in 2019. His pre-referendum Budget was a disaster, and his personal responsibility for 'Project Fear', the failed campaign to inspire a fear of Brexit economics, ruled him out.

Another possibility was Michael Gove. His advisers pushed hard; for them, it was the culmination of a long plan to shake up government. But he had demurred. Gove, 'the Kingmaker', knew well that he could never wear the crown, and had said so many times. His talents lay in affecting change from behind the throne. As his exasperated wife's 'leaked' email to long-time ally and Vote Leave director Dominic Cummings had said, 'What fool would stab his best friends in the back, twice, and expect to be taken seriously? Get over it and focus on the long term.'

A few others flirted with running. Stephen Crabb and Sajid Javid waved a flag for working-class Tory modernisers. Priti Patel bloomed and faded, eclipsed in the referendum by the performance of Andrea Leadsom, the leading Leave woman. She might have run herself, if Boris had fallen under a bus, but was content with a shot at Chancellor, while Gove went for Foreign Secretary and lead EU negotiator, with George Osborne secretly on board as the new Home Secretary.

Crucial to the race was who could tickle the tummies of the 150,000 voting Conservative members. Johnson had correctly calculated that the most likely victor would be the party's leading Eurosceptic. His decision to back the Vote Leave campaign had been cynical; even at the last moment he had written *Telegraph* columns going each way. But Leave was a gamble that paid off.

May had that option, but bottled it. She backed Remain, Cameron's anaemic renegotiation being apparently enough for her to support him. She lost a lot of hard-earned credibility with the grassroots, though her CV for the top job was superior. Her approach was calm, authoritative, and conciliatory, but also dull. She offered stability, a sound pitch in the tumult that followed the vote. But stability of what? Failed austerity? Being sort-of-still-in-the-EU-but-not? Her record on immigration – a series of gimmicks with vans, missing targets and failing to deport criminals – were all easy targets for Boris's skilled communications team.

Much credit for Boris's success lay with his communications director, Martin Tucker. Martin was notable for two things: his famous, albeit estranged, father Malcolm – a self-declared 'huge fucking deal' in the last Labour administration – and a 2015 Tunnock's Teacakes campaign, which had rebranded the sickly Scottish treat as a British confection, principally to generate publicity by exploiting the outrage of SNP activists.

Martin liked stirring things up – for example by seizing on May's technically plausible but politically naive assertion that current EU citizens in the UK might be deported if no reciprocal deal could be made for UK citizens in the EU. Martin's team had a social media campaign out in hours, with pictures of 'Nasty May' packing families into vans, turning her historic strengths into weaknesses. 'Nice Boris', on the other hand, was presented as a steadily more serious politician, able to unite rather than divide the country. His campaign banged out three messages over and over again: 'prosperity, not austerity', the 'best deal for Britain', and the 'best team to deliver it'.

It worked. May stood no chance. Conservative members wanted sparkle, not managerialism. They wanted to remember it was OK to be a Tory, not miserable continuity and lectures on how nasty they looked to metropolitan elites. Most of all, they wanted to have some fun. If Trump could upset the Republican establishment, why not the former Mayor? Boris won by a landslide.

Part 1: 10 October 2016 – Roger the Rascally Rabbit

Britain's new Prime Minister wants to explain how we can leave the EU. Joining him is Sarah Woolley, his new principal private secretary. Sarah's notable father, Bernard, was a PPS in the 1980s. She is a Home Counties girl, educated in all the right schools, connected with the detail and discipline of public life.

BORIS: 'Bounce, bounce, bounce... Roger, Roger, Roger... Out, out, out... At last!...' Well, what do you think?

MARTIN: You sound mentally ill.

BORIS: It's a children's book.

MARTIN: About mental illness?

BORIS: No. *Roger the Rascally Rabbit Leaves the Warren* is about leaving the EU.

MARTIN: Due to mental illness?

BORIS: Sarah, with a view to a more constructive analysis, what do you think?

SARAH: Well, Prime Minister, if you will give me a moment – this, after all, is not the agenda I expected when you called me in to discuss Article 50 of the Treaty on the Functioning of the European Union.

BORIS: You have young children.

MARTIN: None of whom are mentally ill.

SARAH: Thank you, Martin. You are correct, Prime Minister. My children are young.

BORIS: Would you say this story could help them understand how Brexit works?

Sarah: Well, children's literature is not, per se, my area of expertise. But, on balance, with a few tweaks, it could help.

Boris: Tweaks?

Sarah: For example, here on page 7 – where Guy the Ferret pushes Roger out of the room to discuss his free warren plans with Angela the Badger...

Martin: What the fuck is a badger doing living in a rabbit warren with a ferret?

Boris: A good question. I will file it for my next nature documentary.

Sarah: I appreciate that this is how Article 50 is supposed to work. But surely Angela would want to keep Roger in the room to avoid any miscommunication? She does, after all, want to keep selling him carrots. After he's gone.

Martin: Have we considered gassing the badger?

Boris: It might be considered undiplomatic to make a reference to gassing a badger bearing a passing similarity to the former Chancellor of Germany.

Martin: Shooting? I'll call Owen Paterson. Good man for when badgers move the goalposts.

Boris: Thank you, Martin. Please do not call Owen. I see your point, Sarah. It would be nice to think our European partners would talk to us about our deal. Particularly given that we will be chairing the Council of the EU next year.

Martin: Yes, that's going to work well, isn't it? 'What does the chair think of the new Directive on Shopping Trollies?' He thinks he's fucking off – that's what he thinks. Only not in one designed by you lot – it wouldn't get further than Calais and he wouldn't get his pound back...

Boris: Again, thank you, Martin. So how should I explain Article 50, Sarah?

Sarah: Well, it really is very simple, Prime Minister. Having won the referendum you can notify the European Council of your intention to leave. The Notification Bill is now being drafted for Parliament to consider.

BORIS: Any issues in the House?

MARTIN: Are you kidding? Most of the party is sewn up. The last thing they want is another row about Europe. That gets you most of the way. As for the opposition – what opposition? Jeremy Corbyn is abso-fucking-lutely delighted. He's going to have Labour abstain. The crafty fucker.

BORIS: I rarely hear the words Corbyn and crafty used in the same sentence.

MARTIN: Privately he's a Leaver. Only for the sake of unity – for the last year – he has had to do the 'Ode to Joy' singalong with a coalition of MPs that hate him. Sharing a platform with Peter Mandelson. Mandelson, for fuck's sake, the man who'd like to have him shot into orbit on a newly commissioned Trident missile. This in order to ensure that we could find at least one weapon of mass destruction in some desert somewhere. As a precursor to lying about some war.

BORIS: Get to the point, please...

MARTIN: As for the Labour moderates; their bolt is shot. 'Oooh, Jeremy, you can't vote Leave, think of Islington.' 'Oooh, Jeremy, you can't vote Leave, what will *The Guardian* say?' 'Oooh, Jeremy, can we make you appear just a teensy-weensyish bit less shit by pretending you love the big corporate conspiracy you've spent your entire life declaiming as a front organisation for global capitalism?' They will abstain.

BORIS: Thank you, Mart—

MARTIN: The Liberal Democrats are opposed – this week. But there are only eight of them, and Nick Clegg never turns up. Probably wise. Even Nick Clegg doesn't trust which way Nick Clegg is going to vote. The SNP are opposed; those who aren't suspended, drunk, shagging journalists or in jail. But the day we have to rely on them for a parliamentary majority, you might as well have another referendum to let England leave the UK.

BORIS: *Thank you*, Martin! I am reassured that the Notification Bill is safe. Continue, Sarah.

SARAH: Having formally notified the Council of your decision to leave, they will initiate the Article 50 procedure...

BORIS: So if it's the end of 2017 I will notify myself?

SARAH: No, Prime Minister, you will be the chair of the Council of the EU. You will notify the president of the European Council, Donald Tusk.

BORIS: Um.

SARAH: The Council of the EU is the second legislative chamber of the EU, the first being the European Parliament. One represents the governments of the member states, the other the people.

MARTIN: In the rare event 'the people' have the first clue who their MEPs are. Who's your MEP, Prime Minister?

BORIS: Um.

MARTIN: Precisely.

SARAH: Please, Martin. Neither body can initiate legislation. That's the European Commission. Although in this instance it is not the Commission's role to initiate or decide a withdrawal agreement, it can only advise.

BORIS: Um.

SARAH: The relevant body for withdrawal – the European Council – has no legislative role, but it sets strategy and direction for the Union. It also has reserved powers, one of which is to manage Article 50. The withdrawal agreement is not the same thing as the final agreement between the UK and the EU. That will take longer and could be a series of bilateral discussions about different areas of common interest. Those would involve the Commission – but only after we've left.

BORIS: Um.

SARAH: The withdrawal agreement sets out the terms of transition before that happens. It must be agreed by a qualified majority vote.

BORIS: Ah, OK. So I can still agree what aspects of EU rules and institutions still apply, and for how long, or until there is a new deal?

SARAH: No. You will be excluded from any conversation or vote involving the UK withdrawal agreement in the Council.

BORIS: Oh.

SARAH: So, in summary: in an Article 50 process the government of the EU, which is not a government, defers to the president of the EU, who is not a president, to agree with you a future relationship, which is an agreement about a future relationship which is not a relationship. And when I say with you, I mean it may be with you, or it may not be with you, depending on whether or not you can agree about the agreement that is not yet agreed about a relationship that is not yet a relationship. Is that clear?

BORIS: It could be more clear.

MARTIN: Let me rewrite page 9 of the book for you. 'Hi, Donald, it's Roger. Can I talk to you about the trade deal with the weasels?' 'Fuck off.' 'How we're going to manage the fish pond?' 'Fuck off.' 'The 100-acre wood loan agreement?' 'Fuck off.' 'Roger is a sad rabbit.'

BORIS: Oh.

SARAH: Although in reality, Prime Minister, as I explained to you, it is deeply unlikely that the badge— I mean, the Council, would seek to exclude the UK from dialogue or impose a deal. Isolating us serves no purpose, economic or diplomatic.

BORIS: So it can't happen.

SARAH: Well, it can. Unless there is a unanimous Council vote to continue the process, it must conclude after two years. At that point whatever the Council says is the withdrawal agreement is the withdrawal agreement. The worst-case scenario is imposition of a common tariff against us under WTO rules. This is, though, highly unlikely.

MARTIN: Bar that the French are involved at every stage. And they're unmitigated bastards.

SARAH: With whom we are involved on matters of common defence and energy policy. The French national interest is not well served by humiliating Britain.

MARTIN: Though it has been their national pastime for the last thousand years. They're just not very good at it.

BORIS: Well, thank you, both, that has been illuminating. I must go now. I am meeting the BBC about the potential of turning my book into an animated short. They think David Walliams would like to play Roger.

MARTIN: Personally I'd prefer Stephen Fry. He'd be brilliant as a lonely rabbit that sounded completely fucking men—

Boris: Enough! Thank you, both.
Sarah: Yes, Prime Minister.

Part 2: 9 May 2019 – Britain Day

The Article 50 procedure took six months longer than two years. The formal date for Brexit was Monday 9 May 2019. The Prime Minister declared a special bank holiday – Britain Day – much to the irritation of the Labour Party, still inexplicably led by Jeremy Corbyn.

At this point we must note that it was as though events had diverged, as if there were two worlds, one in which Brexit had gone well, the other – not so much. Perhaps it was the craft gin at Britain Day street parties, perhaps the deregulation of cannabis in urban toleration zones, but for some reason our protagonists are now in different realities.

As the Stronger In campaign had predicted, the only deal on the table during the Article 50 process was one named after...

Martin: Norway, Prime Minister. We got fucking Norway!

Boris: It's not that bad.

Martin: Not. That. Bad? We just got handed the deal you explicitly told the British people could never happen.

Boris: Well, if you put it like that...

Martin: What the hell happened? Are you attracted to whales? Were you pining for the fjords? Did you confuse the dribble of cash we have secured from shale gas for a sovereign wealth fund? Is it a blond thing? How the fuck, I mean how the fuck, did we end up back in the European Economic Area? It's a bondage club for gimp nations that want to pay the EU to beat them...

Boris: Donald was very insistent. It was the only way of avoiding tariffs on financial services. The City was very worried.

Martin: But you've had to concede to free movement of people! UKIP are going nuts – sorry, more nuts. Arron Banks has launched a series of 'traitor Johnson' videos showing hordes of Bulgarian navvies ravishing nubile planning inspectors along the route of HS2. One of them winks at the camera and says, 'Thanks, Boris.' He's got Mike Read to sing a cover of the Mr Blobby song with a floppy wig. No one has the first clue what it means. It has, though, been re-tweeted 126,000 times – and only 100,000 of those were by Banks paying for it. It's all going 'tuition fees' on us...

BORIS: We were always going to agree free movement to secure access to the single market.

MARTIN: Of workers! Wanker! And we're paying for access! There's no £10 billion dividend. No war chest for next May. Cameron beamed at you yesterday, for fuck's sake.

BORIS: You're supposed to be advising me on how we sell this to the public.

MARTIN: Fine, fine – if I can sell Boris Island to the Chinese as a glorious opportunity to invest in a swamp full of jet-toasted seagulls, I can do this... First things first – we don't mention fucking Norway!

BORIS: But we're in the European Free Trade Association together!

MARTIN: So is Switzerland. This is Switzerland with British features.

BORIS: Not Norwegian features?

MARTIN: Stop saying Norway! You're obsessed with Norway. Stop thinking about Norway. Don't look at it on a map. Don't talk about the pipelines. If anyone asks you who got to the South Pole first, it was a fucking tie. Think cuckoo clocks; chocolate; think about Roger Federer – actually, no, think about Martina Hingis, more your type.

BORIS: I get the point, Martin.

MARTIN: Oh, you do? Great. Did someone fax it to you? Because that's what the Commission is going to be doing from now on. 'By the way, PM, we're introducing a regulation on vibrators. Would you mind awfully lubing it up for us, and shoving it straight up your—'

BORIS: OK.

MARTIN: Maybe that should be your sequel: *Roger the Rampant Rabbit Gets Rammed*. No more bendy dildos for your warren, Roger, because the Chief Rabbit just agreed to conform to a Belgian stoat's idea of wang harmonisation! What will Missus Roger do now on those lonely nights when you're off ... being a rabbit.

BORIS: All right! It's really not that bad. We've kept control of foreign policy, the North Sea and regional policy. And we've got back fishing.

MARTIN: Oh, well, why didn't you say so? That's brilliant, that is. There's going to be a shoal of ecstatic mackerel near Grimsby, safe in the knowledge that their imminent entrapment and slaughter will be at British hands rather than under the gunnels of a giant ocean-raping Dutch super-trawler. Hell, we can even give them a City Deal to build a new fish finger factory. We'll call it the 'Breadcrumb-coated Brexit bonus for the Northern Powerhouse'. When George has stopped sulking you can have him launch it. Preferably with himself attached somewhere in the Dogger Bank during a hurricane.

BORIS: You could be more positive. It is not as you say. Norway could say no to the Commission more often if they wished. As well as being consulted on new single market rules, and having staff in the institutions, they are represented on international bodies equally with the EU.

MARTIN: You're still saying Norway! And no – we are not going to persuade your half-mad backbenchers that a committee seat on the International Standards Organization sub-committee on biomass boilers represents a win akin to the return of Magna Carta and the restoration of empire. But you're right, we could pick more fights than the N— ... Western Vikings. Their ancestors would have been embarrassed, back in the day. Had some Friesian warlord attempted to impose a standard sword length across the continent, they'd have soon found themselves on the end of a particularly outsized and pointy version. That's a proper renegotiation. These days, their leaders are filling their longboats with Danegeld and apologising to their looters that it can't be more. Eric Bloodaxe would have gutted them like herring, and strung their in—

BORIS: I feel this approach could be counter-productive. A very British cuckoo clock it is. And I'll look into what aggressive neutrality looks like. Probably something like Theresa's response to my last invitation to join the Cabinet.

MARTIN: Just don't mention the Nazi gold.

BORIS: Thank you, Martin.

Of course, a Norwegian option was never likely to fly – not with so many EU members running a trade surplus with Britain. Boris had a very strong hand during negotiations...

SARAH: I am impressed.

BORIS: Thank you, Sarah. I am also surprised...

SARAH: We always knew they would accept some kind of bilateral trade agreement. But I felt sure they would insist on the UK joining the EEA.

BORIS: They tried. Jean-Claude was very insistent that a higher contribution for single market access was essential.

SARAH: Perhaps unwise to make that case at Davos – in Switzerland – surrounded by evidence of a workable relationship outside the single market. Although there are issues...

BORIS: Issues?

SARAH: The Swiss deal irritates them. Constant new negotiations. They've been trying to get a dynamic adoption scheme for years.

BORIS: You mean replacing actual control with a Commission rubber stamp? It's not something the Swiss are very keen on.

SARAH: Nevertheless, Prime Minister, the Commission would prefer they did.

BORIS: Noted.

SARAH: And our diplomatic approach ... You serenaded the president with the opening chorus of 'There'll be 200 EU Directives sitting on the shelf' to the tune of 'Ten green bottles'.

BORIS: They love a good singalong in Luxembourg.

SARAH: You then pointed at his food. You queried whether or not steak tartare tasted any different as a result of the cow being subsidised by the Swiss rather than the Common Agricultural Policy.

BORIS: Yes, he didn't like that very much. Nice steak, though. Tasted like sovereignty.

SARAH: You then dragged over the President of Poland to ask him whether he'd rather have the £2 billion set aside from the foreign aid budget for the continued development of Eastern European infrastructure funded directly by the Treasury. Or filtered through Herr Juncker's Objective 1 bureaucracy.

Boris: A valuable diplomatic intervention from a very fine man.

Sarah: Yes, but when he burst out laughing he spat his Chablis all over the president of the Commission's shoes.

Boris: Not the first time Herr Juncker has had to clean cheap wine off his shoes.

Sarah: An unsubstantiated rumour, Prime Minister – most likely from Martin. I'm not sure, though, that that was what annoyed him most.

Boris: Possibly not...

Sarah: More, I think, when you winked at President Sarkozy and cupped your hands in the shape of a nuclear reactor.

Boris: It's a rum day for any man from the Low Countries when he can't rely on the French to sell out the British. Are other elements of the deal watertight?

Sarah: I believe so. The Germans are relieved we're still funding the east. The Spanish, Portuguese, Greeks and Italians have welcomed your City initiative to refinance elements of their debt repayment programmes. The Swedes are hoping we'll keeping buying all their forests to convert our coal plants to biomass. The Danes think we'll be keeping our lights on with their offshore wind turbines. The Finns think our nuclear power delays will make their project look competent. The Baltic states are praying we can find enough gas under Surrey to reduce the influence of the Russians. Cyprus needs our military bases. Malta needs our used cars. The Hungarians would quite like our used military cars – as would the Croatians, particularly since we told them we were thinking of selling them to the Serbs. Holland will miss us most, although perhaps not for long; their own exit debate has started. The Belgians are too busy being upset with other Belgians to care either way. Luxembourg cares about us nearly as much as we care about them. Ireland are upset, but have opened up several new petrol stations and a duty-free shop near Monaghan.

Boris: So, in brief...

Sarah: Southern Europe is bankrupt and needs us to keep lending to their private sector. Eastern Europe isn't bankrupt but wants our public funds to keep it that way. Northern Europe is hoping we'll spend what's left on their energy projects. The Germans are just relieved we haven't managed to detach from the continental shelf and float away. The Irish are waiting in a service station hoping something will turn up.

Boris: Begorrah!

Sarah: Enjoy Britain Day, Prime Minister.

Part 3: 8 May 2020 – Heavy is the crown of the World King

The 2020 general election campaign was dominated by two themes: the economic record of the Conservative government, and Europe. Voters felt that the Conservatives needed to be punished. However, with Labour a bickering basket case, the Liberal Democrats a parochial irrelevance, and the Greens a fusion of both, people turned to ... UKIP. Their rise, much like that of the SDP in 1983, was not sufficient to break the two-party system, but for the boy who had once said that his fondest ambition was to be 'world king', it was a deeply upsetting day. On 8 May, with the final recounts concluded, he met his staff.

Martin: Two! A majority of two! The ungrateful fucking cunts.

Boris: It's still a majority, Martin.

Martin: It's a liability. Your new administration is one heart attack away from having to rely on the DUP – and I'm pretty sure that unhappy event will be happening in an hour's time, shortly after I've finished talking to the chair of the 1922 Committee about the shambles his colleagues delivered in the marginals. I mean, fuck. Twenty-two UKIP MPs. Gains from us. Gains from Labour. They've even taken three from the Liberals. Diane James is the new MP for Carshalton. For fuck's sake – two-thirds of her constituency think she's a fictional character from a Miss Marple rerun. You know, the posh vicar's wife who poisons her gardener with Baby Bio after he finds her hosting rallies for Rhodesia in the village hall.

Boris: Can you poison someone with Baby Bio?

Martin: I'm willing to try. Nick Clegg looks like he might have drunk a bottle this morning.

Boris: Oh, God, you don't mean...

Martin Yes. He won his seat again.

Boris: Poor sod. Speaking of which...

Martin: Oh, you want me to replay the Isle of Wight count?

Boris: If you would.

TV: 'Nigel Paul Farage (United Kingdom Independence Party), 21,897. Andrew John Turner (Conservative Party), 21,912 ... I therefore declare Andrew John Turner duly electe—'

Martin and Boris: Wahahahahahaha!

Boris: Omigosh, that's never going to get old.

Martin: Every cloud...

Boris: I'm writing a new book – *The Trials of Nigel* – based on *The Oresteia.* I think we just got the punchline.

Martin: Although that incident in Newport was a contender.

Boris: Ah, yes. When he tried to explain his repatriation speech to an 18-stone local shopkeeper; the one with the 9-stone Slovakian wife.

Martin: I really thought the man was going to floor him.

Boris: So did his aides. It quite surprised them when she did.

Martin: Who'd have thought such a small Slav could pack such a large left hook? That sound you can hear next on the tape – MI5's boffins aren't sure if it's Nigel or a dying seagull. Darius Guppy rang to say he wants her number.

Boris: I will choose to ignore that remark.

Martin: Ignore Guppy. To hear is to obey, Prime Minister. I will cancel the hit. *Evening Standard* journalists can sleep safe in their beds tonight.

Boris: And that one. You are skating on very thin ice, Martin. What about Labour?

Martin: Jeremy Corbyn will be resigning at noon.

Boris: That is sad.

Martin: His remaining colleagues, are, as you can imagine, stricken with grief. Tom Watson is furiously chopping onions and smearing them under his eyes.

Boris: I've noticed. Some are so overcome with emotion, they've taken to thanking him personally for their result – and in such colourful language.

MARTIN: It's the New Politics. Why waste time slinging mud at us when you can call your own leader 'a useless bearded wassock' on Sky.

BORIS: I still can't quite believe Tristram Hunt said that.

MARTIN: He'd just lost Stoke-on-Trent! The Potteries went UKIP. It would have been like us losing Tunbridge Wells to Plaid-fucking-Cymru.

BORIS: True, true...

MARTIN: Then Faisal Islam put him on with that monumentally po-faced shite from Momentum, who blamed Hunt's result on him not standing up for Palestinian asylum-seekers on council estates... I'm just surprised the lanky posh prat didn't go all Slovakian midget on him.

BORIS: A fair point, well made.

MARTIN: Momentum, though, have a point. Where the fuck have Progress and the other Blairites been for the last five years? Oh, that's right, failing to organise a coup. And moaning about the good old days to students too young to remember why they should really, really hate them. I actually like Momentum. You know where you are with those hard-left socialist bastards. None of this 'I feel your pain' shit. No attempts to triangulate policies between oily millionaire businessmen, and – well – oily millionaire trade union leaders; just good old-fashioned hatred. 'How are we reaching out to the City?' 'We're not, we're going to line them up against a wall and shoot them.' 'What should we say to appeal to green voters?' 'Here's a shovel, go and do a proper job in the real environment, you recycling-obsessed hipster cockwomble.' 'Do you think Michael Sheen will host a fundraiser?' 'No, fuck off, he's on strike, and so am I.' That's proper socialism, that is.

BORIS: Thank you, Martin, I'm feeling better already. Could you call Sajid? I need to start firing – I mean firing up – the Cabinet.

With an EU free trade agreement in place, mostly on goods, but with some progress on services and capital, the recovering British economy, and an almost balanced Budget, provided the perfect backdrop to Boris's first electoral test as PM.

SARAH: Seventy, Prime Minister, a majority of seventy. Congratulations!

BORIS: Thank you, Sarah. Your acclamation is of course entirely deserved. Bring forth the Cabinet Office Dancing Girls. Summon the Treasury Marching Band. For I – I mean we – have defied political gravity. We have restored the Conservative Party to over 40 per cent of the national vote.

SARAH: By 0.1 per cent, Prime Minister.

BORIS: Yes, yes, but what a 0.1 per cent! There are Tories in Liverpool! We are again a Northern Powerhouse! My eyes are welling up with mawkish sentimentality.

SARAH: Would you like a tissue, Prime Minister?

BORIS: Clacton would have been a gain as well if Carswell hadn't already double-ratted. Such a shame the 2016 Evans coup against Farage's latest resignation failed. Still, their loss, our gains; the prodigal geek has returned. Labour – Labour has secured fewer votes than even Michael Foot. Jeremy Corbyn hasn't so much resigned as been lynched by a bloodthirsty mob. This – this is a glorious day, for here is Boris, undisputed Prime Minister of Britain.

SARAH: Your appointments, undisputed Prime Minister?

BORIS: Cabinet meeting at 3 o'clock.

SARAH: New ministerial appointments on the agenda?

BORIS: No changes. But I don't want them to know that. If you try to sound particularly sympathetic when you ring Matt Hancock, it'll scare the bejeesus out of him. Maybe stop the little shit plotting with Sajid.

SARAH: Very good. I will ask him if he has any imminent holiday plans.

BORIS: Marvellous. Also I would like to see Dav– I mean Lord Cameron – at five.

SARAH: What shall I say is on that agenda?

BORIS: Smiling – lots of smiling; possibly a jeroboam of champagne – and maybe a jig.

SARAH: Anything that might be described as government business?

BORIS: I want him to go with George to China. We have a trade deal to prepare.

SARAH: Very good. When?

BORIS: I imagine he's going to want to take a break from London for the next week. There are only so many times he can say, 'This is marvellous, I'm so pleased for Boris and the party', before turning purple. And he's not as young as he was. We need him alive and calm for the negotiations.

SARAH: Anything else?

BORIS: I suppose I will have to see ... her.

SARAH: Your wife, Prime Minister?

BORIS: Good God, no. She still hasn't forgiven me for that incident at the Hinkley Point ground-breaking dinner.

SARAH: You mean where you enquired of President Sarkozy whether he could introduce you to Marine Le Pen's niece?

BORIS: Possibly, possibly – but no...

SARAH: So who is it you need to see?

BORIS: Her – Nicola. Queen of Smugland.

SARAH: The First Minister of Scotland, Prime Minister?

BORIS: Yes. The fly in the ointment on this day of glory is her increased mandate. It cannot be ignored. The oil price has recovered; they're feeling cocky again; the clans are stirring – the illicit tartan has been seen near Falkirk...

SARAH: What shall I say you wish to see her about?

BORIS: I would love to say: 300 years of bailing out her sorry excuse for a giant rocky swamp; her ludicrous pretensions to statehood; that pitiful facsimile of a national football team; the Runrig reunion tour; and the misery – good God, please do something about the glum...

SARAH: Prime Minister?

BORIS: OK, OK, real issues – no, I'm still thinking about Alex Salmond – in the Tower – watching the crows slowly peck out his treacherous scheming liv—

SARAH: Shall I say you wish to congratulate her in person, one leader to another?

BORIS: Yes, but please make it brief. And organise a trip to the Tower.

SARAH: Yes, Prime Minister.

Part 4: 14 April 2021 – Crouching Boris, hidden agenda

Since gaining market economy status with the World Trade Organization in 2019, the prospects of a free trade agreement between China and the UK, and China with the EU, had been greatly enhanced. The race was then on. Who would be first to secure a deal with the world's largest developing economy? The mighty EU dragon, or the nimble British tiger? We join the team, recouping at the British embassy...

MARTIN: Well, that was a fucking disaster.

BORIS: Oh, come on...

MARTIN: We have agreement on a free trade deal in coal and steel.

BORIS: Important commodities...

MARTIN: Yes – in the Victorian era. At least, you'd have to go back that far to find an example of Britain dominating the world in either of them.

BORIS: I like the Victorian era.

MARTIN: Top hats, industrial accidents, and the clap. I can see why you might. Today, though, today our coal industry is a solitary 87-year-old Welshman, with one lung. He digs up a few lumps every other Monday to burn in the world's smallest blast furnace. This to melt iron ore, the output of which is bashed into a set of novelty steel coffin handles – mostly used locally by the families of former workers from the steel mill. Shut down by Chinese competition.

BORIS: That was hardly our fault.

MARTIN: It doesn't matter. China... China, on the other hand, produces over half a billion tonnes of steel a year. They kill more people in their coal mines, every year, than we've lost soldiers, cumulative, in every conflict this century. And if that wasn't enough, they knock off another million souls annually by burning the fucking stuff in power plants so polluting you can taste it – which does at least take the edge off the street food.

BORIS: I was wondering about the face masks.

MARTIN: Actually those were the police. They were protecting you from a group of students, a little miffed with your comments about getting Hong Kong back on a lease or return.

BORIS: It was a joke!

MARTIN: Never – never – joke with the Chinese about land. We discussed this. The nine-dash line is not something BBC executives do in the bathroom at Annabel's. The Spratly Islands are not a home for really tiny fish. The Senkak— sorry, Dioyutai dispute – is ... really bloody complicated. Taiwan is a part of One China. They're too fucking scared to say otherwise. China doesn't claim Mongolia, but Taiwan does. So they're still arguing the toss about an issue that started in the thirteenth century when the children of Genghis Khan couldn't agree who among them was the biggest bastard. These days – we say they are just visiting Tibet and, oh gosh, is that the time – Dalai who? Never met him... And never, never joke about Britain taking back Hong Kong!

BORIS: Got it, no more introducing Chris Patten as the 'once and future King'.

MARTIN: And stop asking him how his daughters are. He doesn't like it.

BORIS: I don't know what you mean... Your phone is ringing.

MARTIN: It's Straw. Hello. Hello. Yes, hello – oh, it's you, Will. How is the Bank of China? Good – good – I was just talking to the PM about you. No, really... I was just saying, I'm so glad it's a bank he works for, rather than running point for opium dealers. It'd be such a fucking bore to have to have Daddy come over and march you down to the police station again... Yes, yes, that was a long time ago – like that campaign you ran, what was it called? Stronger In? Save Dave? B-S-E? I just can't remember – but then again, neither could the guy you put up to run it... And no, no, I don't have any news about the financial services package... Oh, you heard we've ballsed it all up? ... Well, fuck you very much, you coiffured cunt. How's the whole 'Labour's answer to Justin Trudeau' thing going? Oh, it's not – that's right, because you're working for a fucking bank... Fuck off.

BORIS: How is Straw Minor?

MARTIN: Still a cunt. A polite, well-mannered, reasonable cunt. God, I hate that. He's sitting in the Shanghai Hilton with Danny Alexander, knowing full well we've got diddly squat. I could swear I heard George sniggering in the background as well.

BORIS: Anything constructive in the call?

MARTIN: Yes, the chairman of HSBC told his board he wants to construct a gallows outside Chungking Mansions and hang you from it. HQ migration is back on.

BORIS: Anything actually constructive?

MARTIN: They're also blaming Dave. It appears his year-long sulk did not convince the Chinese of our serious intent.

BORIS: So your advice is to thank Lord Cameron for his heroic efforts, and regret they were ultimately not successful on every point?

MARTIN: Yes, that, and hope to Christ the EU was even less successful than we were.

BORIS: Your phone is ringing again.

MARTIN: Hello. Hello. Oh, hello, Miguel – how is Commissioner Malmström? Oh good, good – we're so pleased... Digital as well... Well, that is just super... Disappointed? No, the Prime Minister understands that our unique circumstances will take longer to integrate into a comprehensive package... Oh, the Norwegians and Swiss are on board? Well they can't get enough of chocolate-coated blubber sweets in Guangdong, I'm sure... No, no, I hadn't heard that the Prudential were seeking to relocate to Frankfurt – must be the lovely weather... No, you take care – so grateful for the call...

BORIS: You've gone very quiet, Martin.

MARTIN: *Fuck!* Jesus fucking cocknobs.

BORIS: Oh dear. That's not even a word, is it?

MARTIN: It bloody will be by the time I've finished editing President Xi's entry on Wikipedia. The conniving, treacherous – fuck it, let's send a gunboat – we may only have one left, and it may be made of Chinese steel, but it worked last time...

BORIS: I can see you need to be alone. I'm just going to go and fire Dave as Trade Envoy – then maybe call Cecilia about whether they'd like us to come in on this deal. Please ensure the BBC cannot find me before the flight home...

What most helped the Prime Minister in his negotiations was his prior experience as London Mayor. His last visit had been a major success. In China, Boris had star quality – something he never tired of reminding his long-suffering trade team: Dave, George and Philip – or the Beijing Beatles, as they didn't like to be called. He was John, apparently; no one wanted to be Ringo.

SARAH: I don't think I've ever seen the ambassador smile before.

BORIS: What's not to love? We're here. The Shangsi Festival of Women is in full swing. And this time next year we'll be selling Land Rovers and Barbours to 2 million wannabe country gentlemen in the Communist Party. Nothing says commitment to the values of Mao better than a Smythson leather-bound copy of the *Little Red Book*. Remind me again what I – I mean we – the team – have achieved.

SARAH: There are still secondary conversations to be had on details. But we have secured an elimination of tariffs, duties and quotas across around 97 per cent of our tradable commodities – 1 per cent more than the Australians managed. Non-tariff conversations on services are progressing as well.

BORIS: Are any of the details important?

SARAH: Not, I think, for you to concern yourself with, Prime Minister. But if you wish to know... In the trade of live animals discussion we secured broad agreement, bar lingering concerns in the fish, crustaceans, molluscs and other aquatic invertebrates line item – specifically the sub-section on molluscs, whether in shell or not, live, fresh, chilled, frozen, dried, salted or in brine, smoked, whether or not cooked before or during the smoking process; across flours, meals and pellets fit for human consumption.

BORIS: What?

SARAH: There are remaining sensitivities in the carriage of Bivalvia Veneridae from the UK to China. Commodity code 0307810010.

BORIS: What?

SARAH: It's the cockles, Prime Minister. They don't want our cockles.

BORIS: Why on earth not?

SARAH: Their agricultural lead is the nephew of one of the pickers drowned in Morecambe Bay. He's making a point.

Boris: Oh. Fair enough. I'll leave that one with Ringo – I mean, Philip. Have we a retaliation?

Sarah: Yes, we're going to retain controls on the import of stinky or fermented tofu – on safety grounds. We can cite a 2008 dispute with Japan where the tofu was contaminated with sewage and iron sulphate.

Boris: Ugh.

Sarah: We also considered soy sauce derived from human hair, artificial eggs, DDT-tainted dumplings, plastic tapioca pearls and 'rabbit' from any district with a shortage of cats. But it was overly fragrant bean curd that won out.

Boris: The poofu has cut through. Turd curd is the word. I sincerely hope this threat helps get our cockles out.

Sarah: Very good, Prime Minister. Would you also like to be briefed on lingering issues with hand-made whips, torque meter wrenches, fixed asset finance option derivatives, or phone apps for the purpose of reading the news? The Chinese are particularly unenthusiastic about that last one. Unless they can install their own filters.

Boris: No, I feel you have convinced me that the detail is not important. How are Team Malmström progressing?

Sarah: Disappointingly, Prime Minister. They have been recalled.

Boris: Gosh, that is disappointing. Why?

Sarah: Several reasons, Prime Minister. Germany could not agree with Poland as to whether or not the investor-state dispute settlement system should be applied to environmental standards. Sweden could not agree with Finland over the inclusion of resin-based pine coatings for self-assembly furniture. Greece disagrees with Belgium about whether Chinese labourers can work in construction, or any public services. Spain disagrees with Portugal over whether Chinese fortified wine can be called port. And in return, Portugal disagrees with Spain over whether Manchurian Manchego is a sufficient differentiation to permit import of copycat cheese.

Boris: The Faux Manchugo is oh-so-no-go?

Sarah: Indeed. Again, very good, Prime Minister. Everyone disagrees with France as to whether their film industry needs special protection from Chinese imports. And France disagrees with everyone as to whether financial services should be part of the package at all. And if they are, whether or not they should be subject to a financial transactions tax.

BORIS: I watched a French film once. I'd be minded to tax them if I ever have to do so again.

SARAH: I will instruct the embassy to cancel next month's schedule of events paying tribute to naturism in French cinema.

BORIS: Perhaps I have judged too hastily...

SARAH: Perhaps. Your flights, Prime Minister. We are due in Malaysia tomorrow, the Philippines next week, and then on to Indonesia.

BORIS: And you bought the 'wish you were here' postcards for Donald?

SARAH: Yes, Prime Minister.

Part 5: 15 September 2022 – Och aye, hell nae

During the Brexit referendum, Scotland voted to remain in the EU by 62 per cent to 38 per cent. This sizeable gap was not mirrored in Wales or Northern Ireland, and was entirely overwhelmed by the substantial lead for Leave in England. The difference helped revitalise Scottish National Party ambitions for independence.

In the background, there was also the 2020 Treaty of Brussels. This included a fast-track accession process for 'former member states or new sovereign entities that were formerly part of a former member state'. It was called the Sturgeon Amendment to Article 49, after substantial lobbying by the First Minister. It was now possible for an Independent Scotland to rejoin the EU in under eighteen months.

Superficially, then, what had been designed as an easy way back for Britain was actually a powerful tool for breaking up the UK. It reassured Scots who had voted for the Union in 2014 that they could still be in a union – just not the one run by Boris Johnson. The SNP easily won the 2021 Scottish elections. Sturgeon used her victory speech to announce a new consultation on a second independence referendum. After a long and careful process of exploring options and building up support, the referendum was held on 15 September 2022. At 11 p.m., the exit polls noted a very clear outcome...

MARTIN: Well, that just about wraps it up for the United Kingdom. Fifty-six per cent out.

Boris: Are you sure? It's not a Survation poll, is it?

Martin: No, it's Ashcroft's new vehicle. The Free Britain Research Institute British Election Survey. Or 'Free English Election Survey with a nod to the Welsh and former terrorists', as we'll be calling it next year.

Boris: Oh God. Has she called yet?

Martin: Queen Merida? No. I imagine she's massing her cyber-savages along Hadrian's firewall and preparing to assault us with a volley of semi-literate gloating. Oh look, it's started: 'Boris byebye #PissoffTories', 'Seeya JK Quisling #Freedom An'take Voldemort widya to', 'I came to Edinburgh, and all I lost was 300 years of history #Borisgohome' – actually I think that last one was from Ruth Davidson.

Boris: This is awful. I can't think.

Martin: Oh, snap out of it. It's fucking brilliant, that's what it is.

Boris: I'm sorry, what?

Martin: Come on Boris, think about it. We're about to be handed permanent Conservative government for the next twenty years. Reliant on the DUP today? In two years' time we can tell Ian Paisley Junior to get back on his don't-mention-the-gays-Bible-bashing-bog-bike and feck off. You're going to have a proper majority again. This isn't a defeat, it's a fucking hostage release.

Boris: I've lost the bloody Union, Martin!

Martin: No, you've allowed democracy to flourish. You are disappointed – of course you are. Furrowed brow. Wobbly lower lip. A solitary tear strategically placed at the corner of your eye. All that shit. But this isn't about you. It's about the British – sorry, Scottish – people taking control of their destiny. It's about two nations reborn. Stronger together, yes, but now celebrating their unique strengths apart.

Boris: Of course it's bloody well about me. The 1922 are going to crucify me. You may not have noticed out there in the press office, but most of the Conservative and Unionist Party actually believe in both parts of our name.

MARTIN: Oh, fuck off, do they. Most of your colleagues believe in one thing: their right to be there. Sure, they like the Union Jack, the Queen, all those lovely crinkly bits in the constitution – because those things help get them elected! Why do you think half your avowedly Eurosceptic pals backed Dave's Remain campaign? There they were, the fey Eurosceptics, for thirty years, banging on about what a fucking outrage the European Union was. Sovereignty, Maastricht, the Common Sheep-fucking Fund – couldn't stop them. But what's this? The leader thinks we should stay? Oh dear – what a dilemma ... decency, principle ... what's that, Prime Minister – a peerage? A ministerial post? Perhaps, on reflection – special circumstances – great renegotiation, Dave! They are careerist cunts – and happily for all of us, so are you. So snap the fuck out of it. Put on your best maudlin and get ready to welcome the bright new dawn.

BORIS: I have mixed feelings. Part of me actually wants to kill you right now.

MARTIN: And the other part?

BORIS: That part wants to kill you as well, but suspects you are right. We can at least blame Gordon Brown again for the campaign.

MARTIN: And Nick Herbert.

BORIS: Why Nick Herbert?

MARTIN: I like blaming him.

BORIS: It is possibly time to forgive him for running the Eurosceptic Remain faction. He was never an Outer. And he has been out of the Cabinet for some time.

MARTIN: I refer you to my earlier remarks about careerists.

BORIS: We will not be blaming Nick. I want him back on the team. Besides, Labour ran this campaign.

MARTIN: Fair enough. I'll call Murdoch's people and the *Mail*. 'Starmer's Scottish Stammer.' 'Kier's Kiertastrophe.' 'The man who cost us Britain.' Screw it, I'm going to ring Dad. I'll tell him he's now a refugee from the Gorbals; come separation, we can deport him. If I wind him up enough, he'll do half the job for us. We'll swamp the morning editions with enough vitriol that the left will spend the next few days attacking the media, not you. Starmer isn't Corbyn; we need to bury him now, before he's really started. This shambles will do.

Boris: Make it so. And when you've finished, we need to work out how to stop them getting all the oil.

But in our happier place...

Boris: Cor! Phew!

Sarah: Four per cent, Prime Minister. Fifty-two to forty-eight. Congratulations!

Boris: We'll have to wait a little longer, to be sure. But it looks sufficient to crack open the English whisky. Will you join me in toasting a wee dram to the crushing of rebels and traitors, Sarah?

Sarah: I believe I will have a small white wine later with the Scottish Office. The Permanent Secretary is hosting a quiet celebration.

Boris: The 'we're all keeping our jobs' party. I'd heard. I was planning on dropping in.

Sarah: They will be delighted. I will warn them to look frugal and restrained for the cameras.

Boris: Before you go, please could you dial Holyrood?

Sarah: It is done. Hello – yes. No. 10. The Prime Minister to speak to the First Minister.

Boris: Hello? Hello? Nicola, what can I say? Congratulations on a very effective campaign – and so very close... Rotten luck about Grangemouth – who'd have thought they'd have threatened to shut it down if you won? Rumours about a threat to block shale gas imports from the US? With our new powers over trade? I'd not heard that before; I'm sure it's just gossip from the darker reaches of cyberspace... Oh, you heard it from Alex – he's quite the storyteller. Will he be coming back? Yes, I'm aware you haven't resigned... No, no, we will be waiting for the official result before issuing a statement. And you – any plans? In the unlikely event you have more free time soon...? Oh. She hung up.

Sarah: Astonishing, Prime Minister. Shall I dispose of the Scotxit Plan now?

BORIS: Yes. Although just summarise it again, I want to use it in my speech later. What would have happened if they'd won?

SARAH: Very well, Prime Minister. One more time. In the event that Scotland had voted to leave the United Kingdom there is no constitutional procedure. We would be making it up as we went along. Nothing would change immediately. But we would begin talks on the separation of institutions, and international recognition for both of us. It is assumed, but not guaranteed, that we would inherit all rights, privileges and obligations of the old UK. It is assumed, but not assured, that Scotland would immediately seek to join the European Union under Article 49 – as well as other international bodies, such as the United Nations and NATO. However, those bodies might not agree to recognise Scotland as a candidate for membership until such as time as our separation negotiations were complete. It is a process...

BORIS: I'm listening.

SARAH: So there would have been a period where Scotland was still a member of the United Kingdom but didn't want to be; but not a member of the EU but did want to be. The EU, meanwhile, would want to start working on making Scotland a member; but could not do so until it was clear what the Scottish nation actually was. We, meanwhile, would wish to separate as fast and as cleanly as possible, in order to avoid any instability in the markets. But we would be in immediate and deep disputes over their ongoing use of the pound, the allocation of national debt and control of territorial waters. We would have had to disaggregate a range of tax and spending decisions. We would need to put contracts that were within the UK on a cross-border basis – for example the National Grid and NHS. We would need a free trade agreement with Scotland. We would have had to find a way to remove Scottish MPs from Westminster. None of this could be done quickly.

BORIS: Got it, got it.

SARAH: In summary, Scotland would have left the UK, but not have left the UK. It would have attempted to join the EU, but not have been allowed to join the EU – until the UK agreed with Scotland what was Scotland and what was the UK. Meanwhile, we would be renegotiating our own free trade agreement with the EU and others to recognise a new border that was not yet a border on the assumption that it would soon be a border: a border with Scotland at first and the EU later. A renegotiation recognising a renegotiation, on the presumption of a further renegotiation when the renegotiation was renegotiated.

BORIS: Dave would have loved that. He did like his renegotiations. You may go now; I'll see you later. Up the union – and send in Martin, I'm going to try to make him understand what you just said.

SARAH: Yes, Prime Minister.

Part 6: 27 August 2023 – They think it's Moldova

Moldova is a European nation of 3 million people, landlocked between Romania and Ukraine. It signed an Association Agreement with the European Union in 2014; this is a preparatory step towards full membership that gives the applicant time to bring their laws and customs into line with the EU accession criteria. Moldova needs lots of time.

Over 70 per cent of the population is ethnically Romanian (or Moldovan). There are also significant Russian and Ukrainian minorities, mostly in the east of the country. This included the autonomous region of Transnistria: a 450km strip of land, to all intents and purposes an independent state. It still hosts a large number of Russian troops and its government is highly autocratic. To the south there is a Gagauz minority of 150,000, mostly in the regional capital of Comrat. Gagauzia has some autonomy, but is not an independent state.

Politically the Moldovan majority lean towards liberalism and the EU. Transnistrians on the other hand, together with other Russophones, and Gagauzians, lean to the left, and against the EU.

The situation was made more complex in 2015–16 by a major corruption scandal in the ruling pro-EU governing coalition. Allegations surfaced that around 20 per cent of GDP had been looted by elites and oligarchs, including the Prime Minister. Several governments fell and there was a notable splitting of Romanian votes towards the opposition parties. This made relations with the EU more difficult, and slowed progress towards EU membership – or it would have done were it not for deeper concerns about Russian activities in Ukraine and Transnistria. The West was obliged to choose between encouraging a corrupt liberal establishment and helping a proto-Communist movement with close links to Putin's Russia.

By 2022, tensions with Gagauzia had become acute. Independence referendums were threatened. Soldiers in unbadged uniforms began to appear in the province. The Moldovan government pressed ahead with a full EU membership application; in response, Transnistria declared full independence and invited Gagauzia to join them. Neither the UN nor the EU agreed to recognise the declaration. Some EU officials were beaten up, and shots were fired into Moldovan enclaves on the east bank of the Dniester. The Romanian Army mobilised.

Given their position outside the EU, the UK offered to host multi-party, multi-institutional talks in London, aiming to de-escalate the tensions and find a workable compromise. On Moldova's annual Independence Day, 27 August, the talks concluded...

MARTIN: Why, Boris? Why?

BORIS: Why what?

MARTIN: Why the fuck did you compare Ms Oğuz of the Gagauzian delegation to Nicola fucking Sturgeon?

BORIS: Well, it's true! They're very alike!

MARTIN: Yes, yes – I grant you they are both small, impossibly annoying and keep popping up in your peripheral vision – like Columbo, 'with just one more thing to discuss' – but they all thought it was political code.

BORIS: Oh.

MARTIN: They bloody well phoned Edinburgh to find out how she pulled off independence. In the middle of the fucking talks.

BORIS: Not ideal, I agree.

MARTIN: The latest Moldovan Prime Minister, meanwhile, thought that is precisely what you were encouraging them to do – stormed out, and sent two companies of the Moldovan Army into the suburbs of Comrat.

BORIS: Bit of an overreaction, I thought.

MARTIN: Not quite as much as the Strela missiles that were then fired from

Transnistria, narrowly avoiding bringing down a helicopter full of British journalists. We were thirty feet and a gusty day away from losing *The Guardian*'s Eastern Europe correspondent – and Piers Morgan…

Boris: You seem more troubled by that than I would have thought likely.

Martin: We. Do. Not. Want to lose some of the most effective advocates for this government that money can't buy. Every time they write or broadcast one of those ranty little sermons about us, usually attached to a demand for state controls and higher taxes, it scares the willies out of the floating voters – who cling to us. It's why Dad hated them so much. And besides, do you really want to martyr Piers Morgan? Is that a eulogy you'd be happy to give? 'Piers was a friend of mine, a great broadcaster, bon viveur … and … arrghh. Fuck, I can't do it – just bury him in lead and put lime in the casket.'

Boris: I think I would manage. Please get back to the review.

Martin: The Russians were laughing. They've gone back to the Ritz to dispose of whatever they were going to slip into the Moldovan PM's food. No need now. Instead, 2,000 heavily armed sociopaths, without uniforms but all called Ivan, are clambering into their attack choppers, preparing to defend plucky little Gagauzia from Western aggression. We have given Vladimir Putin the moral high ground.

Boris: In fairness, Moldova did that.

Martin: Oh, yes, let's blame Moldova: a country currently run by a man whose last job was selling used cars to Bulgarians. Who won his election by being the only leader in his four-party coalition who wasn't on bail for fraud. Largely, I suspect, because none of his automobile customers survived the trip home from the showroom long enough to press charges. Why don't we blame the people who put him there? The fucking EU.

Boris: I really don't think that would be wise…

Martin: Oh, come on, it's perfect. There they are, sitting in Chişinău, around a table with a dozen locals of questionable character, dangling before them the grifter opportunity of a lifetime: a golden ticket to the Brussels subsidy factory. While outside, 60,000 angry protesters are rioting on Stephen the Great Boulevard. Principally about what a bunch of thieving criminals their government are. And wondering why the EU is propping them up.

BORIS: That may be true. But's it not very relevant to what happened today.

MARTIN: It's entirely relevant. The E-fucking-U could have stopped this sooner by ditching that bunch of thieving nonentities, and getting stuck in with the other side's bunch of thieving nonentities. This before Vlad the Invader could get a look in. We would then at least have confused public opinion, rather than a million people getting all misty-eyed about hammers, sickles, and a man who likes to bare-chest wrestle bears...

BORIS: I'm getting rather lost here, Martin...

MARTIN: Look, the EU thinks it's a neutral actor in these post-cold war disputes. It isn't. In this one it's Romania. In Cyprus it was Greece. In former Yugoslavia it's everyone who isn't the bloody Serbs. It's not neutral. It's deeply influenced by whoever is currently in it – and worse, it doesn't see it. The Commission think they're building the New Europe, where national identities don't matter, where we all go skipping hand in hand, like a sodding Coke commercial written by John Lennon. They are completely blind to their own prejudices – or rather those of their members. Then they go wading in, waving the chequebook, principally at groups most like the current membership, and wonder why all the others – the ones who've been nursing blood-feud grievances for several hundred years – are not embracing the new era of brotherly love. They never know when to back off. They have caused this escalation.

BORIS: Ah. So what do you want me to say?

MARTIN: We deeply regret today's events. Now is the time for all parties to step back from the brink. We remind President Putin that Moldova is a member of NATO. We will not tolerate an incursion into NATO territory by Russian forces. Not officially. Nor those excitable enthusiasts from Odessa who appear to have accidentally taken a wrong turn at the Ukrainian border. We note the deep and real anger felt across Moldova at their government. We strongly urge all parties to support free and fair elections as soon as possible – and the suspension of the EU accession process until there is confidence that the new government has widespread support for that process to continue.

BORIS: And Piers Morgan?

MARTIN: Send him to interview Nicola Sturgeon. Two birds with one stone...

Boris was a very popular international leader in Moldova, in part helped by his success in holding together the United Kingdom and in part due to the tireless work of the ambassador. Carefully explaining the British approach to dispute resolution. How to defend your sovereignty without pulling apart. Groundwork that was essential to peace talks in London...

SARAH: Thank you, Ambassador, that is excellent news. I will report back to the Prime Minister. He will be delighted. Your recall? I'm sure it's only a matter of time. I will raise it ... goodbye.

BORIS: How is Dominic?

SARAH: Ambassador Cummings sounds tired but relieved. We have progress. He did, though, ask again when he's going to be allowed to come home.

BORIS: It is certainly under consideration. He was, however, a very popular choice for this posting. I wouldn't wish to go against the mood of the party.

SARAH: Prime Minister?

BORIS: I don't think many ambassadors have had their job supported by a letter from ninety-six MPs, several of whom were former leaders.

SARAH: Lord Duncan Smith wanted him sent to Moldova?

BORIS: Technically the letter said 'a place far, far, away'; I think it was drafted by a *Star Wars* fan. That was after the bit about 'properly rewarding his extraordinary contribution to the referendum campaign'.

SARAH: You mean the 'unofficial' Vote Leave posters of the now Foreign Secretary grinning while Jean-Claude Juncker picked his pocket?

BORIS: Yes, I'm sad to say George can hold a grudge. Possibly the poster itself – but more likely the days of speculation on social media as to where exactly the Commissioner's hand was – linked, I think, to George's facial expression... It was very unfair, that's just the way he looks when he's happy. Anyway, what did the ambassador have to say?

SARAH: Well, first, he wanted to be sure you'd really read the background notes. I think Martin said something to him about the time you confused the Macedonians in Macedonia with the Macedonians in the Former Yugoslav Republic of Macedonia, and both of them with the ancient Macedonians.

BORIS: Yes, yes, yes – but, to be sure ... remind me: why are they fighting?

SARAH: It's very historic. Moldova in antiquity was a place you invaded in order to get somewhere else. The Dacians were occupied by the Romans. The Romans were booted out by the Bastarnae, who in turn competed with the Scythians and Samarians. There's something of a divide in this between the Dacians and the Free Dacians, who may or may not have been precursors to the modern Romanians...

BORIS: A little too far back, I think...

SARAH: In the early Middle Ages things got more complicated.

BORIS: Oh God, really?

SARAH: Periodically they were invaded by the Goths, Huns, Avars, early Hungarians, early Russians, Turkic nomads, Cuman Empire, and the Mongols. Although historians are divided as to whether the Mongols were just passing through.

BORIS: Moldova, not good enough for the Mongols. Got it.

SARAH: The Bulgarians occupied it twice, and the Genoese popped in for a bit. There was a brief period of independence: the Principality of Moldavia, most notable in popular culture as a conquest of the protagonist in *Ghostbusters 2*.

BORIS: So our main opportunity for a cultural reference, to lighten the mood, is to that of Vigo the Carpathian? A despotic homoerotic madman trapped in a painting by happy slime. And you want me to mention that within earshot of a Putin hit-squad?

SARAH: Possibly not. If I may continue? Moldavia included areas of Romania and Ukraine, in part contributing to today's territorial mess; but it was subsumed into the Ottoman Empire as a vassal state, which was then carved up at various points between them, the Russians and the Habsburgs. In 1812, the Ottomans recognised Russian control over most of what is now Moldova, which they called Bessarabia.

BORIS: I will refer instead to 1812 overtures from the Russians.

SARAH: Very contemporary, Prime Minister. Transnistria, though, was not in Bessarabia. They had been part of early Russia, the Grand Duchy of Lithuania, the Polish-Lithuanian Commonwealth and the Crimean Khanate. They were absorbed into the Russian Empire proper, earlier than the rest of Moldova. To all intents and purposes they were Russians. Or at least closest to that tradition. And proud of it.

BORIS: Proud?

SARAH: Partly because Bessarabia was something of a joke in the Russian Empire. It had very low levels of literacy and high levels of poverty. In many Russian stories they were the punchline. And on that note, please don't—

BORIS: I will not compare Moldova to Liverpool.

SARAH: Thank you, but just remember that history impacts how they think about each other – as does the way in which the Russians industrialised Bessarabia – which led, in part, to immigration from Bulgaria into the Gagauzian region. At various points in the nineteenth century the Russians, Romanians and Ottomans fought over who owned what, until the Ottomans collapsed and the Russians had a revolution. This left the Romanians in charge, at least of Bessarabia; Transnistria remained in the Soviet Union as an Autonomous Soviet Socialist Republic.

BORIS: Much like Liverpool.

SARAH: Prime Minister! You promised.

BORIS: Sorry!

SARAH: The Nazis then sold out the Bessarabians to the Soviets: they made the Romanians give up the province in 1940. A new Soviet republic was created by the Russians, including the most Moldovan bits of Transnistria. This is where today's borders come from, and why the UN considers one part of the other. But the Nazi-Soviet alliance didn't last long. Romania was in charge during the war, and many bad things happened to the ethnic Russians. Then the Soviets were back after the war, under Stalin, and a lot of bad things happened to everyone, through deportations and famines.

BORIS: Meaning?

SARAH: Modern Moldova was forged as a result of betrayal and genocide. Twice.

BORIS: Don't mention the war...

SARAH: Or the Warsaw Pact... or really anything much about the twentieth century. When the Soviet Union collapsed most of the inter-ethnic and territorial tensions resurfaced. Moldovan nationalists seized power, but managed to alienate Russians and Gagauzians in the process. There were bitter rows that culminated in Transnistrian secession and a short war, only stopped by the intervention of the Russian Army. Who have been there ever since. The nationalists then botched the transition to a market economy, leading to the collapse of much industry, widespread corruption, and emigration. About 40 per cent of the economy today comes from money sent home by Moldovans, including a lively community in London.

BORIS: Yes, Martin showed me their Facebook group.

SARAH: I think that's enough history. To return to the point of the ambassador's call – there is a ceasefire. The Moldovan government has suspended their accession talks with the EU. The Gagauzian delegation has suspended its independence demands, but want further talks on deeper autonomy. The Moldovans have agreed to this provided the Gagauzians agree to support resumption of the EU talks when devolution is concluded. The Transnistrians are holding victory parades for Russians in Tiraspol. The Romanian and Russian armies have agreed to return to their bases. *Russia Today* is interviewing Putin tonight about his claim that he could knock out a horse with one punch. MI5 believe it's a coded message.

Boris: Pity, Martin offered to set me up with the Blackpool donkey sanctuary – to avoid losing face. Do you think I should explain Transnistria as being like Blackpool to Moldova's Liverpool? But with no pleasure beach?

Sarah: Please don't. Just be aware, though, that the issue is not entirely resolved. There are still territorial disputes between Moldova and Transnistria over villages on both sides of the Dniester, left over from the 1992 war.

Boris: Noted. But for now we can say that the London Conference has been a complete success. The EU and the Russians have retreated – and, once again, perfidious Albion has saved Europe from conflict. Please drop a note to the ambassador, thanking him for all his hard work and welcoming the contribution he is still to make – on the ground – to the very long and difficult process of reconciliation between the factions. Be sure to copy in George.

Sarah: Yes, Prime Minister.

Part 7: 20 June 2024 – Let us In

Although the London settlement was able to hold the peace in Moldova for most of the winter, by spring tensions had resurfaced, mostly around the status of particular villages. The conflict resumed.

By April, there was a full-blown refugee crisis. Half a million Moldovans were on the move, most pouring over the border into Romania, and from there on to the rest of the EU. During the Syrian refugee crisis, countries such as Hungary, Croatia and Slovenia had built significant structures for managing temporary increases in refugee numbers. These slowed the flow, but did not stop it. By the end of May the Sangatte refugee camp in Calais was filling with desperate families keen to be united with their cousins and friends in London.

Among them were a large number of young men from Ukraine and Belarus, all claiming to be Moldovans. This caused tensions, and occasionally fighting between the genuine refugees and the economic migrants. On 20 June 2023 – UN World Refugee Day – there came a crisis.

Martin: Jesus Christ, there are Moldovans in the Tunnel!

Boris: I am aware. COBRA will be meeting soon. I need to be ready and briefed.

Martin: OK, OK, no need to panic. We are not panicking. We are calm.

Boris: Martin? What do we know?

Martin: At 3 a.m. Ukrainian youths set fire to a food tent in Sangatte. The fire spread, and by 4 a.m. large parts of the camp were being evacuated. During the process fighting broke out between rival groups. In the confusion a large group of refugees fled. An advanced party stole a truck. With the police distracted, they were able to drive it through fencing and enter the Tunnel.

Boris: Have they...?

Martin: Yes, we believe they crossed the territorial border about fifteen minutes ago.

Boris: So...?

Martin: The French have indicated they are now our problem. The cunts. This is going to put us through the migration cap.

Boris: That never included asylum-seekers. It's a limit on foreign workers.

Martin: Oh, you think the *Daily Mail* is going to give a toss? They'll call it an invasion.

Boris: What about sending them back to France?

Martin: Well, other than the deep illegality of failing to process those claiming asylum – which will be all of them – and assuming they're not just here because they're mad keen on a fast train to Edinburgh, there is the problem of our recent rows over the Dublin Convention.

Boris: Ah. The arrangements concerning conditions of return for asylum shoppers?

Martin: Yes, that was a brilliant home goal, wasn't it? Having kept the Dublin Convention out of Brexit discussions, we should have been fine – but oh, no, when it came to revisions, to the creation of Dublin IV, some of the backbenchers noticed that it would be the Commission doing the redrafting. They threw their toys out of the pram about control. The twats. Meanwhile, half the Labour Party got overexcited about proposals to use face-recognition software to check and register entrants. They voted to oppose implementation on privacy grounds. Double twats.

BORIS: That's a lot of twats.

MARTIN: So we're not part of the latest controls. At least, not yet.

BORIS: Surely we can just use the previous arrangements? They haven't been revoked.

MARTIN: Oh, yes, Dublin III. How can I put this...? Try to imagine back to when you were a teenager. You've just gone on a date. You're in the car, and she's looking at you expectantly.

BORIS: Sounds familiar. If memory serves she was driving, and wearing this very exciting red—

MARTIN: This is a disturbing allegory. Please don't make it worse with reality. You reach into your pocket and pull out 'old faithful' – the trusty Dublin III prophylactic. Surely, surely, this will stop the little blighters gaining unwanted access to a warm room for nine months? There's an impenetrable barrier – she can send them back to the point of departure for reprocessing – or a tissue.

BORIS: —with lacy suspenders that were just visible...

MARTIN: Shut up. But what's this? What has little Boris done wrong? Why is she buttoning up her blouse? Why has the look of love been replaced by one of moody disappointment and bureaucratic indifference?

BORIS: Sadly, that sounds familiar as well...

MARTIN: Is it perhaps that the trusty Dublin III is about as much use a rubber sieve? Has the European Court of Human Rights insisted that we put holes in it? So Boris's brave little swimmers don't have their right to a family life impeded? Or suffer inhuman or degrading treatment by being returned to a squalid disposable facility?

BORIS: Like Sangatte?

MARTIN: Precisely.

BORIS: So you're saying?

MARTIN: Never buy a condom approved by a European court.

BORIS: Less allegorically?

MARTIN: Leaving the EU has made fuck-all difference to our inability to control our borders in a crisis.

Boris: Hang on, there's a message from CT Command: 'Moldovan protesters in London have set fire to Stamford Bridge.' Crikey. Chelsea is burning.

Martin: Putin FC? Finally your cuts to London's Fire Brigade are paying dividends.

Boris: Please call Abramovich and extend our support. Then get me on the lunchtime bulletins.

Martin: Drafting the lines now. Standing firm in the face of terrorism – respect for property – genuine refugees welcome – nothing to fear – may have to detain Tunnel arrivals longer to check for links with local extremists, etc. You can have the new Home Secretary issue one of those position papers on new counter-terrorism measures she keeps on standby. Priti looks fantastic when she's saying slightly sinister things about investigatory powers.

Boris: The Patel pouty power-play it is. Thank you, Martin. Unleash the securocrats!

The UK was not, and rarely had been, the most popular target in Europe for either asylum-seekers or economic migrants. That, though, did not prevent immigration from being one of the top three issues of concern for British voters for much of the twenty-first century. The politics of migration favoured tough rhetoric, managed entry procedures and limits to numbers. Brexit added most EU migrants to these procedures.

During wars and refugee crises, Britain instead favoured the provision of support near the source: processing claims and creating good facilities near the borders to disincentivise risky travel. The Johnson administration was something of a pioneer of this twin-track method. Borrowed in part from Australia. When the Moldova crisis reignited, Britain's approach, at home and abroad, was able to forestall the worst outcomes. Prior to a major speech to a UN refugee conference in London, Sarah is briefing the Prime Minister.

Sarah: Prime Minister, I have to alert you to a small difficulty that has emerged.

Boris: What is it?

SARAH: The Moldovan situation has inadvertently created a crisis for one of our research facilities.

BORIS: Explain.

SARAH: Prior to the resumption of hostilities, the Culham Centre for Fusion Energy had been in advanced talks with a Professor Rădăuțanu from the Academy of Sciences in Chişinău. He and some of his team were set to move to their facility to join a major new centre of expertise in niobium-tin material science.

BORIS: I think I recall a paper about something very complicated a few months ago.

SARAH: Yes, Prime Minister, I had one of the team draw you a picture. In brief, though, niobium-tin is a superconductor. It is essential to the magnet system in the tokamak fusion reactor. Culham is a part of that. They are soon to conclude their EU funding pitch, and success depends on guaranteeing the presence of Professor Rădăuțanu and his team.

BORIS: You lost me somewhere around the magnets.

SARAH: Fusion. Cheap energy for ever – without carbon emissions; or radioactive waste. But very hard to do. There's a big international programme to try to deliver it – based in France, but supported by a number of research establishments around the world, one of which is here in Culham. You visited it two years ago.

BORIS: Oh, yes, they did a very nice cheese sandwich. And the host – I think she was called Svetlana, from Georgia – probably – really knew her cheese sandwiches! I should visit again…

SARAH: We co-fund them through our Engineering and Physical Sciences Research Council and the EU's Horizon 2025 programme – co-funding we nearly lost after Brexit given the row about free movement rules.

BORIS: I recall we made special provision for science researchers across the EEA to resolve the stand-off.

SARAH: Correct. And that's why we're still cooperating with each other, most recently on this new material science centre for the tokamak.

BORIS: But?

SARAH: Without Professor Rădăuțanu the bid will collapse. £20 million of funding from the EU gone, much more from the spin-off programmes with the nuclear Catapult and commercial sponsors.

BORIS: We have nuclear catapults? I wish I'd known that before I agreed to Trident.

SARAH: Very droll, Prime Minister. As I am sure you are aware, the Nuclear Advanced Manufacturing Catapult is how we finance the commercialisation of new science in this area. These magnets could revolutionise a range of other fields, from super-efficient wind turbines to electric cars.

BORIS: So where is our Moldovan investment – I mean, the professor – now?

SARAH: Well, he was halfway through a Tier 1 exceptional talent migration process, with the support of the Royal Society. His laboratory assistant was on Tier 2, and there were three post-grads with Tier 4 student visas. However, we'd already lost one of the post-grads due to a previous Tier 5 error: an au-pair visa over-stay. She is barred from reapplication until that is resolved. Rather unfortunate, as we think she's why the professor's wife and children won't be joining him.

BORIS: A wandering eye for exceptional talent?

SARAH: Quite, Prime Minister. Our Tier 2 applicant was borderline. We had to triple his pay to meet our salary threshold, and he barely made it through the English language test. We then lost a few weeks when a shopping spree put his bank balance below the savings test in the middle of the ninety-day commitment period.

BORIS: An expensive trip. What was he buying?

SARAH: A suitcase, Prime Minister.

BORIS: An unfortunate reason for a travel ban.

SARAH: Indeed. We nearly lost the professor himself when that delay meant that we'd already exhausted our quota of 500 for this year's Tier 1 applications.

BORIS: Did we resolve that?

SARAH: Yes, it turned out that two arts applicants were the same woman from Amsterdam.

Boris: Ah, a double Dutch cap breach meant our new arrival was possible.

Sarah: Correct, Prime Minister. It is only years of professional training that are preventing me from being amused. But to get back to the point: this all became moot when the separatists bombed Chișinău. The professor and his colleagues fled and ended up in our co-sponsored holding facility in Romania.

Boris: Excellent. How is the Balfour Beatty refugee camp and repatriation college?

Sarah: Working well, Prime Minister. We've identified fifty migrants with skills in the shortage occupation list who will be fast-tracked. Around 200 more have enrolled on the building skills courses; they'll be capable of training others to British construction standards by the winter. Many of these have indicated they want to come to the 'Little Moldova' garden city site in Cheshire, to start building their own accommodation for resettlement – which means that for each refugee house, three are built for locals.

Boris: Yes, I did enjoy pointing out to the Campaign to Protect Rural England that our new 'emergency brake' powers allow the partial suspension of green belt and other planning restrictions on humanitarian grounds: the one good idea to come, indirectly, out of Dave's botched renegotiation. Just reassure me it's a Labour seat we picked for the demonstration project?

Sarah: You'll have to ask Martin, Prime Minister. Suffice it to say that I believe you've now got anti-fracking, anti-immigration and anti-development protesters arguing with each other about how best not to use 200 acres of mud near Nantwich.

Boris: Jolly good, I will dispatch Nick Boles to listen to their valid concerns. He loves that sort of thing. But on the subject at hand: if the professor's team is in the camp, why can't we just conclude their migration processes on site?

Sarah: In the confusion of exit he allowed his fingerprints to be taken at the Romanian border, before they reached the British camp. Technically, then, the Home Office says he's started an asylum process in Romania. This would likely preclude, or at least confuse, his prior migration request. His citizenship is now open to question. He's not being very helpful about this; we think he's still sulking about his missing post-grad. If he does seek asylum in Romania, he could still come here – our free movement of scientists agreement would enable that. But that would be too late for the funding application to succeed.

BORIS: I take it the Romanians are no better than we are at processing asylum claims?

SARAH: Worse, they've got their own stake in the fusion project and might see slowing him down as a way of taking our funding. They are now very insistent on his sincere desire to stay. So, in summary, Prime Minister, our fusion foundation funding with the French is resting on a Moldovan who may be a Romanian but wants to be British, due to Romanians who want him to remain in Romania – not go back to Moldova, to get his leg over, when the war isn't over. We would like him to be British, although the Home Office is skittish. We've four applicants on three tiers, with three applicants' applications dependent on the fourth application, which may now not be an application, dependent on whether a second application was really an application or merely the misapplication of an application for asylum to a non-applicant.

BORIS: Oh, bloody hell. Set up a call with the Romanian Prime Minister. I'll remind him exactly how much money we're currently putting in that camp and appeal to his sense of reason.

SARAH: You mean you're going to bribe him, Prime Minister?

BORIS: I am going to facilitate a change of heart. Meanwhile, make it crystal clear to the Home Office that they are to fast-track the original requests, including the nuclear science au pair – and make sure a minister takes personal responsibility for liaising with the fusion team and the EU. Get Truss on the case. She talks Scientist. When this is over, we're going to review this nonsense. I see a bright future for the red-tape challenge on immigration; we'll call it Johnson's No More Tiers Review. Now get me the phone.

SARAH: Yes, Prime Minister.

Part 8: 9 May 2025 – Borxit?

The general election of 2025 pitted Prime Minister Johnson against opposition leader Keir Starmer. The UK's economic performance was unremarkable, towards the bottom end of the G20 for growth – but there had been no collapse.

Yet voters were fed up. Fifteen years of Conservative government were long enough. There was a mood for change, a desire to punish the incumbents. They had, after all, failed to secure major new markets, lost Scotland and complicated a foreign war. Johnson himself was personally tainted by an immigration scandal. Rumours persisted throughout the election that he had got himself intimately involved in manipulating the application of a Moldovan au pair.

Labour wasn't perfect, either. Starmer had pulled them back from the madness of the Corbyn years, but he was still presiding over a coalition of interest groups rather than a coherent political force. But this didn't matter. The mood was populist, he himself was credible, and his team, a diverse group of younger MPs, didn't look like a Communist book group. On Europe he backed the status quo, but promised more cooperation through bilateral agreements.

The result could only go one way...

MARTIN: It's been a pleasure, Prime Minister. Most of the time you were not a cunt.

BORIS: Thank you, Martin, I'm deeply moved. What will you be doing next?

MARTIN: The Dutch want me to run their Out campaign. It's relatively simple, we're going to compare the EU to the sea, Dutch sovereignty to the sea wall, the pro-Europeans to the hole, and voting out as shoving an enormous finger in...

BORIS: Very colourful.

MARTIN: We'll also be trying to stop Geert Wilders fronting it. He terrifies the Dutch even more than Farage did our lot.

BORIS: Farage! Whatever did happen to UKIP?

MARTIN: Continuity UKIP has twenty councillors, mostly in Weston-super-Mare. The Free Britain Party still has a representative in the Welsh Assembly. Nigel Farage's English Parliament movement is almost invisible, and – ah, who cares – they're gone, and so are we. What will you do next?

BORIS: Not sure. Still got a constituency to manage – write a book or two – make insightful remarks about the bitter feud that's about to engulf the party... In fact I think a Roger sequel is in order – *Roger and the Sack of Ferrets*; the bitter ungrateful, resentful ferrets. What will they split over next? I wonder if the illustrators can do a scheming vole that looks like Hancock? Labour are threatening to do something about the House of Lords. Looks like I'll be running for the new Senate at some point – if called upon to serve... Might need a good campaigner... Might you...? Oh, he's gone. Better off alone, I guess... I could murder a cheese sandwich right now – Svetlana? Oh, that's right – deported last week... Hello? Hello? Is there anyone there?

The United Kingdom in 2025 was in good shape. It had agreed more trade deals with more parts of the world than any country bar Switzerland. It enjoyed a thriving technology and financial services sector, with high-value manufacturing and agriculture underpinned by cheap energy from a shale gas boom and Scottish renewables.

Johnson borrowed from Harold Wilson's playbook to bestride the centre ground: the white heat of technology, Boris buses on biofuels, Boris bikes with Boris batteries one day to be powered by limitless – almost free – fusion power. There was a Boris buzz.

He faced ongoing difficulties on domestic issues. The NHS was grumbling, he hadn't solved the growing cost of an ageing population, other public services occasionally flared up in dispute. But as for public spending, who'd notice a little extra borrowing on the £2 trillion of national debt?

Not Labour, certainly. They were not incompetent, but not ready either. Their campaign seemed weak and anaemic by comparison with the Prime Minister's dynamism – still too parochial and obsessed with things that mattered to Labour activists, not the public. They attacked the Conservatives on migration, for example, but this simply allowed the Tories to paint them as open-border extremists who would let anyone in. Appeals to human rights and compassion seemed a little feeble when the Conservatives had a Moldovan candidate standing in Cheshire, based on his positive experience of being trained to build his own home – and that of his Labour opponent.

The majority was down. But a win's a win...

Boris: So, just one more time, so I can really believe it...
Sarah: Yes – Prime Minister.

Postscript

With deep apologies to Armando Iannucci (*The Thick of It*), Jonathan Lynn and the late Antony Jay (*Yes, Minister*). Satire remains Britain's finest export. With special thanks to Helen Mayer of Vote Leave, who after a small renegotiation process, stuck with our historic union, and supported this project. Further thanks to Iain and Duncan, the Institute of Economic Affairs, Campaign for Science and Engineering, European Commission, Britain Stronger in Europe, and Steve 'bury me in Chişinău' Coventry, former adviser to the Moldovan government.

Chapter 22

What if Jeremy Corbyn became Prime Minister? (I)

Tom Harris

The critics and commentators got it dead wrong.

The scarlet standards that were waved so fiercely in Downing Street on the night of Thursday 7 May 2020 were, if anything, a paler shade of the red that coloured the faces of the experts who had predicted consistently that Labour under Corbyn could never win office.

But that, of course, was before the Euro referendum and the implosion of David Cameron's Conservatives. The drama of that infamous period in British history – the result itself, Cameron's resignation as Prime Minister, the legal challenges, the splits, the dramatic aftermath – is a tale that historians and journalists will report on and analyse for generations to come.

But among the many and far-reaching epoch-shattering consequences of the Tory meltdown, by far the most significant was the turning, by a demoralised, unenthusiastic and reluctant electorate, to Corbyn's Labour, elected on a historically low share of the vote in a five-party contest.

As the results came in on election night, there were echoes of Corbyn's first election five years earlier as Labour leader. The 71-year-old, looking at least ten years older following his four and a half years of struggle with his rebellious parliamentary party and a hostile media – including a second leadership election, and victory, in 2016 – seemed unprepared or unwilling to accept that he was about to walk through the doors of No. 10 as Britain's next Prime Minister. Aside from welcoming his own re-election in Islington, he flatly refused to comment on the extraordinary national result until, at precisely 11.06 on Friday morning, 8 May, Labour crossed the finishing line with exactly 301 of the Commons' 600 seats. The eventual overall majority would, later that day, be confirmed as an almost-healthy eighteen.

The tired, grim-faced Prime Minister-elect at last appeared on his own doorstep. His words were carefully chosen (although no one present thought their composition in any way accounted for the inordinate delay in their being delivered), for they amounted, it transpired only later, to the most explosive constitutional challenge to the monarchy ever mounted.

Head down, his voice and hands trembling noticeably, Corbyn announced to the media throng and the world that he would shortly be heading to Downing Street to begin forming his new government. Ignoring all questions, Corbyn politely thanked those present for their time and retreated indoors. It was only after Corbyn's entourage had arrived at SW1A (via public transport, naturally) that the new dispensation was clarified. Outside No. 10, Corbyn extended a gracious invitation to Her Majesty to visit him here, at the centre of government, to give her blessing, should she so choose, to the country's new government. Corbyn himself, it became obvious, would not be going to the Palace to be appointed as the Queen's Prime Minister; that honour, Corbyn told a stunned media pack, had already been bestowed by the people, and he intended to respect that decision, with or without the approval of 'a hereditary figurehead'.

Corbyn returned inside No. 10 as the crowd that had been allowed beyond the iron gates which normally sectioned off Downing Street from Whitehall sang 'The Red Flag' and their tears of joy flowed.

The first few hours of the first Labour government in ten years were no less dramatic. Corbyn's first appointment, John McDonnell as Chancellor of the Exchequer, was expected. However, the new Chancellor's announcement, made at the same podium that the Prime Minister had spoken at earlier in the day, shook the markets, if not the public. The 'experiment' of Bank of England independence had failed, McDonnell announced. Interest rates were a political weapon that should be wielded by politicians, not financiers. And he would consult on what kind of structure the bank would need in order to fulfil its most important function of guaranteeing full employment.

The move had been anticipated by some, but its absence from Labour's election manifesto had persuaded most that warnings of exactly this move were based on nothing more than scaremongering.

The next few hours saw a succession of MPs and Lords walk up the famous street to receive their commission from the new Prime Minister. Clive Lewis, the new Defence Secretary, confirmed to the press what was already virtually guaranteed: that the UK's independent nuclear deterrent would be removed from British soil as soon as possible.

Emily Thornberry, the new Foreign Secretary, was uncharacteristically quiet during her first twenty-four hours in office. But when, on Saturday afternoon, she held a press conference at the Foreign and Commonwealth Office, it became clear that she shared her leader's policy agenda entirely. She announced that she had invited the Israeli ambassador to her office in order to inform him that his government would be expected to enter immediate peace talks with Hamas and the Palestinian Authority with a view to drawing up a new two-state solution. A failure to do so would result in full economic, cultural and academic sanctions against Israel by the UK and a closure of its embassy and consulates. She also warned that she expected to talk to the EU's foreign affairs representative to encourage his support.

When pressed on the wisdom of the UK intervening in a sovereign country's affairs to such an extent, Thornberry prompted outrage and condemnation by describing Israel as 'a not entirely legitimate state'.

The ensuing furore almost overshadowed the last great controversy of Labour's first weekend in office. Debbie Abrahams, now Secretary of State at the renamed Workers' Rights Department, waited until the late afternoon of Sunday to announce, via Twitter, that the new government, as a priority, would introduce an enabling Bill that would allow every major trade union reform of the past thirty years to be repealed in one go. General secretaries throughout the country broke out the finest champagne and were still drinking it when the sun rose on the Monday morning of the first full week of Jeremy Corbyn's premiership.

Despite an angry, public appeal by the defeated Prime Minister, Theresa May, whose tenure as Leader of the Opposition was to last only eight weeks, Prime Minister Corbyn insisted that the previous cross-party agreement to delay the reconvening of Parliament for a full week should be honoured. The arrangements had been put in place in the expectation of a hung parliament and the inevitably prolonged coalition discussions that would result. But, as with the experts' predictions five years earlier, no one had expected a government to emerge with a majority, let alone a majority of nearly twenty – and for a *Labour* one!

So, for a full ten days, the new government was free to exercise full executive power without the inconvenience of its ministers having to be held accountable to the Commons. Speaker Hoyle was understood to have advised the Prime Minister that he would earn the respect of the House by agreeing an early meeting. Sources at No. 10 suggested that in return the Prime Minister had advised Hoyle that he would earn the gratitude and support of the Labour benches if he kept his nose out of government business and his mouth shut.

Corbyn was not reluctant, in fact, to face the elected Commons as a whole. But he was wary indeed of having to face the massed ranks of the Parliamentary Labour Party (PLP). Despite threats and actual attempts to deselect as many rebel Labour MPs as possible by Momentum, the hard-left campaigning group that had served as Corbyn's Praetorian Guard after he won the leadership in 2015, their efforts had been less than successful. (The only major scalp they had been able to secure had been that of the shadow Foreign Secretary, Hilary Benn, now duly appointed by Corbyn to the Lords, where he was expected to remain on the back benches.)

Labour's National Executive Committee had traditionally ruled that in situations where two or more sitting MPs were contesting the right to be the candidate in the same, redrawn, seat, no new candidates could enter the contest. A deft organisational manoeuvre by deputy leader Tom Watson had made sure that the NEC upheld this rule, meaning that even where an anti-Corbyn MP had been defeated for their chosen berth, it was usually by a colleague with similar views. And provided the losing MP could establish that at least a part of their old constituency now made up a part of a new one, they could expect to get something of a free run in that new seat, provided that the trade unions, who controlled the fabled 'trigger ballot', played ball. Thanks to Watson, they usually did. The political obituaries that Corbynistas had gleefully anticipated – those of Chuka Umunna, Tristram Hunt, Stella Creasy and Liz Kendall, to name but a few of a very long target list – would not be written yet.

So the new PLP, although now more malleable than its previous incarnation, thanks to the election of about fifty new hard-left MPs, was nevertheless largely composed of unreconstructed centre-left so-called 'moderates'.

Having publicly snubbed the Queen's presumed right to invite her Prime Minister to form a government, there was speculation that Corbyn might even take the monarch's place at the State Opening of Parliament ten days later, reading out his government's agenda to a joint gathering of Commons and Lords in Westminster Hall. This seemed to have been an idea that was seriously considered and was only rejected after the intervention of Baron Livingstone of Brent, the new Leader of the Lords, who argued successfully that such a move would distract attention away from the substance of the Queen's Speech itself.

And what a speech it was.

Every fear that had been expressed about the instincts and inclinations of the hard left found expression in that twenty-minute oration by a visibly irritated monarch. Her government would move immediately to 'clarify our membership of NATO', as well as 'strengthen our conventional forces through the removal of the United Kingdom's weapons of mass destruction'. On immigration, her government would 'set in place a new dispensation to welcome to Britain the world's poor, hungry and dispossessed, irrespective of their economic situation in their home country, or the threats they may or may not face there'. This was what the right-wing press and, according to polls, large swathes of the wider electorate, had feared: an 'open door' immigration policy that was liberal, progressive and massively unpopular.

The rest of the speech seemed to go out of its way to irritate and offend Corbyn's opponents inside and outside his party. All benefits sanctions were to be scrapped, as was the controversial Work Capability Assessment introduced by the previous Labour government and used enthusiastically by its successor. As signalled by Abrahams, a new right to strike without a proper ballot, the legalising of secondary picketing and the reintroduction of the closed shop would 'bring a new era of solidarity to the United Kingdom's workplaces', Her Majesty declared stiffly.

And, in listing her planned foreign trips over the coming year, the Queen confirmed what had already been briefed by No. 10: her government would do all it could to apologise and make amends for her country's 'ill-advised and misguided interventions in the affairs of other nations'.

~

Barely two years later, two events within weeks of each other sealed the government's fate and ended Britain's brief love affair with radical socialism. But before then, the new government's programme had to be implemented.

John McDonnell's first Budget, delivered to a packed House and a watchful, nervous nation on 24 June 2020, defined Corbyn's short-lived government in the eyes of most. The 10 per cent rate of income tax – introduced by Gordon Brown as Chancellor in 1999 and then scrapped by the same man after he became Prime Minister – was resurrected. It is now suggested that McDonnell fully expected the opprobrium heaped on him almost from the moment of this announcement, but at the time most witnesses were united: McDonnell expected to be cheered to the rafters, carried on the shoulders of the low paid as they applauded their new socialist hero. Unfortunately, in order to meet the cost of his largesse, the new Chancellor reduced the tax threshold from the £12,500 he inherited to £10,000, which meant a tax hike for the poorest paid in the country.

More damaging, however, was the announcement that the higher rate of tax would be raised by ten pence to fifty pence in the pound. Those who had previously paid forty-five pence on earnings over £150,000 now found themselves paying seventy-five pence instead. This, McDonnell told an appalled Commons, would allow the government to pay off the deficit without demanding that the poorest pay for it. The headline writers truly felt spoiled for choice when, in the peroration of his speech, and with a flourish, Chancellor McDonnell announced a super tax, levied at an eye-watering 90 per cent on earnings of more than £250,000 a year.

When Standard & Poor's announced it was downgrading Britain's credit rating to BBB, the Chancellor didn't even bother to make an official comment, leaving it to his spokesman to inform the world that the government 'would not be bossed around by the financiers' bank manager'.

Meanwhile, the economic data that had sparked S&P's concerns in the first place – the unprecedented levels of borrowing that the government needed to fund the spiralling cost of welfare following Abrahams's 'reforms' – meant fresh doubts about whether the government could afford to meet the commitments it had made to public sector workers. The new 'People's Living Wage' McDonnell had announced on Budget day was set at £14 an hour, a level the opposition, CBI and even many Labour backbenchers warned was suicidally extravagant. As predicted, it cost employers – and employees – dearly and the unemployment numbers began to edge up ominously. Meanwhile, local authorities, ministers decreed, would be expected to increase their recruitment levels to compensate for the shrinking of a private sector that, McDonnell decided, was acting to type by putting profit before people.

But higher levels of public sector employment meant higher wages bills, higher than the amount the government had already budgeted for. 'That's what the council tax is for,' an unnamed Treasury Minister was reported to have said, gifting the media with the government's first genuine 'Marie Antoinette' story.

As unemployment soared and inflation reared its head in a serious way for the first time in two decades – breaking the iconic double-digit barrier in April 2021 – Corbyn and McDonnell emulated their Labour predecessors by inviting the TUC General Council to Downing Street – not for 'beer and sandwiches', as one Labour MP remarked, but for 'croissants and mineral water'.

Yet by now even some of the left-leaning union bosses were becoming nervous of Corbyn's and McDonnell's preferred solutions to the economic crisis, which seemed to revolve around more state ownership, borrowing and spending. They were even less convinced by their insistence that it was all the fault of the international financial world and (inevitably) the Americans. The previously named 'special relationship' between the US and the UK was now more commonly referred to as 'Cold War II' and, following the initial row over interference in Israel's affairs, transatlantic trade had reduced catastrophically, adding more woes to the Chancellor's agenda.

The new Governor of the Bank of England, Lord McCluskey, had welcomed the Chancellor's decision to hike interest rates virtually monthly throughout 2021 in an attempt to curb the inflationary threat, and by year's end the base rate stood at an eye-watering 7.25 per cent. Repossessions rocketed and the level of new mortgages plunged to a post-war low.

The renationalisation of the UK rail industry was accomplished, at least in part, as swiftly and as efficiently as ministers had claimed at the start of the parliament. Despite the fact that the actual trains themselves remained in the hands of the banks, which had bought them when the system was first privatised, the franchises were back in the comforting embrace of the Department for Transport by the end of 2021. Train operating companies which protested that their franchises still had years to run were told that they were welcome to continue running services if they wished, but only as contractors for the new owners – the government. Threats of legal action nevertheless ensued. In the meantime, for the first time since 1996, the UK railways were unified: on 1 January 2022, British Rail returned!

The first UK-wide rail strike in a quarter of a century began on 2 January 2022. The cause of the action differed, depending on which trade union leader was speaking at the time. The important point was that following the government's reforms, no national ballot was necessary, and any drivers and other staff who didn't respect the picket lines could be physically prevented from getting to work, thanks to the support from other trade unions representing workers from sympathetic industries. Euston and King's Cross saw the worst violence, with pickets vastly outnumbering police officers. TV viewers watched in astonishment as passengers were forced to flee the country's largest railway stations for their own safety.

Paddington saw similar scenes, with a brand new Crossrail train actually set on fire (though it had already been evacuated and no one was injured). Across the country not a single train left its depot on that day, nor on any following day for exactly four weeks. The RMT announced that it had been the most successful trade union action seen in Britain since the miners' strike in 1984/85. The difference was that, in 2022, the strikers actually won.

The government did not.

Ministers found themselves facing in many different directions during and after the strike. McDonnell seemed genuinely delighted when the Transport Secretary, Andy McDonald, announced that every one of the RMT's demands – higher pay for all staff, increases in staffing and more flexible working practices – would be met. But the emergency across-the-board rise in fares to help pay the bills was, McDonald made clear, a direct result of the Chancellor's decree that no new money would be available in the current financial year from what he had already detailed in the government's Red Book. Relations between the two went further downhill when McDonnell agreed to join a protest against the fares rise by passenger groups in McDonald's own constituency.

When the end came, however, it came from a direction predicted by none of the pundits.

Whether Corbyn or any of his senior allies could be blamed for the first event remains an unanswered question, so long as the former Prime Minister sticks to his insistence in not giving evidence to the ongoing public inquiry headed by Lord Johnson. Speculation about conversations between ministers and itchy-fingered Irish Republicans have created a smokescreen through which it is difficult to make out the truth. Yet it is certainly true that signals were given, through certain channels, that the new government intended to make progress towards a united Ireland, using an often-overlooked clause of the Good Friday Agreement. Most observers assumed – and the Ulster Unionists dreaded – that this meant the implementation of the Agreement's provision for a referendum on unification. That was a decision that could only be taken by the Secretary of State for Northern Ireland, Dave Anderson. In the Commons on 1 March 2022, however, answering an Urgent Question tabled by the Democratic Unionists, Anderson made it clear that the government would do no such thing. Visibly angry at the situation he felt he had been put in by those briefing for No. 10, Anderson then privately demanded of the Prime Minister that any briefings to the contrary had to cease.

Just after 4 o'clock on the afternoon of Wednesday 16 March, a massive explosion ripped through the main entrance hall of Belfast Town Hall, killing fourteen people and injuring many more. At the same time, gunmen, later revealed as supporters of the New IRA, assassinated a Sinn Féin Northern Ireland Assembly minister and her assistant as they walked to their car at Stormont. The subsequent shoot-out between the terrorists and the minister's close protection officers left the attackers as well as the minister dead. The terrorist organisation announced via the Press Association that the twenty-year ceasefire had been ended because of a lack of progress towards a united Ireland, that Sinn Féin were now seen as Unionist quislings and that the 'armed struggle' would only end with the removal of the border between the six counties and the rest of the island.

In scenes of chaos and confusion that many hoped had been consigned to Northern Ireland's history, First Minister Arlene Foster announced that she was requesting a surge of British Army troops in order to stabilise the security situation.

Defence Secretary Lewis, who was the guest of honour at a Stop the War Coalition fundraising dinner when the news came through, seemed taken by surprise by Foster's request but said, as he left in his ministerial car for Downing Street, that he was open-minded to it. An hour later, sombre but silent, he stood beside the Prime Minister as Corbyn announced to the nation that any increase in the numbers of British troops 'on Irish soil' would only exacerbate the situation 'in the north'. He would not repeat Harold Wilson's mistake of 1967, he said. The Unionists of Northern Ireland were to be left to fend for themselves.

As the bombings and killings started to escalate in Northern Ireland, and as Corbyn, Lewis and Andy Burnham, the Home Secretary, continued to hold fast to their determination to keep out of it, another, arguably more serious, threat emerged to Britain's international prestige.

As opposition leader, Corbyn had made clear his view that Britain had no right to claim sovereignty over Gibraltar and that, since the UK was now no longer even a member of the European Union, there was every reason to strengthen relations between the two countries by entering negotiations on Gibraltar's 'long-term constitutional future'.

The Spanish authorities almost certainly interpreted events in Northern Ireland as a sign of the UK government's reluctance to safeguard the rights of citizens outside the British mainland.

They interpreted correctly.

When, on Thursday 19 May, without a single shot having been fired, Spanish troops raised their national flag above the Rock for the first time in more than 300 years, a nation that had suffered both economic and constitutional humiliations in recent years suddenly found a reason to unite, and to celebrate.

Speaker Hoyle, known for his passionate support for Britain's claim to the territory, created a new precedent by summoning, without consulting the Prime Minister, an emergency session of the Commons on Saturday 21 May – the first such sitting since the Falklands crisis had erupted in 1982. Meanwhile, on that remote group of islands in the South Atlantic, fearful eyes darted between the UK and Argentina; it remains a mystery why the Argentinians failed to take advantage of the situation while Corbyn was Prime Minister, when British resolve in foreign matters had been seen to be so unreliable.

The emergency debate was the most extraordinary anyone present or watching could recall. Despite government objections, Speaker Hoyle accepted a cross-party amendment (signed by more Labour MPs than Conservative) that added the situation in Northern Ireland to the motion of censure before members. Opening for the government, the Prime Minister began by making clear that the government, rather than raise any kind of objection with the Spanish authorities, would instead begin negotiations with them. Tempers flared and unparliamentary language went unchecked by the Speaker. Eventually, twenty minutes into Corbyn's speech, the Speaker suspended the session to allow members 'to calm down and catch their breath'. When the session resumed, the atmosphere was hardly less explosive. Then Leader of the Opposition Dan Hannan made what most observers considered to be the best speech heard in the chamber since Hilary Benn's on Syria in 2015. His demand that both Northern Ireland and Gibraltar must remain 'British, yesterday, today, now and for ever!' found its way into the next day's newspapers' front pages (and Hannan himself inevitably photoshopped onto the body of Olivier's Henry V).

The sleeping beast known as 'Moderate Labour MPs' seemed unexpectedly to awaken that day. Having spent the earlier part of the parliament grudgingly respecting the Labour whip – and particularly the manifesto on which Prime Minister Corbyn had been elected – exactly 101 of them voted for the substantive motion, blasting the government for 'cowardice in the defence of the nation'. That night, Corbyn's spokesman announced that every one of them would be suspended from the party whip with immediate effect.

A little-known and paradoxical paragraph of the Labour Party rulebook instantly became the subject of fevered speculation: MPs who lose the whip are nonetheless expected to obey it, or forfeit the chance of ever returning to the fold. If an election were called while such a suspension was active, the MPs would be unable to stand as Labour candidates.

Would the 101 oblige by offering their continued support for the administration? If not, they had not only deprived the government of its majority, but had gifted 'largest-party' status to the Conservatives.

The following few days were comparatively quiet in political terms; no task force was being dispatched to southern Spain, after all, and even the New IRA seemed to be obeying some form of self-denying ordinance while events in London developed. TV screens were filled with knowledgeable talking heads, confidently describing the constitutional situation and its precedents.

Except, as the wiser studio guests pointed out, there were no precedents.

Fortunately for Corbyn and his government, the following week's Whitsun recess allowed for some calm to descend on the still-busy corridors of the Palace of Westminster. Ministers still went about their work but the green leather benches of the Commons were vacant.

Hannan's now-famous Matthew Parker address changed everything – the country, British politics, the Labour Party, the monarchy and the constitution. As an MEP, Hannan had campaigned enthusiastically to make himself unemployed by taking a leading role in the Leave campaign during the referendum of 2016. But when exit negotiations concluded, the powerful orator found himself in some demand by the membership of a number of Conservative associations who were looking for new candidates in safe seats in the Shires. When the 2020 election finally arrived and the Conservatives, led by Prime Minister Theresa May, stumbled to an unexpected and catastrophic defeat, Hannan had found himself on the green benches of the Commons, then almost immediately thrust into the position of favourite to succeed May after the latter's inevitable resignation.

Still bullish from the unanimously positive reviews of his speech to the Commons four days earlier, Hannan used a hastily arranged speech at Conservative Party HQ to call for an intervention by none other than the Queen herself. Before an invited audience that included all three living former Tory Prime Ministers – Major, Cameron and May – Hannan declared his party the 'true, democratic government of our nation' and the 'government in exile'. Only Her Majesty could put an end, once and for all, to the uncertainty and chaos that gripped not only her kingdom, but also her overseas dominions. Deliberately echoing his predecessor, David Cameron, Hannan announced that he was making a 'big, open and comprehensive offer' to the now whipless Labour rebels to join with him in a national government that would re-establish constitutional government, reassert Britain's pride and authority at home and abroad, and then call an early general election one year hence, at which the public could decide the fate of both main parties.

An excitable press pack now turned its attention to Buckingham Palace and to the acknowledged leader of the Labour rebels, Dan Jarvis. Would he now expect the Cabinet position of Deputy Prime Minister? The former paratrooper declined to comment, but the impression given by some of the 101 was that Hannan's offer represented the least worst scenario on offer.

The final sticking block, it appeared, was the Queen herself. Would she openly declare her hostility to her Prime Minister by inviting Hannan to try to form a government? To do so would surely be snubbing the voters who, as friends of Corbyn repeatedly told reporters, had a mandate to govern.

Buckingham Palace let it be known that Her Majesty would look very seriously at what role she might play in the current circumstances. Even this ambiguous phrasing was enough to spark speculation at a mighty gallop.

On the Thursday after Whitsun, 26 May 2022, the Prime Minister's weekly audience with the Queen had been expected to be conducted by phone, since she had planned to be in Balmoral. However, in the early hours of Thursday, it was announced that Her Majesty had decided to return to London to meet Corbyn face to face.

A reluctant Corbyn turned up late. The audience lasted less than ten minutes. When he left the palace, ashen-faced and without comment, he returned, not to Downing Street, but to his party's offices in Victoria Street.

After a delay of nearly two hours, Corbyn emerged into the spotlights of the world's press to tell them what they already knew: he had been dismissed by the Queen as Prime Minister and replaced by Dan Hannan as the head of a new, national government. The most left-wing government in British history had lasted precisely 750 days.

This was a 'constitutional and anti-democratic outrage', said Corbyn in his trademark soft tones. Flanked by his media adviser Seumas Milne and both the (now shadow) Foreign Secretary and Chancellor (the Leader of the Lords was nowhere to be seen), Corbyn appealed to the voters who had given him his mandate to govern not to sit back and accept dictatorial rule from an 'unelected and undemocratic dictator'. When reporters asked for clarification as to whom he was describing – the Queen or Hannan – Corbyn spat, 'She knows who I'm talking about!'

It was at that point that his fate was sealed. The electorate had love for neither Corbyn nor Hannan by that point, but the Queen, despite the controversy, still enjoyed the combined support of both camps, and more.

Stop the War and its left-wing and anarchist affiliates staged an impressively large demonstration the following Saturday against what it labelled 'the palace coup'. It claimed a turnout of more than 1.5 million; the police estimated the figure to be nearer 25,000.

Observers there that night in Victoria Street maintain that Corbyn seemed more energised and determined than they had seen him since he took office just over two years earlier. Some suggested that this clash of philosophies – Queen *v.* Parliament, the unelected hangover from an undemocratic era versus the democratically elected progressive socialist

– had inspired Corbyn, had reminded him at the last moment of his career and what he had entered politics for.

But those who knew him rather better suggested a simpler and more convincing explanation: Corbyn was back where he felt most comfortable – out of office, without responsibilities, with no obligation to make decisions, and free again to take high-minded and principled positions without having to justify them.

Histories of subsequent events, of the emergence of New Labour as a party in its own right and the death of the old party it left behind, of Prime Minister Hannan's long reign at No. 10 and of the Mediterranean wars, are better left to other writers to chronicle. But the history of the demise of the Labour Party, from its 180+ majority under Tony Blair in 1997 to its miserly twenty-five seats at the general election held less than thirty years later in 2025, is one that will keep political historians busy for many years to come.

Chapter 23

What if Jeremy Corbyn became Prime Minister? (II)

Francis Beckett

At first it looked as though the establishment was going to accept the people's verdict gracefully.

The morning after the election, newspapers which had tried hard to destroy Jeremy Corbyn seemed almost to be running up the white flag. Even the *Daily Mail* editorialised, 'There are voices of sanity in the Labour Party and in the civil service. We have to hope that Mr Corbyn will have the sense to listen to them, and not to the wild-eyed Marxists around him.' *The Times* intoned sonorously:

> British political history is full of wild Labour leaders with revolution in their rhetoric who became moderate and respectable as soon as they were faced with the responsibilities of government. Mr Ramsay Macdonald, it is often forgotten, was once a left-winger, and Mr Harold Wilson once resigned from government in support of his hero, the left-wing Mr Aneurin Bevan.
>
> It seems highly likely that, faced with the responsibilities of government, Mr Corbyn will turn out to be more or less harmless. It may be wise for the Conservatives and the right wing of his own party to let him have the occasional bauble to show his supporters, so long as he shows no inclination to reach for the crown jewels.

Corbyn himself discovered that you can still run on adrenalin when you're seventy. The new Prime Minister had not slept, yet sitting in his own kitchen with a cup of tea and a few close advisers at eight in the morning, he felt fresh and excited, and anxious to get to work. The world's media was camped on his doorstep. He would have to face them some time, but there was no hurry.

The grim ideologue Andrew Murray, now seconded from the trade union Unite to be his chief of staff, looked suspiciously across the kitchen table at the Prime Minister. 'Jeremy, I hear you want to put off announcing the New Deal. I hope you're not going to panic, now of all times.'

Corbyn reflected, not for the first time, that Murray had a way of sounding as though you had sinned whenever you diverged from what he considered correct political thinking. And Corbyn knew that his first battle had begun.

~

Four hours earlier, as soon as it was obvious that Labour was going to be the largest single party and would form a government with the SNP support they had been promised, he had made what friends and enemies agreed was the most graceful victory speech from a new Prime Minister for years.

He stepped softly out of the Islington council offices. As soon as the big front door of the quiet period building was opened for him, the roaring of the crowd outside hit him like a tornado. He stepped onto a makeshift platform, on which the world's broadcasters had clipped their microphones, and held up his hands in a futile attempt to quiet the huge crowd shouting his name. Even at 4 a.m., excited supporters blocked Upper Street for a mile in both directions. Most of them could not see him, but they knew he was there, and that was enough. Those who could see him took his raised hands as a cue to shout yet louder.

At last a grizzled trade union leader with a crumpled suit and a voice like a foghorn heaved himself onto the platform beside the leader and roared into the microphone, 'Comrades, let Jeremy speak!' The message trickled through the crowd and Corbyn took the microphone again.

Even now he was not going to bellow. He had got to this point without bellowing, even when he faced David Cameron at his shoutiest during PMQs. He knew things about life that younger politicians had yet to learn. He was not going to abandon his studied quietness now.

'Comrades and friends, you have waited a long time for this. Now we have, for the first time in most of your lifetimes, a Labour government that believes in Labour values.'

The roar from the crowd made it impossible for him to speak again for several minutes, and commentators in broadcasting stations throughout the world flannelled heroically until Corbyn's raised hands produced another slight reduction in the noise level.

> You never gave up hope. So the new government has a sacred duty to deliver the better and fairer society you have voted for. If we don't, the chance won't come again in my lifetime, perhaps not even in yours. I pledge that every waking moment I have will be devoted to delivering it.

With one last wave, he stepped down from the platform and walked swiftly through a corridor of Unite shop stewards with linked arms, hastily assembled by his communications chief Seumas Milne to hold off reporters, and back into the Town Hall to take a telephone call from Buckingham Palace.

~

Four hours later, in Corbyn's kitchen, Andrew Murray protested that the speech was dreadfully unspecific. When was his boss going to announce the New Deal?

'You going to settle for the occasional bauble then, Jeremy?' said Murray, not unkindly, but with a sort of grim earnestness.

'No, but I think we need to wait a few days,' said the Prime Minister firmly. 'Of all the things we're going to do, this is the one that's going to have the City and the press down on our heads. We think the New Deal is a way to deal with the migration crisis. They think it's an attack on capitalism.'

The migration crisis had been the big issue of the election. Ever since the Brexit vote, there had been first a trickle, then a flood of people fleeing the country for the safer economies of France, Belgium and Germany. The National Health Service had pretty well collapsed for lack of doctors and nurses. New home-building was almost at a standstill as Britain's Polish builders went to make holiday homes on the Côte d'Azur and elegant dwellings along the banks of the Rhine.

Theresa May's government had tried to solve the problem with border controls, but the camp outside Dover was now a running sore on the south coast, and every night hundreds more Indian doctors, Polish builders and other key workers sneaked onto lorries, braving armed customs officers in their determination to get into the European Union.

Corbyn's New Deal was another approach. Instead of stopping them at the border, he would persuade them to stay with vastly inflated pay settlements paid for by deficit budgeting along Keynesian lines. He had talked of it in general terms during the election, but he also had a detailed plan, which only his closest advisers knew about.

Murray looked down at the table, clasped his hands in front of him and said, 'I didn't think you'd panic this early.'

'That's not fair, Andy.' Seumas Milne, all good looks and Wykehamist charm, often did this good-cop/bad-cop routine with Murray. It puzzled Corbyn, who thought they were lifelong friends from their days in the Straight Left faction of the British Communist Party.

Milne turned to the Prime Minister and added, 'But I think you're being over-cautious here, Jeremy.'

Corbyn said, 'We need time for you to brief sympathetic journalists, Seumas. We need time for Miriam to bring as much of the Parliamentary Labour Party onside as possible.'

'Miriam! Are you behind this?' asked Milne, turning sharply to the fourth person in the room, an elegant woman of thirty who had just been elected as the youngest new MP of the 2020 intake. She had risen fast, via a Labour-supporting think tank, to a post in the leader's office and now to Parliament, and she was known to have the leader's ear.

'Jeremy is right. We need a couple of days,' said Miriam. 'The hardline Blairites are a lost cause, but we've still got a lot of waverers among our own MPs. And we need to make sure the Scot Nats are on side.'

'Who cares about the SNP? They're unprincipled sectarians,' said Murray, glaring at the youthful interloper.

Murray never understood where Miriam had come from, but wherever it was, he was pretty sure it did not meet his standards of correct ideology. The late-middle-aged, grey-haired, grim-faced Murray, veteran of a lifetime of ideological struggle fought out in trade union offices and smoke-filled back rooms, looked at the stylish young convert from the Green Party with no background he understood or respected as though she was a creature from a different planet. Somehow, thought Murray, this clever, pretty young woman had wormed her way into Jeremy's inner circle – which he thought was the preserve of men and women who had been with Jeremy for years – and he was sure she was up to no good.

The Scottish National Party, which held the balance of power, had already made it clear that they did not want to be in government. They remembered what had happened to the Liberals after the 2010 election. The price for their support in Parliament was generally one Corbyn could pay without tears, even though giving more powers to the Scottish Parliament left the West Lothian question embarrassingly urgent and unanswered. But then it had remained unanswered for forty-three years; a few more could do no harm.

Corbyn had resisted Murray's suggestion that he should turn on the SNP during the election campaign. The idea had been that he should do what Ed Miliband had done in 2015, calling the SNP unfit to have a voice in government and promising to do no deals with them. But Corbyn had listened instead to Miriam.

'It's what cost Miliband the election in 2015,' she told Corbyn. 'The Tories were saying, "whoa, dreadful SNP people, must never be contaminated by them", and that panicked Ed into saying the same thing. And the voters thought, well, if both Labour and Tories say they're that dreadful even talking to them could contaminate you, then we'd better vote for the party that won't have to talk to them. Labour will have to talk to them before it can form a government. The Tories won't. So they voted Tory. Voters are quite logical, sometimes.'

Jeremy had accepted her argument and refused to say that he would never talk to the SNP. He had earned the hatred of Scottish Labour, which failed to win a single Scottish seat and blamed Corbyn, but the election outcome did not reflect the English terror of the SNP that had helped to sink Miliband in 2015.

Nonetheless, hatred of the SNP in Labour circles was historic and visceral. Now, as he formed his government, Corbyn was having the same argument again. 'A lot of your friends will be appalled if you talk to those bourgeois nationalists,' said Murray.

'Sorry, Andrew,' said Jeremy, 'but Miriam's right. We need our own people on board, we need the SNP walking into the lobby behind us. We wait. We release the plan on Monday afternoon. Until then we say nothing.'

Miriam smiled, pushed her chair back from the kitchen table and crossed her legs in a way that made the Prime Minister, just for a moment, wish he was a younger man.

~

'Prime Minister, Saudi Arabia is one of our most important markets.'

That afternoon, sitting in the Cabinet room for the first time and still without sleep, the new Prime Minister, with Miriam at his side, was listening to a large, erect, abrupt man in military uniform and a small, round, crumpled middle-aged man with a fleshy, honest face, who was from MI5.

The spy said, 'You may not be aware, Prime Minister, but the mere fact of your election will cost this country dear in Saudi trade, unless you act now to limit the damage. The Saudi government does not think of you as a friend.'

Corbyn knew that it was true. Soon after he was elected Labour leader, the Saudi ambassador to the UK had written an article in the *Daily Telegraph* complaining of Corbyn's attitude to his government. In particular, the ambassador was angry that, in Corbyn's first conference speech as Labour leader, he had called on the Prime Minister to intervene to try to stop the execution of Ali Mohammed al-Nimr, who had been sentenced to death for taking part in protests. Shortly afterwards, Corbyn had called for the Ministry of Justice to stop working with a Saudi justice system that, he said, punished almost all dissent and had doubled the number of beheadings in the previous twelve months.

'Billions of pounds we'll lose,' said the soldier. 'Think what that means for your people.'

'By my people, you mean...?'

'Workers. Chaps who build the bloody things. Aren't they the chaps you're supposed to be in favour of?'

'I think what the general means,' said the spy smoothly, 'is that a good many British jobs depend on trade with Saudi Arabia and any reduction in that trade would result in unemployment. Which, he rather assumes, you would consider a regrettable state of affairs.'

'Exactly. Saudi prince thinks you're a fucking Sunni.' The general seemed to think the last word rhymed with 'bunny'.

'Shia. He thinks Mr Corbyn is a Shia,' said the spy impatiently. 'The crown prince himself is a Sunni.'

'Why does he think Jeremy is a Shia?' asked Miriam.

'It's that bloody silly letter you wrote,' began the general, before the spy looked hard at him.

The spy said smoothly, 'You may remember, Prime Minister, that a few years ago you asked the then Prime Minister to reconsider the Overseas Security and Justice Assistance policy, commonly known as OSJA. You said, and I quote, that it was "little more than a rubber-stamping exercise, enabling the UK to be complicit in gross human rights abuses". I fear our Saudi partners thought that was an unkind reference to them.'

'It was.'

'Be that as it may. British companies sell billions of pounds' worth of arms to that country. We are Saudi Arabia's biggest arms supplier. Should they decide to buy elsewhere, the contracts will go to France. I do not think you were elected to export British jobs to Toulouse.'

'Thank you for all that, gentlemen,' said the new Prime Minister. 'I will make sure your views are heard at Cabinet next month – we can't discuss it at our first Cabinet, naturally, but we will take the decision next month.'

'No you bloody won't...' started the general, but the spy broke in before he could go on.

'Our soundings suggest', he said, 'that there will be no decision to be taken next month. Prime Minister, unless you take immediate action to repair your personal relations with the crown prince, all trade will cease next week. Other nations, and particularly France, will take our place, and you will be blamed for the consequent unemployment and hardship.'

Miriam was watching the spy closely, and now she spoke. 'Suppose the Prime Minister were to do what you suggest. Do you think that, in exchange, the crown prince might halt the current treason trial and let those young people go free?'

'No,' said the spy. 'Next Monday, fifteen young men, ten of them still in their teens, who are accused of attending a protest march, are to be crucified and then beheaded. Twelve young women, two of them teenagers and one of them a British citizen, are to be whipped in public for unspecified crimes of immorality. We have so far kept it out of the newspapers, but we will be unable to do so when the sentences are carried out. Our information is that the crown prince intends to make this a test of the new British Prime Minister. Should you speak on their behalf, our trade with that country will be at an end.'

As he got up to leave, he held the Prime Minister's hand for a few seconds longer than necessary and said quietly, 'Next Monday, Mr Corbyn. It gives you the weekend to think. Use it well. Make up your mind by Monday. Or others will make it up for you.' He looked into the Prime Minister's eyes. 'Government is hard, Mr Corbyn,' he said, 'hard and cruel. Did no one tell you?'

~

The spy was back half an hour later. There was, he said, something he did not wish to say in front of the general.

'It's about your official spokesman, Mr Milne.'

'What about him?'

'He'll have to go. He's a security risk.'

'Seumas! What on earth do you mean?'

For answer, the spy handed over an old yellowing cutting from *The Guardian*. In an article by Seumas Milne he had highlighted these words: 'But political corruption and the implacable opposition of the spooks and military to progressive change are the traditional forms of anti-democratic politics, in Britain, as elsewhere.'

'You do understand, don't you, Prime Minister? The security services cannot work with you while you have this man on your staff.'

~

The weekend was for government-making. Newspapers were occupied, as always on these occasions, by the comings and goings in Downing Street: who would serve, who wouldn't, who was in, who was out. Making a Cabinet, Corbyn found, was much easier than making a shadow Cabinet. If you had real Cabinet positions to offer, people tended to forget that they had sworn they would never serve under you.

The dining rooms of London's top clubs were kept busy. Spooks and soldiers and scribblers, commercial moguls and sleek men and women from the City – everyone wanted to be in on the action, whatever the action turned out to be.

And on Monday morning, in a private room at the Royal Society of Arts, an elegant building near Charing Cross, a simple lunch was being discreetly laid out. The sign at the entrance gave its subject as 'Inspirational management: managing inspiration – Brainstorming seminar by the Ideas Shower.'

A middle-aged woman politician, once a member of Tony Blair's Cabinet and now the public affairs consultant to two oil-rich Middle East ruling families as well as a life peer, hurried through the open meeting spaces, past young men and women in suits who were talking about shareholder value and bringing in low-hanging fruit, to a private room at the end. There stood a tall, lean man with discretion written all over his face, who held open the door for her and told her in a low voice as she passed, 'Lunch is laid out already. The staff won't need to come in. I've told them not to, until everyone's gone.'

'Thank you, Matthew,' said the public affairs consultant, and Matthew Taylor, the RSA's chief executive and once Tony Blair's chief of staff, closed the door and melted discreetly into the background. A younger woman seated at the table got up and came towards her, and they kissed on both cheeks. 'Miriam,' said the consultant fondly. 'How is life in the belly of the beast?'

'Oddly consoling,' said Miriam. 'I hadn't realised that such charming simplicity still existed. You know everyone, don't you?'

In addition to the two of them, there was a journalist known to have the ear of Rupert Murdoch, the chief executive of one of the country's biggest outsourcing companies, and a rotund man in a crumpled suit whose profession no one ever asked, for they were pretty sure he worked for MI5. By the time they turned their attention to the desserts laid out on the side table, everyone knew the score. Miriam's report made it clear that Corbyn was not going to behave sensibly. He not only intended to implement his New Deal, he had detailed plans for doing it. So plans had to be made and acted on that very afternoon.

~

'We're doing this with great regret, but the man is imbued with old-fashioned male chauvinism,' the public affairs consultant and life peeress was telling the journalist on the phone an hour or so later. 'I speak for at least twenty Labour MPs and several members of the House of Lords who take the Labour whip, and who cannot tolerate Jeremy Corbyn continuing to lead our party. He has – how can I put it? – a problem with women.'

'Really?'

'You just have to look at his government. The top jobs are held by men. The Cabinet is dominated by men – they hold 60 per cent of the posts. This man clearly does not like women and does not want to work with them. Is that enough?'

'Women have 40 per cent? That's a bigger percentage than any previous government, isn't it?'

'It's a shocking lack of ambition for a Labour government. Will that do? I have a lot of calls to make.'

'It's fine.' The journalist did not waste time asking why the consultant had herself declined a post in government, or why she hadn't voted for the woman candidate for deputy leader – Diane Abbott – back in 2015. The story was clear: Labour was already dangerously split, and members of his own party were making the deadly accusation that Corbyn was anti-woman.

~

'We are speaking out now because the matter won't wait,' the chief executive told the business editor. 'Billions of pounds' worth of exports were lost on Friday alone because of the uncertainty created by having Jeremy Corbyn in Downing Street. Unless a change to a moderate figure is made within twenty-four hours, many big British businesses will be bankrupted.'

'Aren't you exaggerating a bit?'

'No. By the way, I think you may find Tony Blair has something interesting to say.'

'He hardly counts, these days, does he? He's already left the Labour Party. Anyway, he never takes our calls.'

'He will today,' said the chief executive, and gave the journalist a telephone number in Kazakhstan to ring.

~

'I'm afraid there's no possibility of error,' the spy was telling the *Guardian* columnist. 'Corbyn met at reception, and shook hands with, a senior official in Hamas. He is definitely an anti-Semite.'

'Fifteen years ago, you say?' said the columnist.

'An anti-Semite. Do I make myself clear?'

'Of course,' said the columnist, who had never really doubted it.

~

'I'd rather not be identified as the source for this document,' the spy was telling the BBC's political editor. 'But it's a full list of the Islamists, terrorists and Communists that Jeremy Corbyn and his advisers, associates and friends have known for the last fifty years.'

'Isn't the connection a bit tenuous in some cases? I see it says here that his brother Piers once knew someone who knew someone else who knew someone...'

'Every one of them', said the spy firmly, 'is a person MI5 has had to warn the BBC against employing, or against allowing on air. Do I make myself clear?'

He did.

~

In the Cabinet room, Seumas Milne was briefing his boss on the blizzard of media calls his office was taking.

'I have to tell you something, Jeremy. Miriam is a spook.'

'Of course she is,' said the Prime Minister. 'That's how they know we're releasing our New Deal plans this afternoon.'

'So what are we going to do?'

'Release them, on schedule,' said the Prime Minister.

~

'JEZZA "HATES WOMEN"', shrieked *The Sun*, alongside a picture of a model in a bikini, just in case the reader might not know what sort of person Corbyn was supposed to hate. She was quoted as saying, 'If Corbyn thinks women aren't fit to be in government, I think he's just wrong.'

'CORBYN "TAKES SCYTHE TO BRITISH JOBS"' was the *Daily Mail*'s offering, and on an inside page it had an exclusive. Apparently, several months previously, Corbyn had turned down an invitation to speak to a north London feminist group and the group's spokeswoman interpreted this as a snub to all women. The spokeswoman, whose only previous media exposure in her many years of political activism had been in the pages of *Socialist Worker*, was quoted at length on how this proved the new Prime Minister cared nothing for what women thought.

The story ended: 'A spokesman said Mr Corbyn would have accepted if the meeting had not coincided with the Labour Party conference.'

The *Today* programme gathered together a small panel of veteran female broadcasters to discuss the social significance of the new Cabinet, and the consensus among them was that the real problem was the absence from the government of a woman of Corbyn's age or older. This tempted them into one more trip down memory lane to recall their struggles against the BBC hierarchy, and Corbyn was compared unfavourably with John Birt.

In the blogosphere, Guido Fawkes – Paul Staines to Westminster insiders – had a scoop, naturally. By employing his famous investigative skills, Mr Staines had managed to make contact with the daughter of a Saudi oil billionaire who had once met Corbyn at an embassy reception. Corbyn had apparently been openly bored by her tale of the problems of finding good domestic help in London. 'I realised', she told the blogger, exclusively and indignantly, 'that Jeremy Corbyn is just not interested in women's issues.'

Mr Staines had, of course, a proud record of investigating the dark side of Jeremy Corbyn. Only the previous year he had revealed that a man who had been a close university friend of Corbyn's brother thirty years previously now kept his money in an offshore trust, which exposed the hypocrisy of Corbyn attacking Conservative politicians for doing just that.

The *Financial Times* led on a prediction from an economic think tank that Corbyn would bankrupt Britain within a month, while the *Telegraph* featured an interview with former Prime Minister Tony Blair in which he exclusively revealed to his old friend and fellow Catholic Charles Moore his decision to join the Conservative Party. 'It's the responsible thing to do,' he was quoted as saying. 'Jeremy Corbyn will ruin the country.'

It was a seriously worried communications chief who walked into the Cabinet room that afternoon. 'If only you'd listened to me,' said Seumas Milne, 'our plans for the New Deal and stopping arms sales to the Saudis would be on all the front pages, instead of this crap.'

'Yes,' said the Prime Minister, 'they would. Good day to bury the news, wasn't it?'

~

'Shame you don't drink,' said Miriam. 'I feel we have something to celebrate. We could open a bottle of champagne.'

'I drink,' said Jeremy. 'Just not very often, and not very much. If you make that Merlot, I'll join you. You'll find a bottle in that cupboard.'

'A month in, and you're looking stronger than ever,' said Miriam as she placed the bottle on Jeremy's kitchen table and expertly extracted the cork. 'The Saudi ban went through as an Order in Council and no one's noticed, particularly. The New Deal isn't going to have any trouble now – none of our people are going to oppose it because there's no press storm to latch onto. And everyone said you were too straight for dark and devious politics.'

'They often say that,' said the Prime Minister with a smile. 'How do they think I survived on the Bennite left all through the '70s, '80s and '90s? They were man-eaters, that lot. You never met anyone with such sharp teeth. But I couldn't have done this without you. How does it feel to be a double agent? I've often wondered.'

'Great,' said Miriam. 'It means I can tell you what they're going to do tomorrow.'

'And what's that?'

'They're going to insist that you break off negotiations with Iran. Otherwise there's a media storm brewing about every contact with every suspect group in the Middle East that you and everyone you know has ever had. They've got a file two inches thick. The charge is anti-Semitism. It'll be nasty. Very nasty.'

'War drums getting louder. Is it time to throw them Seumas?'

'Too big for that, I'm afraid. Everyone knows he can go straight back to *The Guardian* and write op eds,' said Miriam. 'No, I'm afraid it's time for Plan B.'

'Oh dear. Do we have to?'

'We knew we'd have to one day. I'm afraid the day has come. I hope you've warned Laura. They always go to the wife, you know.'

'Oh, well,' said the Prime Minister. 'If we must. You'd better tell your friends in MI5 about our, er, arrangement. And I suppose I'll have to stay tonight.'

~

The spy was on the telephone to the editor of *The Sun*.

'I'm now in a position to confirm the story I mentioned over lunch yesterday. Yes, it's Miriam. Yes, Corbyn's adviser Miriam. Yes, Miriam and the Prime Minister. Yes, they've been… Yes, as it happens, I can do just that. He will leave her flat about 1 a.m. this morning. There are street lights there for your photographer. Yes, I will have a word with the local authority. I will make sure they're not being turned off in that street to save electricity. Yes, I have a former friend of hers who will say it's been going on for about three months. I'll text you a name and address.'

He put the phone down and looked into the middle distance. He wasn't a bad man, and he didn't much like what he had just done. But government is cruel, and sometimes, he thought sadly, you have to do grubby things for Queen and country.

ALSO AVAILABLE FROM BITEBACK PUBLISHING

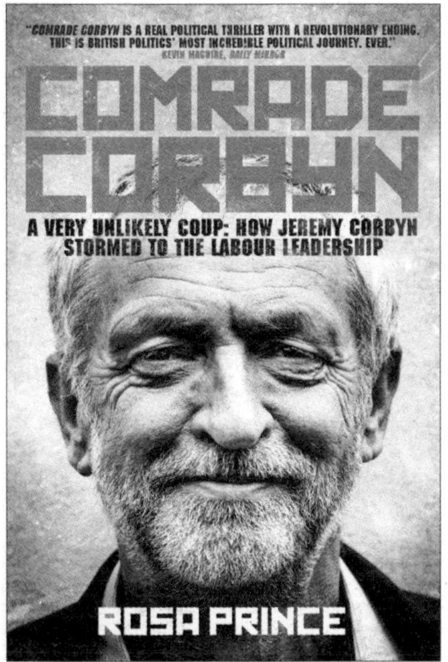

432PP PAPERBACK, £10.99

"An engaging and accomplished analysis."

Jason Cowley, *Sunday Times*

"Fascinating and forensic … Essential reading for anyone who follows politics."

Mary Riddell, *Daily Telegraph*

This new edition of the critically acclaimed biography brings the Jeremy Corbyn story fully up to date, setting out how this very British iconoclast managed to snatch the leadership of a party he spent forty years rebelling against … and how the party has rebelled against him in turn.

Engaging, clear-sighted and above all revealing, *Comrade Corbyn* explores the extraordinary story of the most unexpected leader in modern British politics.

— AVAILABLE FROM ALL GOOD BOOKSHOPS —

WWW.BITEBACKPUBLISHING.COM

ALSO AVAILABLE FROM BITEBACK PUBLISHING

HARDBACK, £25

— AVAILABLE FROM ALL GOOD BOOKSHOPS —

WWW.BITEBACKPUBLISHING.COM